# CARBENE CHEMISTRY

# ORGANIC CHEMISTRY

## A SERIES OF MONOGRAPHS

*Edited by*

## ALFRED T. BLOMQUIST

*Department of Chemistry, Cornell University, Ithaca, New York*

• • • • • • • • •

# CARBENE CHEMISTRY

BY

## WOLFGANG KIRMSE

*Chemisches Institut der Universitaet Marburg*
*Marburg, Germany*

WITH CONTRIBUTIONS BY

H. M. FREY

PETER P. GASPAR

GEORGE S. HAMMOND

1964

ACADEMIC PRESS    New York and London

ACADEMIC PRESS INC.
111 Fifth Avenue, New York, New York 10003

*United Kingdom Edition published by*
ACADEMIC PRESS INC. (LONDON) LTD.
Berkeley Square House, London, W. 1

LIBRARY OF CONGRESS CATALOG CARD NUMBER: 64-21669

PRINTED IN THE UNITED STATES OF AMERICA

# PREFACE

Carbene chemistry has experienced a tremendous growth and wide interest in the past decade. The investigation of divalent carbon intermediates proved to be rewarding to both physical and preparative organic chemistry. Many research groups have excelled in contributing to our present knowledge of the elusive carbene species.

By now, carbene chemistry has outgrown the dimensions of review articles, and the task of providing a comprehensive monograph seemed timely. On considering the objectives of such a publication, it appears that full coverage is best achieved by a single author, whereas the most authoritative treatment may come from various experts dealing with their own fields of research. The present volume attempts to combine the advantages of both procedures. In the first ten chapters, I have tried to give an essentially complete survey of carbene chemistry. Literature citations extend through late 1963, and a few early 1964 references have been included. Scope and emphasis devoted to the various topics are undoubtedly influenced by the author's personal interests. Therefore, advance apologies are tendered to any of my colleagues who find their own work discussed inadequately, and to those whose findings I have inadvertently overlooked. Although the subject demanded a careful and critical discussion of mechanistic problems, the discussion has been kept to a minimum in the first ten chapters in anticipation of the contents of Chapters 11 and 12. In these chapters, theory is applied consistently to the interpretation of carbene reactions in those fields where it is most advanced. It is a pleasure to thank Professors H. M. Frey, P. P. Gaspar, and G. S. Hammond for their valuable contributions.

Furthermore, I wish to express my gratitude to numerous colleagues who have participated in the preparation of this volume by stimulating discussions, by constructive criticism, and by disclosure of unpublished results. I am especially indebted to Dr. Robert B. Hager who read the entire manuscript.

*Marburg/Lahn*                    WOLFGANG KIRMSE
*May 1964*

# CONTENTS

# CHAPTER 1

# Introduction

## I. SCOPE AND LIMITATIONS

CARBENES MAY BE DEFINED as "divalent" carbon intermediates. More precisely, the carbene carbon is linked to two adjacent groups by covalent bonds, and possesses two nonbonding electrons which may have antiparallel spins (singlet state) or parallel spins (triplet state). The formal relationship of carbenes to other simple intermediates is presented in Table I. Triplet carbenes may be considered as diradicals although the location of two unpaired electrons at the same carbon atom may give rise to some peculiarities. Singlet carbenes are electron-deficient species, comparable to carbonium ions; on the other hand they possess a nonbonding pair of electrons, comparable to that of carbanions. The electrophilic or nucleophilic character of singlet carbenes depends, therefore, strongly on the ability of adjacent groups to withdraw electrons from, or supply electrons to, the carbene carbon.

TABLE I
SIMPLE INTERMEDIATES IN THE CHEMISTRY OF CARBON COMPOUNDS

| | | Number of covalent bonds | Number of valence electrons |
|---|---|---|---|
| Carbanions | $\diagup\!\!\!\diagdown\!C\!:^{\ominus}$ | 3 | 8 |
| Radicals | $\diagup\!\!\!\diagdown\!C\cdot$ | 3 | 7 |
| Carbonium ions | $\diagup\!\!\!\diagdown\!C^{\oplus}$ | 3 | 6 |
| Carbenes | $\diagup\!\!\!\diagdown\!C\!:$ | 2 | 6 |

With most of the intermediates mentioned in Table I, the existence of moderately stable species (e.g., triarylmethyl derivatives) has provided a basis for the investigation of transient analogs. In contrast, little useful information is provided by stable compounds with formally "divalent" carbon. In carbon monoxide, isocyanides, and fulminic acid derivatives, resonance stabilization of the "divalent" carbon by neighboring groups is extremely strong. Determinations of atomic distances, dipole moments, etc., have clearly revealed that triple bonded structures make a major contribution to the resonance hybrid. As a consequence, the "divalent" carbon of these compounds displays nucleophilic reactivity.

$$\left[\,|\,C=\overset{..}{O}\rangle \;\leftrightarrow\; |\,\overset{\ominus}{C}\!\equiv\!\overset{\oplus}{O}\,|\,\right] \qquad \left[R\!-\!\underset{..}{N}\!=\!C\,|\;\leftrightarrow\; R\!-\!\overset{\oplus}{N}\!\equiv\!\overset{\ominus}{C}\,|\,\right]$$

The possible contribution of a carbene structure to the resonance hybrid of tetraphenylallene-dianion (*1*) may be mentioned:

$$\left[\,Ph_2C\!=\!\overset{\ominus}{C}\!-\!\overset{\ominus}{C}Ph_2 \;\leftrightarrow\; Ph_2\overset{\ominus}{C}\!-\!\overset{..}{C}\!-\!\overset{\ominus}{C}Ph_2\,\right]$$

Although the challenge of preparing compounds having properties intermediate between those of the unstable carbenes and the strongly resonance-stabilized structures has not been met with much success so far, this field is at present being actively investigated. Two nitrogen atoms linked to the carbene carbon exert a strong influence in compounds such as I, which appears to dissociate with formation of a resonance-stabilized, nucleophilic carbene (II) (*2*).

(I)                          (II)

No comparable effects have been noted with other tetraamino-ethylenes (*3*); steric factors are obviously important, but not yet fully understood. Carbenes containing one $\alpha$-oxygen or sulfur atom are still moderate electrophiles (*4*) whereas there is some indication of nucleophilic behavior with two sulfur atoms (*5*). To summarize, attachment of hetero atoms by *single bonds* to divalent carbon affords transient intermediates rather than stable compounds.

As an exception to this rule, the hybrid structure IV has been attributed to crystalline, moderately stable compounds obtained from *N*-alkylbenzthiazolium halides (III) by treatment with base (*5a*).

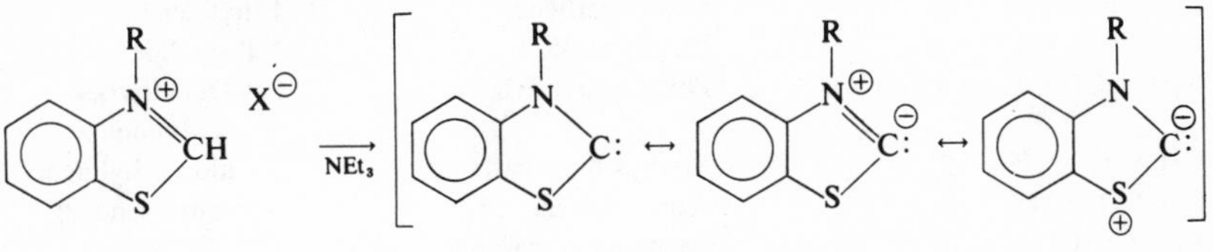

(III)                                                    (IV)

Substituents less capable of resonance, such as halogen, carbonyl, aryl, and alkyl, render the "divalent" carbon atom increasingly reactive. In the dihalocarbene series, maximum resonance stabilization may be expected with difluorocarbene. "Half-lives" of 0.5 and 20 msec. have been observed in solution (*6*) and in the gas phase (*7*), respectively. Thus, in spite of resonance, difluorocarbene is a transient intermediate, although it is about $10^3$ times longer lived than methylene.

The foregoing survey shows a distinction between reactive, unstable carbenes and stable compounds with "divalent" carbon, the latter group being characterized by a hetero atom *doubly bonded* to the "divalent" carbon. It appears appropriate, therefore, to deal with these two groups separately. Only the reactive, transient carbenes will be treated in the present monograph.

## II. NOMENCLATURE

The term "carbene," collaboratively conceived by Doering, Winstein, and Woodward, and first presented at the 119th Meeting of the American Chemical Society, 1951 [cf. (*8*)], seems well suited to describe the class of reactive divalent carbon compounds defined in Section I. "Carbene" is to be employed in the same way as "carbinol" (*9*). Difficulties arising with cyclic carbenes may be eliminated by use of the prefix "carbena," to be employed in the same way as "aza," "oxa," etc.

The "carbene" nomenclature conflicts with established rules of the International Union of Pure and Applied Chemistry (IUPAC) Organic Nomenclature Committee. It has been pointed out that substances with a merely transient existence should be classified as radicals. The ending for a $>C=$ radical is -ylidene.

TABLE II

NOMENCLATURE COMPARISON

| | "Carbene" | "Ylidene" |
|---|---|---|
| $CH_3CH$: | Methylcarbene | Ethylidene |
| $CH_3CH_2CH$: | Ethylcarbene | 1-Propylidene |
| $(CH_3)_2CH—\underset{.}{C}—CH(CH_3)_2$ | Diisopropylcarbene | 2,4-Dimethyl-3-pentylidene |
| $CH_3—\underset{.}{C}—Cl$ | Methylchlorocarbene | 1-Chloroethylidene |
| $CH_3CO—CH$: | Acetylcarbene | Acetonylidene (?) |
| $EtO_2C—CH$: | Carboethoxycarbene | — |
| $Cl_2C$: | Dichlorocarbene | — |
| $CH_2=CH—CH$: | Vinylcarbene | Propenylidene |
| (cyclohexenyl with $CH_3$): | 3-Carbena-4-methyl-cyclohexene | 6-Methylcyclohex-2-enylidene |

It will be seen that the "ylidene" procedure cannot be applied consistently unless at least one group linked to the divalent carbon atom is alkyl. In cases such as $Cl_2C$:, $Ph_2C$:, and $RO_2C—CH$: names have to be based on "methylene," which, in this use, is synonymous with "carbene." It appears more difficult to locate the divalent carbon atom if formulas are transcribed in the "ylidene" nomenclature. Furthermore, the "ylidene" procedure may be misleading as the term "ylidene" will frequently refer to compounds not containing a divalent carbon atom (e.g., cyclohexylidenecyclohexanone), although it does not occur as an ending in this case.

Because of its clearness, simplicity, and consistency, the "carbene" nomenclature will be applied in this monograph. As mentioned above, "carbene" is synonymous with one of the several definitions of "methylene." In order to differentiate the spin states of the carbenes in question, it has been suggested that "all triplet states be given the traditional names of methylene derivatives and the name carbene be reserved for singlet states" (10). As a necessary amendment, it has been proposed that this nomenclature should apply to the ground state (11).

Although the ground state multiplicity of some carbenes has been established, there is considerable controversy about others. Furthermore, carbene reactions frequently involve excited states, the multiplicity of which may or may not be identical with that of the ground states. For these reasons, all transient intermediates with "divalent" carbon will be termed "carbenes" in this text; spin states, where known, will be specified by adding "singlet" or "triplet."

## III. HISTORY

The first attempts to prepare methylene were made at a time when the quadrivalency of carbon was not yet established. Dumas (12) and Regnault (13) tried to dehydrate methanol by means of phosphorus pentoxide or concentrated sulfuric acid. The pyrolysis of methyl chloride was studied by Perrot (14) with the aim of eliminating hydrogen chloride. Butlerov (15) treated methylene iodide with copper powder in a sealed tube, but obtained only ethylene.

A second period of carbene research was initiated by the discovery of isonitriles and fulminic acid derivatives. Nef, stimulated by his own work in this field (16), proposed a "general methylene theory" (17) which explained most substitution reactions by the sequence of $\alpha$-elimination and addition. Only few of the contemporary chemists accepted these views. Nef also announced that methylene would become available in the near future. Obviously he still though that methylene, once prepared, would be a stable compound.

The pioneering work of Staudinger and his associates (1912–1916) (18–21) on the decomposition of diazo compounds and ketenes contributed much to the recognition of carbenes as merely transient species. As radicals were the intermediates *en vogue* in the following decades, carbenes were generally regarded as diradicals, and methods of radical chemistry, such as the Paneth (22, 23) and Polanyi (24–26) techniques, were applied to the identification and production of carbenes.

Recent approaches to carbene chemistry have taken place along two lines. First, when the insertion of methylene and other carbenes into carbon-hydrogen bonds was observed (27, 28) and adequately interpreted (28), it became clear that carbenes were a unique type of intermediate, giving characteristic reactions not encountered with radicals. Second, the studies of Hine (29) *et al.* on haloform solvolysis reactivated the concern with $\alpha$-elimination as a potential route to carbenes. The two fields of research were shown to be related by the discovery of dihalocarbene addition to olefins (9). Since then, research on carbenes has rapidly expanded and has made important contributions to both preparative and theoretical organic chemistry. Ample justification of this statement may be found in the following chapters.

## REFERENCES

1. W. Schlenk and E. Bergmann, *Ann.* **463**, 228 (1928).
2. H. W. Wanzlick, *Angew. Chem.* **74**, 129 (1962).
3. N. Wiberg and J. W. Buchler, *Angew. Chem.* **74**, 490 (1962); *J. Am. Chem. Soc.* **85**, 243 (1963); *Chem. Ber.* **96**, 3000 (1963).
   H. W. Wanzlick, F. Esser, and H. J. Kleiner, *Chem. Ber.* **96**, 1208 (1963).
4. U. Schöllkopf and A. Lerch, *Angew. Chem.* **73**, 27 (1961); U. Schöllkopf, A. Lerch, and W. Pitteroff, *Tetrahedron Letters* **1962**, 165, 241.
5. U. Schöllkopf and E. Wiskott, *Angew. Chem.* **75**, 725 (1963).
5a. H. W. Wanzlick and H. J. Kleiner, *Angew. Chem.* **75**, 1024 (1963).
6. V. Franzen, *Chem. Ber.* **95**, 1964 (1962).
7. J. P. Simons and A. J. Yarwood, *Nature* **187**, 316 (1960).
8. W. v. E. Doering and L. H. Knox, *J. Am. Chem. Soc.* **78**, 4947 (1956).
9. W. v. E. Doering and A. K. Hoffmann, *J. Am. Chem. Soc.* **76**, 6162 (1954).
10. R. M. Etter, H. S. Skovronek, and P. S. Skell, *J. Am. Chem. Soc.* **81**, 1008 (1959).
11. A. M. Trozzolo, R. W. Murray, and E. Wasserman, *J. Am. Chem. Soc.* **84**, 4990 (1962).
12. J. B. Dumas, *Ann. chim. phys.* [2] **58**, 28 (1835).
13. H. V. Regnault, *Ann. chim. phys.* [2] **71**, 427 (1839).
14. A. Perrot, *Ann.* **101**, 375 (1857).
15. A. M. Butlerov, *Ann.* **120**, 356 (1861).
16. J. U. Nef, *Ann.* **270**, 267 (1892); **280**, 291 (1894); **287**, 265 (1895).
17. J. U. Nef, *Ann.* **298**, 202 (1897).
18. H. Staudinger and O. Kupfer, *Ber. deut. chem. Ges.* **44**, 2197 (1911); **45**, 501 (1912).
19. H. Staudinger and R. Endle, *Ber. deut. chem. Ges.* **46**, 1437 (1913).
20. H. Staudinger and J. Goldstein, *Ber. deut. chem. Ges.* **49**, 1923 (1916).
21. H. Staudinger, E. Anthes, and F. Pfenninger, *Ber. deut. chem. Ges.* **49**, 1928 (1916).
22. F. O. Rice and A. L. Glasebrook, *J. Am. Chem. Soc.* **55**, 4329 (1933); **56**, 2381 (1934).
23. T. G. Pearson, R. H. Purcell, and G. S. Saigh, *J. Chem. Soc.* **1938**, 409.
24. C. E. H. Bawn and W. J. Dunning, *Trans. Faraday Soc.* **35**, 185 (1939).
25. C. E. H. Bawn and J. Milsted, *Trans. Faraday Soc.* **35**, 889 (1939).
26. C. E. H. Bawn and C. F. H. Tipper, *Discussions Faraday Soc.* **2**, 107 (1947).
27. H. Meerwein, H. Rathjen, and H. Werner, *Ber. deut. chem. Ges.* **75**, 1610 (1942).
28. W. v. E. Doering, R. G. Buttery, R. G. Laughlin, and N. Chaudhuri, *J. Am. Chem. Soc.* **78**, 3224 (1956).
29. J. Hine, *J. Am. Chem. Soc.* **72**, 2438 (1950), and subsequent papers, cf. Chapter 8.

# CHAPTER 2

# Methylene

THE PARENT CARBENE, methylene, has been the object of much research, including quantum mechanical calculations (*1–7*) and spectroscopic studies in addition to preparative and kinetic work. An absorption near 4050 Å, previously assigned to methylene (*8–10*), is now attributed to $C_3$ (*11–14*). The true spectrum of methylene has been recorded after a long search making use of the flash photolysis of gaseous diazomethane (*15, 16*). The bands assigned to methylene on the basis of isotopic shifts ($C^{13}$, D) consist of two entirely different systems in the vacuum ultraviolet (1415 Å) and in the far red region (8190, 7315, and 6531 Å). The former absorption is consistent with a linear (triplet) structure, whereas the red bands indicate a bent (singlet) configuration. According to the observed dependence of the two absorption systems on inert gas pressure, the linear (triplet) state may be taken as the lowest energy state.

Regardless of the nature of the ground state, singlet methylene is formed in most cases as a consequence of spin conservation. Present evidence indicates that methylene also reacts in the singlet state, before undergoing a singlet-triplet transition, unless extreme conditions are selected. Exceptions pertaining to the mode of formation or reaction will be mentioned in due course.

Conflicting results have been obtained concerning the heat of formation of methylene. Mass spectrometry has been applied to study the appearance potentials of various ions in the mass spectra of methane, methyl, and methylene (*17–21*). The ionization potential of methylene obtained by most workers using this method is 11.9 e.v., corresponding to $\Delta H_f^\circ(CH_2) = 66.4$ kcal. per mole (*18*). On the other hand, the Rydberg series in the vacuum ultraviolet spectrum of methylene (1415 Å) converges to give an ionization potential of 10.4 e.v. (*16*). The spectroscopic evidence casts grave doubt on the interpretation of the appearance

7

potential data. $\Delta H_f^\circ(CH_2) = 82 \pm 2$ kcal. per mole recently has been obtained by observing the equilibrium concentration of methylene over hot carbon in an atmosphere of hydrogen (22). [For a critical review of the evaluation of $\Delta H_f^\circ$ (CH$_2$) see also (23).]

Some of the theoretical problems mentioned here but briefly are discussed in more detail in Chapters 11 and 12. This chapter is concerned mainly with the chemistry of methylene.

## I. FORMATION OF METHYLENE

### A. Methylene from Ketene

The pyrolysis of acetone at high temperatures produces ethylene and carbon monoxide instead of the expected ketene (24). Staudinger (25) explained this observation by assuming a thermal decomposition of ketene:

$$2CH_2{=}C{=}O \rightarrow CH_2{=}CH_2 + 2CO$$

When ketene itself was pyrolyzed, considerable quantities of methane were formed in addition to ethylene and carbon monoxide (26, 27).

Much work has been devoted to studies of the photolysis of ketene, and the major reactions occurring in this system are now well known. If radiation of a wavelength shorter than 2800 Å is absorbed, the primary photochemical process is

$$CH_2{=}C{=}O \xrightarrow[< 2800\,\text{Å}]{h\nu} :CH_2 + CO \tag{1}$$

Light quanta of sufficiently high energy immediately dissociate the ketene molecule. The quantum yield of carbon monoxide ($2.12 \pm 0.15$) is independent of pressure and temperature (28). At longer wavelengths a predissociation mechanism has been suggested, involving excited ketene molecules (29, 30):

$$CH_2{=}C{=}O \xrightarrow[> 2800\,\text{Å}]{h\nu} CH_2{=}C{=}O^* \tag{2}$$

$$CH_2{=}C{=}O^* \rightarrow :CH_2 + CO \tag{3}$$

$$CH_2{=}C{=}O^* + CH_2{=}C{=}O \rightarrow 2CH_2{=}C{=}O \tag{4}$$

The occurrence of collisional deactivation [Eq. (4)] leads to smaller quantum yields which depend on pressure and temperature (e.g., 0.54 at 3660 Å, 27°, $1.5 \times 10^{-6}$ moles per liter). Under these conditions, added oxygen virtually eliminates the dissociation of ketene [Eq. (3)] by reacting with excited ketene molecules. Within experimental error the quantum yield of carbon monoxide formation is equal to that of oxygen consumption, and the yield of ethylene is very small $(31)$. In the short wavelength region, oxygen has little influence on the quantum yield of ethylene $(28)$.

It should be noted that the dissociation of ketene is reversible. When ketene was photolyzed in the presence of carbon monoxide-$C^{13}$, considerable amounts of $C^{13}$ were incorporated in the recovered ketene $(32, 33)$.

Two mechanisms of ethylene formation were considered for more than 20 years: (a) dimerization of methylene $(34)$:

$$2 : CH_2 \rightarrow CH_2 = CH_2 \tag{5}$$

and (b) reaction of methylene with ketene $(35)$:

$$:CH_2 + CH_2 = C = O \rightarrow CH_2 = CH_2 + CO \tag{6}$$

Recently, overwhelming evidence in favor of Eq. (6) has been accumulated. The quantum yield of 2 of carbon monoxide formation is compatible only with Eq. (6). When excess ethylene was used as a scavenger for methylene, the smaller quantum yields indicated that part of the carbon monoxide arises from subsequent reactions of methylene $(36)$. Kistiakowsky and Sauer $(37)$ photolyzed mixtures of ethylene and ketene, and an inert gas and ketene, under identical conditions. In the cell containing the large excess of ethylene, intervening methylene was trapped by addition to ethylene, and reaction (6) was eliminated. The ratio of carbon monoxide formation in the two cells provided a measure of the dimerization reaction (5). Although this ratio was slightly smaller than 2, no change was observed over a wide range of light intensities. Without noticeable effect the same amount of light energy was administered either as constant radiation or as a series of flashes. This result excludes a significant contribution of Eq. (5) even under favorable (flash) conditions.

The mechanism of reaction (6) has not yet been completely established. The intervention of an excited molecule of cyclopropanone has been suggested $(37)$, which might break to give the radicals A and B:

$$:CH_2 + CH_2 = C = O \rightarrow \begin{array}{c} CH_2 - C = O^* \\ \diagdown \quad \diagup \\ CH_2 \end{array} \begin{cases} \cdot CH_2 CH_2 \dot{C}O \quad (A) \\ \\ \cdot CH_2 CO - CH_2 \cdot \quad (B) \end{cases} \tag{7}$$

Radical A is thought to give ethylene and carbon monoxide very rapidly, whereas B may be somewhat longer lived. There are several indications of a comparatively stable intermediate in ketene photolysis. The quantitative application of the Paneth technique (removal of tellurium mirrors in a flow system) yields an apparent half life of the order of 0.1 sec. (38, 39). More information was obtained by a combination of flash photolysis and mass spectrometry (40). No increase of mass 14 ($CH_2$) was observed, but a peak of mass 55 ($C_3H_4O$) formed and disappeared gradually. Both observations may be due to the presence of the radical B.

The ratio of carbon monoxide to ethylene in ketene photolysis is always a little greater than 2 (approximately 2.2). Some polymer formation is always observed and accounts for a part of the deficiency of ethylene. In addition, appreciable quantities of ethane and acetylene are formed as first-stage products (41). As their formation is completely suppressed in the presence of small quantities of oxygen, they may arise from radical (abstraction) reactions of methylene. If ketene is photolyzed by flashes of high intensity, acetylene and hydrogen become major products (42). The differences, as compared to lower intensities, are probably due to the adiabatic nature of the process, which leads to very high temperatures.

It should be remembered that the rather complex pattern of ketene photolysis is due to excited ketene molecules and to secondary reactions of the methylene formed. The picture becomes much clearer if light of sufficiently short wavelength is used, and an acceptor for methylene is added in large excess. Under these conditions many reactions of methylene have been successfully studied.

## B. Methylene from Diazomethane

### 1. Photolysis and Pyrolysis

The pyrolysis of diazomethane has long been thought to yield methylene. Staudinger (25) pyrolyzed diazomethane in the presence of carbon monoxide and obtained some ketene, probably arising from the combination of methylene and carbon monoxide:

$$CH_2N_2 \rightarrow N_2 + :CH_2 \xrightarrow{CO} CH_2{=}C{=}O \qquad (8)$$

The Paneth technique was applied to diazomethane by several workers (*38, 39, 43*). The decomposition products of diazomethane were able to remove mirrors of Se, Tb, Sb, and As, but not mirrors of Zn, Cd, Tl, Pb, Bi, and Hg. (All of these metals react with methyl radicals.) The product obtained from Te was identified as polymeric telluroformaldehyde $(CH_2Te)_x$, whereas methyl radicals yielded volatile $(CH_2Te)_2$. The apparent half life of methylene, determined by this technique, however, is by far too long in view of our present knowledge of the rate of methylene reactions. Therefore it appears improbable that the removal of metal mirrors is due to free methylene.

Rabinovitch and Setser (*44*) pyrolyzed diazomethane in the presence of hydrocarbons and obtained the same products as are formed by the photolysis of similar mixtures at room temperature. At present this work constitutes the most conclusive evidence for methylene formation in the pyrolysis of diazomethane. Above 250° the decomposition appeared to be homogeneous and first order, $k = 1.2 \times 10^{12} \exp(-34,000/RT)$ sec.$^{-1}$. Shantarovitch (*45*), studying the decomposition of diazomethane in the presence of nitrogen in a flow system, obtained $k = 8 \times 10^{10} \exp(-31,750/RT)$ sec.$^{-1}$.

The photochemical decomposition of diazomethane was observed in the first decade of this century (*46, 47*). According to Kirkbridge and Norrish (*48*) the quantum yield is approximately 4 with light of 4360 and 3650 Å wavelength. Most probably the primary reaction is

$$CH_2N_2 \overset{h\nu}{\rightarrow} :CH_2 + N_2 \tag{9}$$

Ethylene is the major product of diazomethane photolysis and appears to result from interaction of methylene and diazomethane:

$$:CH_2 + CH_2N_2 \rightarrow CH_2{=}CH_2 + N_2 \tag{10}$$

Frey (*49*) has provided a careful analysis of the gaseous hydrocarbons formed when diazomethane is photolyzed in the presence of an inert gas:

| | | | |
|---|---|---|---|
| Ethylene | 63.5% | 1-Butene | 9.0% |
| Ethane | 2.7 | trans-2-Butene | 1.0 |
| Acetylene | 2.6 | cis-2-Butene | 0.9 |
| Propylene | 7.0 | 1-Pentene | 3.8 |
| Propane | 2.0 | trans-2-Pentene | 1.1 |
| Cyclopropane | 1.4 | cis-2-Pentene | 0.8 |

The pattern of reaction products is hard to explain in terms of secondary reactions of methylene. The high yields of 1-alkenes may result from reactions of vibrationally excited molecules with diazomethane (23):

$$C_2H_4{}^* + CH_2N_2 \rightarrow C_3H_6{}^* + N_2$$

$$C_3H_6{}^* + CH_2N_2 \rightarrow C_4H_8{}^* + N_2, \text{ etc.} \tag{11}$$

$$C_nH_{2n}{}^* + M \rightarrow C_nH_{2n} + M$$

## 2. Catalytic Decomposition

The decomposition of diazomethane is catalyzed by various boron compounds (50-55) [in the order of increasing efficiency: trialkyl borates < boron trifluoride < trialkyl boranes (50)]. Most of these reactions yield crystalline polymethylene of high molecular weight and essentially linear structure. Without doubt the first step is some coordination of the electron-deficient catalyst with the carbon atom of diazomethane, but there is some argument about the subsequent steps leading to the polymer. Most authors prefer the following mechanism:

$$R_3B + CH_2N_2 \rightarrow R_3\overset{\ominus}{B}-CH_2-\overset{\oplus}{N}{\equiv}N \rightarrow R_3\overset{\ominus}{B}-\overset{\oplus}{C}H_2 \xrightarrow{CH_2N_2}$$

$$R_3\overset{\ominus}{B}-CH_2-\overset{\oplus}{C}H_2 \xrightarrow{CH_2N_2} R_3\overset{\ominus}{B}-CH_2-\overset{\oplus}{C}H_2-CH_2, \text{ etc.} \tag{12}$$

The reaction of diazomethane with a large excess of boron trifluoride affords $F_2B-CH_2F$ (56),. and related aluminum compounds $R_2Al-CH_2X$ are formed with ease at low temperatures from dialkyl-aluminum halides and diazomethane (57). These cases of halogen shift suggest an alternative mechanism of polymethylene formation:

$$BF_3 + CH_2N_2 \rightarrow F_2B-CH_2F \xrightarrow{CH_2N_2} \underset{\overset{|}{\oplus}CH_2}{F_2\overset{\ominus}{B}-CH_2F} \rightarrow F_2B-CH_2CH_2F \tag{13}$$

A competition of both mechanisms has been proposed (55), but since neither of them involves methylene the arguments need no detailed discussion at this point.

A second group of catalysts comprises metals such as copper (58, 59), iridium (60), and vanadium (60) (but not silver, iron, zinc, and nickel), and metal salts such as cupric sulfate (59), cupric stearate (53, 54), cuprous cyanide (59), cuprous iodide + amines (60), cuprous chloride, cuprous bromide (61, 62), auric chloride (63), iridium trichloride, vanadium trichloride, platinum tetrachloride (60), zinc iodide (64), and zinc chloride (65). The products obtained from the reaction of diazomethane with these inorganic compounds are polymethylene, or ethylene, or organometallic compounds of the structure $M(CH_2X)_n$. In a recent comprehensive study, Wittig and Schwarzenbach (66) have related the various products to the reduction potential of the metal involved:

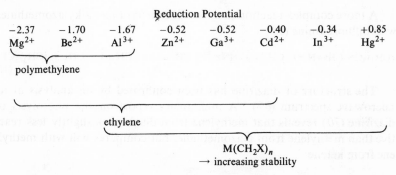

Reduction Potential

| $-2.37$ | $-1.70$ | $-1.67$ | $-0.52$ | $-0.52$ | $-0.40$ | $-0.34$ | $+0.85$ |
| $Mg^{2+}$ | $Be^{2+}$ | $Al^{3+}$ | $Zn^{2+}$ | $Ga^{3+}$ | $Cd^{2+}$ | $In^{3+}$ | $Hg^{2+}$ |

polymethylene

ethylene

$M(CH_2X)_n$
$\rightarrow$ increasing stability

Diazomethane, if decomposed by such catalysts, shows some of the reactions of methylene (e.g., addition to olefins), but not others (e.g., insertion). The particular problem is whether the addition to olefins should be attributed to a methylene of lowered reactivity or to the organometallic compound $M(CH_2X)_n$. In the case of dialkylaluminum halides (57) and zinc halides (66), where the organometallic intermediates have been isolated and their reactions have been checked independently, the latter explanation most probably holds. The situation is less clear with copper and copper salts. Some authors prefer to talk about the intermediates produced by these catalysts in terms of "coordination complexes of methylene." Because of their preparative value the various "modified methylenes" are included in the present review.

## C. Methylene from Diazirine

Diazirine, the cyclic isomer of diazomethane, has been prepared recently by oxidation of diaziridine (67) which is made from formaldehyde, ammonia, and chloroamine:

$$CH_2O + \begin{matrix} NH_3 \\ NH_2Cl \end{matrix} \rightarrow CH_2\begin{matrix} NH \\ | \\ NH \end{matrix} \xrightarrow{Cr_2O_7^{2-}} CH_2\begin{matrix} N \\ \| \\ N \end{matrix} \qquad (14)$$

Cyclization and oxidation have been brought about in a single step by reaction of a methylene-bis-ammonium salt with hypochlorite (*67a*):

$$H_2C \begin{array}{c} NH_3^{\oplus} \\ NH_3^{\oplus} \end{array} \begin{array}{c} X^{\ominus} \\ X^{\ominus} \end{array} \xrightarrow[\text{ClO}\ominus]{\text{HO}\ominus} \left[ H_2C \begin{array}{c} NHCl \\ NH_2 \end{array} \right] \xrightarrow{\text{HO}\ominus} \left[ H_2C \begin{array}{c} NH \\ | \\ NH \end{array} \right]$$

$$\xrightarrow{\text{ClO}\ominus} H_2C \begin{array}{c} N \\ \| \\ N \end{array}$$

A more complex reaction involves treatment of *tert*-alkylazomethines with difluoroamine (*68*):

$$(CH_3)_3C-CH=N-C(CH_3)_3 + HNF_2 \rightarrow CH_2 \begin{array}{c} N \\ \| \\ N \end{array} + (CH_3)_2C=CH_2 + (CH_3)_3CF \tag{15}$$

The structure of diazirine has been confirmed by an analysis of its microwave spectrum (*69*). A preliminary report on the photolysis of diazirine (*70*) reveals that methylene from diazirine is slightly less reactive than methylene from diazomethane, but compares will with methylene from ketene.

## D. Methylene from Hydrocarbons

In a kinetic investigation of the pyrolysis of methane, Kassel (*71*) concluded that methylene was involved in the formation of ethane:

$$CH_4 \rightarrow :CH_2 + H_2 \qquad :CH_2 + CH_4 \rightarrow CH_3-CH_3$$

$$CH_3-CH_3 \rightarrow CH_2=CH_2 + H_2 \tag{16}$$

$$CH_2=CH_2 \rightarrow HC\equiv CH + H_2$$

Since then methylene has been postulated quite often as an intermediate in the "cracking" of hydrocarbons under the action of heat, catalysts, electrical discharge, and radiation. Only the few reasonably substantiated examples are mentioned here [for a more comprehensive treatment see (*72*)].

Acetylene and hydrogen, in addition to some ethylene and ethane, are the products resulting from electrical discharge in methane, and have been accounted for by a mechanism similar to that in Eq. (16). Under these conditions, tellurium mirrors are removed with formation of polymeric telluroformaldehyde (*73*). $CH_2D_2$ was obtained as the major product from mixtures of $CH_4$ and $D_2$, and $CH_4$ and $CD_4$ (*74*). Photolysis of methane by 1470 and 1295 Å radiation (xenon resonance lines) yielded a similar product mixture (*75*). The intervention of methylene in such systems appears probable in view of recent experiments with deuterated alkanes (e.g., $CH_3CD_3$). Photolysis in the vacuum ultraviolet region led to abstraction of molecular hydrogen predominantly from the same carbon atom (76). The remaining fragment of the molecule should be a carbene.

The irradiation of alkanes (from methane to pentane) with a $Co^{60}$ source in the presence of $I^{131}$ afforded up to 20% yields of labeled methylene iodide (77). Direct iodination did not occur under these conditions as no radioactive hydrogen iodide was formed. The observation of $CH_2I_2^{131}$ has therefore been taken as evidence of a methylene intermediate.

The interaction of recoiling carbon-11 atoms, produced by the $C^{12}(n,2n)C^{11}$ reaction, with hydrocarbons (ethane, propane, pentane) appears to involve methylene. The product composition showed a definite phase dependence. The change from gas to liquid and solid phase reduced the yields of ethylene and acetylene, with a concomitant increase of apparent methylene insertion products (77b). Observations on the statistical nature of the formation of various hexanes from $n$-pentane (77a) were confirmed with propane. The ratio of $n$-butane to isobutane approached 3:1 in the liquid and solid phase (77b). Indiscriminate reaction with carbon-hydrogen bonds is characteristic of methylene (cf. Section II,D,1).

## E. Methylene from Methyl Halides

The $\alpha$-elimination of hydrogen chloride from methyl chloride may be brought about by phenyl sodium (78) or amyl sodium (79). The major reaction in both cases, however, is displacement (Wurtz reaction):

$$CH_3Cl + R-Na \begin{cases} \longrightarrow R-CH_3 + NaCl \\ \longrightarrow R-H + :CH_2 + NaCl \end{cases} \tag{17}$$

Products resulting from the addition of methylene to olefins or to excess organometallic compound ($R-Na + :CH_2 \rightarrow R-CH_2Na$) were found in low yield. Both observations can be explained equally well in terms of organometallic intermediates, $CH_2ClNa$ (cf. Section II,H). If any methylene is involved it appears to be of very low reactivity.

## F. Methylene from Methylene Halides

The formation of alkyl radicals from alkyl halides and sodium in the gas phase is a well-known reaction [Hartel and Polanyi, for a review see (80)]. Sodium vapor, diluted by an inert carrier gas, is introduced into a stream of vaporized alkyl halide. Methylene halides were investigated under similar conditions by Bawn *et al.* (*81–83*). Starting with methylene chloride, methylene bromide, or methylene iodide in nitrogen as a carrier gas they obtained ethylene, whereas in a hydrogen atmosphere methane was the major product. They proposed the reaction scheme (*18*).

$$CH_2X_2 + Na \rightarrow \cdot CH_2X + NaX$$
$$\cdot CH_2X + Na \rightarrow :CH_2 + NaX$$
$$2:CH_2 \rightarrow CH_2{=}CH_2 \tag{18}$$
$$:CH_2 + H_2 \rightarrow CH_4$$

The observation that ethylene was the major product even in methane as a carrier gas casts some doubt on the intermediacy of methylene. According to our present knowledge of the reactions of methylene, ethane formed by insertion should be expected. An alternative mechanism of ethylene formation involving haloalkyl radicals should be considered:

$$2 \cdot CH_2X \rightarrow X{-}CH_2CH_2{-}X \xrightarrow{Na} CH_2{=}CH_2 \tag{19}$$

Ethylene has in fact been obtained from 1,2-dihaloethanes under the conditions of the Polanyi experiment.

The elimination of bromine from methylene bromide can be achieved by organolithium compounds. The reaction is initiated by a halogen-metal exchange, i.e., one bromine atom is removed as a cation:

$$CH_2Br_2 + R{-}Li \rightarrow R{-}Br + LiCH_2Br \xrightarrow{?} :CH_2 + LiBr \tag{20}$$

Addition of methylene to olefins (*84*) and, predominantly, to excess lithium alkyl (*79*) has been observed. These subsequent reactions may be due to the organometallic intermediate, $LiCH_2Br$, as well as to methylene (cf. Section II,H). The reaction between the sodium salt of pyrrole and methylene iodide to give pyridine (0.5% yield) (*85*, *86*) possibly involves a similar elimination.

The treatment of methylene iodide, or methylene bromide, with magnesium (*87*) or aluminum (*88*) affords ethylene. Under favorable conditions intermediates of the structure $XMCH_2X$ have been detected. Presumably ethylene arises from these intermediates and not from the dimerization of methylene. On the other hand, the reaction of lithium with methylene chloride, or bromochloromethane, in tetrahydrofuran has been reported to yield "methylation products" (not specified) of the solvent (*89*). This observation, if confirmed, would indicate the formation of methylene capable of insertion.

Iodomethylzinc iodide, $IZnCH_2I$, is accessible from methylene iodide and zinc-copper couple (*90, 91*), as well as from diazomethane and zinc iodide (*64, 66*). It is a very useful reagent which converts olefins to cyclopropanes in fair yields (cf. Section II,E,1,b). Although the mechanism of these reactions is not yet fully elucidated, a dissociation of the organometallic compound to give methylene appears improbable.

## G. Methylene from Ylides

Trimethylammonium methylide is usually prepared from tetramethylammonium halides by treatment with phenyl lithium. It is obtained under these conditions as a moderately stable complex with lithium halide (I). The complex decomposes at elevated temperatures, or in suitable solvents (e.g., 1,2-dimethoxyethane), with formation of polymethylene (*92*). If phenyl sodium is used in place of phenyl lithium, methylene may be trapped by reaction with cyclohexane or triphenylphosphine (*93*) [Eq. (22)].

$$(CH_3)_4\overset{\oplus}{N}X^{\ominus} + LiPh \rightarrow (CH_3)_3\overset{\oplus}{N}-\overset{\ominus}{C}H_2 \cdot LiX \rightarrow (CH_3)_3N + (CH_2)_x \qquad (21)$$

$$(I)$$

$$(CH_3)_4\overset{\oplus}{N}X^{\ominus} + NaPh \xrightarrow{Ph_3P} Ph_3P=CH_2 \qquad (22)$$

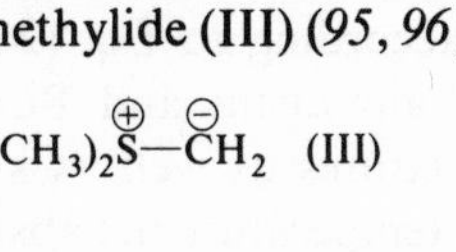

Methylene transfer, involving nucleophilic attack at *polar* double bonds, has been reported recently with dimethylsulfoxonium methylide (II) (*94*), and dimethylsulfonium methylide (III) (*95, 96*).

$$(CH_3)_2\overset{\oplus}{S}-\overset{\ominus}{C}H_2 \ (II) \qquad (CH_3)_2\overset{\oplus}{S}-\overset{\ominus}{C}H_2 \ (III)$$
$$\underset{O}{}$$

Although cyclohexene would not be expected to react with either II or III, competition experiments appear desirable to establish the electrophilic character of the intermediate in reaction (22).

## II. REACTIONS OF METHYLENE

### A. Reaction with Hydrogen

The product composition of many systems involving methylene is profoundly influenced by the presence of hydrogen. Two mechanisms must be considered for a reaction between methylene and hydrogen:
(a) Addition of methylene to the hydrogen molecule to give methane:

$$:CH_2 + H_2 \rightarrow CH_4 \tag{23}$$

(b) Abstraction of a hydrogen atom, leading to methyl radicals and affording methane and ethane as the major products:

$$:CH_2 + H_2 \rightarrow CH_3\cdot + H\cdot \qquad\qquad 2CH_3\cdot \rightarrow CH_3CH_3$$

$$CH_3\cdot + H_2 \rightarrow CH_4 + H\cdot, \text{ etc.} \tag{24}$$

Evidence for both of these mechanisms has been presented. The photolysis of diazomethane without added hydrogen yielded 4% of methane, whereas 14% of methane were obtained in the presence of an equimolar amount of hydrogen (48). The gas phase reaction of methylene bromide with sodium vapor (81–83), if carried out in a hydrogen atmosphere, afforded methane rather than ethylene. Electrical discharges through mixtures of $CH_4$ and $D_2$ resulted mostly in the formation of $CH_2D_2$ with minor amounts of $CH_3D$ and $CHD_3$ (74). These observations are most easily explained in terms of Eq. (23). It should be remembered, however, that the intervention of methylene is unequivocally established only in the photolysis of diazomethane.

Rosenblum (97), and Gesser and Steacie (98), observed little or no methane in the photolysis of ketene and hydrogen mixtures at room temperature. At higher temperatures they observed the formation of methane in addition to other products (e.g., ethyl methyl ketone) derived by attack of methyl radicals on ketene. They proposed an abstraction mechanism according to Eq. (24). Entirely different results were obtained by Chanmugam and Burton (99) who photolyzed ketene and deuterium mixtures as well as ketene and hydrogen. They concluded that at room temperature the abstraction reaction (24) is negligible compared to the addition reaction (23). Ethane-$d_1$ was not formed in ketene–$H_2$–$D_2$ photolysis, an argument against a process involving methyl radicals.

In a recent reinvestigation of the methylene and hydrogen system,

Bell and Kistiakowsky ($100$) have concluded that the abstraction reaction (24) is the net result of three reactions:

$$:CH_2 + H_2 \rightarrow CH_4^* \tag{25}$$

$$CH_4^* + M \rightarrow CH_4 + M \tag{26}$$

$$CH_4^* \rightarrow CH_3 \cdot + H \cdot \tag{27}$$

The addition reaction, Eq. (25), leads to vibrationally excited methane which decomposes to give methyl radicals by Eq. (27) unless collisionally deactivated [Eq. (26)]. Most probably hydrogen is very ineffective in stabilizing the excited methane molecules. This may be the reason why an increase in hydrogen pressure exerts only a small effect on the yield of methane. Previously conflicting observations may thus be reconciled. The results of $D_2$ experiments may be used for a choice between the direct abstraction [Eq. (23)] and the addition-decomposition mechanism [Eqs. (25)–(27)]:

Abstraction:

$$:CH_2 + D_2 \rightarrow CH_2D \cdot + D \cdot$$

$$D \cdot + CH_2N_2 \rightarrow CH_2D \cdot + N_2$$

Addition:

$$:CH_2 + D_2 \rightarrow CH_2D_2^*$$

$$CH_2D_2^* \rightarrow CH_2D \cdot + D \cdot$$

$$\rightarrow CHD_2 \cdot + H \cdot$$

$$D \cdot + CH_2N_2 \rightarrow CH_2D \cdot + N_2$$

$$H \cdot + CH_2N_2 \rightarrow CH_3 \cdot + N_2$$

For the abstraction reaction only ethane-1,2-$d_2$ is expected as the product. On the basis of the addition mechanism one would predict the formation of $CH_3$—$CH_3$, $CH_3$—$CH_2D$, $CH_3$—$CHD_2$, $DCH_2$—$CH_2D$, $D_2CH$—$CH_2D$, and $D_2CH$—$CHD_2$. The observed isotopic composition of the ethanes is in accord with the addition mechanism ($100$).

More evidence is furnished by the results of experiments with added oxygen. The reaction of oxygen with methylene is slow (cf. Section II,C), whereas the reaction with methyl radicals is rapid. The addition of oxygen to the methylene and hydrogen system produced a dramatic reduction in the yield of ethane, but had a much smaller effect on the methane and ethylene yields. Methane still arises, under these conditions, from the collisional deactivation process [Eq. (26)], and ethylene from the reaction of methylene with diazomethane. Ethane formation, which is a result of methyl association, is almost entirely eliminated.

Direct evidence for the occurrence of methyl radicals in the methylene and hydrogen system has been obtained spectroscopically from the flash photolysis of diazomethane with a large excess of hydrogen (16).

## B. Reactions with Carbon Monoxide and Carbon Dioxide

The reaction between methylene and carbon monoxide to give ketene was first observed by Staudinger and Kupfer (25) upon passing a mixture of diazomethane and carbon monoxide through a hot tube. The same reaction has been detected by photolyzing mixtures of ketene and carbon monoxide-$C^{13}$, which led to the formation of labeled ketene (32). A recent detailed study revealed (33) that the combination of methylene and carbon monoxide results in the formation of excited ketene molecules which redissociate unless collisionally stabilized:

$$:CH_2 + CO \rightleftharpoons CH_2{=}C{=}O^* \tag{28}$$

$$CH_2{=}C{=}O^* + M \rightarrow CH_2{=}C{=}O + M \tag{29}$$

Ketene itself is rather effective as a "third body," M. The addition reaction [Eq. (28)] is about twice as fast as the reaction of methylene with ketene. In view of this evidence it is not surprising that ketene is obtained in yields up to 50% by photolyzing diazomethane in a solid nitrogen-carbon monoxide matrix at 20°K. (101).

Carbon dioxide, previously thought to be inert toward methylene, in fact reacts with the formation of carbon monoxide and, probably, formaldehyde (a peak of mass 29 was observed in the mass spectrum) (37). The rate of the reaction was determined by following the formation of $C^{13}O$ from $C^{13}O_2$, and turned out to be sixty times slower than the rate of reaction of methylene with ketene. The reaction between methylene and carbon dioxide, formally a displacement, may proceed via an $\alpha$-lactone:

$$:CH_2 + CO_2 \rightarrow O{=}C\overset{CH_2}{\underset{O}{\diagup\!\!\!\big|}} \rightarrow CO + CH_2O \tag{30}$$

## C. Reactions with Oxygen and Nitric Oxide

Oxygen and nitric oxide are frequently used as radical scavengers. Their behavior toward methylene is of interest in evaluating the spin state of methylene, at the moment of reaction, by chemical methods.

There is little evidence of any interaction of oxygen or nitric oxide with methylene, a result which suggests that the reactions of singlet methylene are usually faster than transition to the triplet ground state.

When added to the photolysis of ketene (3660 Å), oxygen quenches the formation of ethylene by reaction with excited ketene molecules, and not with methylene (28, 30). The influence of oxygen on ketene photolysis is small at 2654 Å and room temperature. It becomes pronounced at elevated temperatures, being again due to radical reactions rather than those of methylene (102). Nitric oxide does not affect the yield of ethylene in the 0°–50° range (103).

The presence of oxygen in the photolysis of diazomethane leaves the characteristic insertion pattern of methylene unchanged, but eliminates minor radical abstraction reactions (104). It follows that the reaction of methylene with oxygen is slow as compared to the insertion reaction. The sensitivity of methylene toward oxygen increases, however, in the presence of a large excess of inert gas (105). This effect is attributed to the singlet-triplet transition of methylene brought about by many collisions with inert gas molecules.

## D. Reactions with Carbon-Hydrogen Bonds

### 1. Insertion

Insertion into carbon-hydrogen bonds is the most characteristic reaction of methylene. There is evidence (106) that the reaction proceeds by a "three-center" mechanism without a detectable intermediate:

$$\text{>C—H} + :CH_2 \rightarrow \text{>C} \cdots\cdots \text{H} \rightarrow \text{>C—CH}_2\text{—H} \qquad (31)$$
$$\overset{\cdots}{CH_2}$$

Diazomethane was photolyzed in the presence of isobutene-1-$C^{14}$, and insertion into the allylic carbon-hydrogen bonds was shown—by degradation of the 2-methyl-1-butene obtained—to proceed without significant mixing of the $C^{14}$ label (106) (cf. Section D,2 as to some mixing which occurs in the gas phase). This result excludes from consideration any intermediate capable of allylic resonance.

$$(CH_3)_2C{=}C^{14}H_2 + :CH_2 \rightarrow H\cdots\cdots CH_2{-}\underset{CH_3}{\overset{|}{C}}{=}C^{14}H_2$$
$$\overset{\cdots}{CH_2}$$

$$\rightarrow CH_3CH_2{-}\underset{CH_3}{\overset{|}{C}}{=}C^{14}H_2 + \cdots\cdots \qquad (31a)$$

The insertion reaction with saturated hydrocarbons was investigated in the liquid phase by Doering *et al.* (*107*). It was shown that the various types of carbon-hydrogen bonds in *n*-pentane, 2,3-dimethylbutane, and cyclohexene were attacked randomly. Thus for diazomethane and *n*-pentane the relative yields of *n*-hexane, 2-methylpentane, and 3-methylpentane, at $-75°$ and $+15°$, were 48:35:17 and 49:34:17, respectively (statistical values are 50:33.3:16.7). Studies on a large number of $C_6$–$C_8$ alkanes (*108*) have confirmed the classification of methylene as "the most indiscriminate reagent known in organic chemistry" (*107*). Experiments designed for intermolecular, instead of intramolecular, competition gave identical results (*108*).

Some discrimination was observed in the gas phase reactions of methylene. Photolyses of mixtures of diazomethane and *n*-butane, and diazomethane and isobutane, were carried out in the gas phase (*109*). Methylene was found to react 15–20% faster with secondary than with primary carbon-hydrogen bonds, and about 50% faster with tertiary than with primary carbon-hydrogen bonds. Considerably larger rate differences were noted using ketene as the source of methylene. The relative rates of attack on primary, secondary, and tertiary carbon-hydrogen bonds were approximately 1:2:7 (*110*). The difference in selectivity of methylene produced from diazomethane and ketene was rationalized in terms of "hot" methylene. It was assumed that the methylene formed by diazomethane photolysis carried energy in excess of the methylene formed from ketene. Much additional evidence to support this hypothesis has been published (cf. Chapter 11).

As a consequence of "excess energy," the products of gas phase insertion of methylene may arise in an excited state and, unless collisionally deactivated, they may isomerize or decompose. Thus cyclopropane (*111–113*) and cyclobutane (*114*) gave high yields of methylcycloalkanes only in the liquid phase or at high pressures in the gas phase, whereas extensive isomerization to olefins occurred at low pressures in the gas phase.

The reaction of methylene with methane is not a simple one as might be expected. Investigators of this system have been confronted with a dilemma similar to that of the methylene-hydrogen reaction. Vanpee and Grard (*115*) photolyzed ketene in the presence of methane and found ethylene and ethane as the major products. The formation of ethane was attributed to the reaction

$$:CH_2 + CH_4 \rightleftharpoons CH_3{-}CH_3^* \xrightarrow{+M} CH_3{-}CH_3 \tag{32}$$

Ethane was thought to arise in an excited state which is either stabilized by collision or dissociates to give methylene and methane. The formation of methyl radicals was considered to be too exothermic.

Chanmugam and Burton, using $CD_4$, found very little $C_2H_2D_4$; there was considerably more $C_2H_6$. They concluded that reaction (32) does not occur. A reinvestigation of the $:CH_2$ and $CD_4$ system (100) revealed, however, that the results are best explained by a modification of Eq. (32). Excited ethane molecules will, on redissociation, give two methyl radicals rather than methane and methylene:

$$:CH_2 + CD_4 \rightarrow CH_2D\!-\!CD_3\text{*} \xrightarrow{\;+M\;} CH_2D\!-\!CD_3$$

$$CH_2D\cdot + CD_3\cdot \tag{33}$$

$$DCH_2\!-\!CH_2D \qquad D_3C\!-\!CD_3$$

The observed isotopic distribution was consistent with Eq. (33). As expected, the amount of ethane-1,1,1,2-$d_4$ relative to all the ethanes produced increased with increasing pressure. In the presence of oxygen the ethane formed is almost exclusively ethane-$d_4$ as the association of methyl radicals is eliminated by the radical scavenger.

In attacking the carbon-hydrogen bonds of ethers (116), amines (117), and alkyl chlorides (118), methylene discriminates in favor of the $\alpha$-position. Quantitative studies established an $\alpha:\beta$ ratio of 1.23 in diethyl ether, and of 1.26 in tetrahydrofuran (photolysis of diazomethane in the liquid phase) (116). The contribution of polar resonance structures to the transition state may account for these effects (116).

With olefins and aromatic compounds, insertion of methylene into carbon-hydrogen bonds and addition to the double bonds compete at comparable rates. No discrimination between aliphatic and allylic hydrogen was observed in cyclohexene (photolysis of diazomethane in the liquid phase) (107). A slight preference of methylene for the vinyl hydrogen of cyclohexene (107) and isobutene (106) was indicated, but the reverse holds for propylene (113).

An isotope effect of $k_H/k_D = 1.3$ has been found for the insertion of methylene into secondary carbon-hydrogen bonds, using propane-2,2-$d_2$ (119). cis-2-Butene and cis-2-butene-$d_8$ have been compared in their reactions with methylene (produced by photolysis of ketene). The isotope effects for methylene insertion into the allylic and vinylic carbon-hydrogen bonds were $k_H/k_D = 1.96$ and $k_H/k_D = 1.55$, respectively.

These values indicate some C—H bond extension in the activated complex. The secondary isotope effect for double bond addition was small (6–9%) (*119a*). Stereochemically, the insertion of methylene appears to proceed with retention of configuration. The bridgehead hydrogens of bicyclic compounds such as bicyclo[2.2.2]octane undergo insertion at a normal rate although an attack from the rear is prohibited (*120*). The reaction of methylene with the diacetates of the 1,2-cyclopentanediols was studied by Franzen (*121*). Insertion into the $C_1$—H (or $C_2$—H) bonds occurred with at least 95% retention.

It may be useful to ask whether insertion is characteristic of carbenes or pertains to other excited molecules as well. No generally valid answer can yet be given. It has been suggested that excited ethylene molecules formed by mercury-sensitized irradiation may insert directly into the carbon-hydrogen bonds of propane (*122*). In a recent reinvestigation of this system, using propane-2,2-$d_2$, Chesick (*119*) has concluded that excited ethylene does not undergo one-step insertion reactions to any appreciable extent.

### 2. Abstraction

The reactions between methylene and hydrocarbons in the gas phase afford, in addition to the products of direct insertion, various compounds which are best accounted for by a radical component of the over-all reaction. The following scheme has been proposed for the methylene-propane system (*104*):

$$
\begin{aligned}
:CH_2 + CH_3CH_2CH_3 &\rightarrow n\text{-butane} \\
&\rightarrow \text{isobutane}
\end{aligned} \Bigg\}\ \text{insertion}
$$

$$
\begin{aligned}
&\rightarrow CH_3\cdot + \cdot CH_2CH_2CH_3 \rightarrow n\text{-butane} \\
&\rightarrow CH_3\cdot + CH_3\dot{C}H{-}CH_3 \rightarrow \text{isobutane} \\
2\,CH_3\cdot &\rightarrow \text{ethane} \\
2\cdot CH_2CH_2CH_3 &\rightarrow n\text{-hexane} \\
2\,CH_3\dot{C}H{-}CH_3 &\rightarrow 2,3\text{-dimethylbutane}
\end{aligned}
\tag{34}
$$

$$
\cdot CH_2CH_2CH_3 + CH_3\dot{C}HCH_3 \Big\langle \begin{aligned} &\nearrow 2\text{-methylpentane} \\ &\searrow \text{propane} + \text{propylene} \end{aligned}
$$

Quantitative analysis indicated that 78% of the products came from direct insertion, and 22% from a radical path. Formation of the "radical products" was suppressed in the presence of oxygen.

The origin of the intervening radicals has not yet been completely elucidated. Two mechanisms are conceivable: One-step abstraction of a hydrogen atom by methylene (*104*):

$$:CH_2 + R-H \rightarrow CH_3 \cdot + R \cdot \tag{35}$$

Alternatively, there may be insertion into a carbon-hydrogen bond to give an activated molecule with a methyl group at the insertion site. If the molecule is not quenched by collision, it may dissociate to give a methyl radical (*100*):

$$:CH_2 + R-H \rightarrow R-CH_3{}^* \rightarrow CH_3 \cdot + R \cdot \tag{36}$$

Equation (36) has been clearly demonstrated for the reaction of methylene with methane (*100*), but it appears less likely with higher hydrocarbons. Here the internal distribution of excess energy is very rapid as may be seen from Butler and Kistiakowsky's work on activated methylcyclopropane (*113*). The isomerization products were identical regardless of whether the activated molecules were obtained from cyclopropane and methylene (insertion), or from propylene and methylene (addition). We cannot, therefore, expect an activated molecule to break exclusively at the site of insertion, as implied in Eq. (36). Reaction (36) is probably restricted to low pressures and small molecules where the excess energy is concentrated in a few molecular vibrations. There is evidence that direct abstraction [Eq. (35)] occurs at pressures where all excited molecules would be collisionally stabilized. It has been noted that the reactivity of the various carbon-hydrogen bonds in the abstraction process corresponds to that encountered with methyl radicals (*104*).

Abstraction of hydrogen from the allyl position of olefins produces resonance-stabilized allyl radicals, and may result in a migration of the double bond. The formation of 1-butene and 3-methyl-1-butene by photolysis of diazomethane in the presence of *cis*-2-butene in the gas phase was explained in this way: (*123*)

$$\underset{H}{\overset{CH_3}{\diagdown}}C=C\underset{H}{\overset{CH_3}{\diagup}} + :CH_2 \rightarrow CH_3 \cdot \quad + \begin{bmatrix} CH_3CH=CH-CH_2 \\ \updownarrow \\ CH_3\overset{\cdot}{C}H-CH=CH_2 \end{bmatrix} \text{(IV)} \tag{37}$$

$$IV + R-H \rightarrow R \cdot + CH_3CH_2CH=CH_2$$

$$IV + CH_2N_2 \rightarrow N_2 + \underset{\underset{CH_2 \cdot}{|}}{CH_3CH-CH=CH_2} \xrightarrow{+R-H} \underset{\underset{CH_3}{|}}{CH_3CH-CH=CH_2}$$

The reaction of IV with diazomethane was considered a more realistic route to 3-methyl-1-butene than the recombination of IV with the methyl radical.

The photolysis of diazomethane in the presence of isobutene-1-$C^{14}$ led to 8% "mixing" of the isotopic label in the gas phase, whereas only 1% of "mixing" was observed in the liquid phase (*106*):

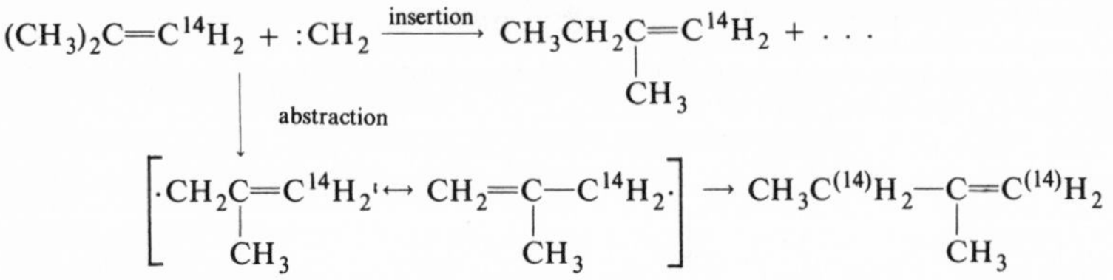

$$(CH_3)_2C{=}C^{14}H_2 + :CH_2 \xrightarrow{\text{insertion}} CH_3CH_2\underset{\underset{CH_3}{|}}{C}{=}C^{14}H_2 + \cdots \tag{38}$$

$$\Big\downarrow \text{abstraction}$$

$$\left[ \cdot CH_2\underset{\underset{CH_3}{|}}{C}{=}C^{14}H_2{}^{'} \leftrightarrow CH_2{=}\underset{\underset{CH_3}{|}}{C}{-}C^{14}H_2\cdot \right] \to CH_3C^{(14)}H_2{-}\underset{\underset{CH_3}{|}}{C}{=}C^{(14)}H_2$$

Because of the 50-50 distribution of $C^{14}$ over the positions 1 and 3 of the methallyl radical, 8% of "mixing" indicates a 16% contribution of the abstraction reaction in the gas phase. Even if radicals were formed in the liquid phase, the operation of the cage effect would almost certainly prevent appreciable mixing.

## E. Reactions with Multiple Bonds

### 1. Olefins

Carbon-carbon single bonds are inert toward methylene even in highly strained small ring compounds such as spiropentane (*120*). Carbon-carbon double bonds add methylene easily to form cyclopropanes:

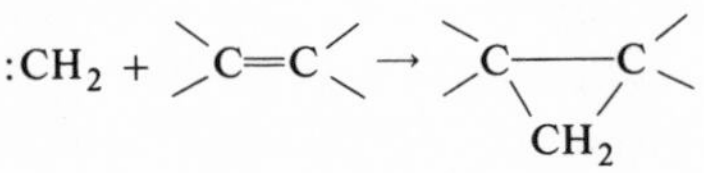

$$:CH_2 + {\scriptstyle >}C{=}C{\scriptstyle <} \to {\scriptstyle >}C\underset{\underset{CH_2}{\diagdown \diagup}}{\phantom{x}}C{\scriptstyle <} \tag{39}$$

Most addition reactions of methylene are stereospecific *cis* additions (*109, 124, 125*), e.g., *cis*-1,2-disubstituted cyclopropanes are obtained from *cis*-olefins, and *trans*-1,2-disubstituted cyclopropanes from *trans*-olefins. The stereospecificity is thought to reflect the singlet state of the reacting methylene (which is not in its ground state). Deviations from stereospecificity, although undesirable for preparative purposes, are of theoretical interest and have received much attention.

*a. Photochemical Reactions.* Methylene produced by photolysis of diazomethane and ketene carries excess energy (cf. Section D,1 and Chapter 11). Cyclopropanes formed by addition of such methylene to double bonds are originally in an excited state. In the liquid phase, and under high pressures *of the reactant* in the gas phase, the excited molecules are immediately stabilized by collision, and the geometry is retained. At low pressures in the gas phase the excited molecules may undergo *cis-trans*-isomerization (*126, 127*). The *apparent* nonstereospecificity under these conditions is due to subsequent reactions of the products which are initially formed in a stereospecific manner. The pressure limit for stereospecific addition decreases with increasing molecular weight of the olefin, i.e., increasing internal distribution of the excess energy.

It has been shown that the activation energy of geometrical isomerization is much smaller than that of structural isomerization (*126, 127*). (The former process obviously does not involve the complete rupture of a carbon-carbon bond.) Consequently, higher pressures are required to suppress geometrical isomerization as compared to structural isomerization.

In contrast to the apparent nonstereospecificity discussed in the preceding paragraph, the addition process itself will be nonstereospecific whenever methylene reacts in its triplet state. In the gas phase, under high pressures *of inert gas,* the methylene radicals may collide many times and may be converted to the triplet state before they react with the olefin. Nonstereospecific addition of methylene to *cis*- and *trans*-2-butene has been observed under these conditions (*128, 129*).

Alternatively, methylene may be produced immediately in the triplet state by sensitized photolysis. This technique involves energy transfer from the triplet state of a sensitizer to diazomethane, exciting the latter to the triplet state. Benzophenone (in the liquid phase) (*130*) and mercury (in the gas phase) (*131*) have been used as sensitizers.

It should be noted that the addition of triplet methylene to *cis*-2-butene affords appreciable amounts of *trans*-1,2-dimethylcyclopropane, whereas *trans*-2-butene gives mainly *trans*-1,2-dimethylcyclopropane with only traces of the *cis* isomer. This observation indicates that the rate of spin inversion in the diradicals involved here is comparable to the rate of rotation about carbon-carbon single bonds.

The addition of methylene to olefins is accompanied by insertion into the various carbon-hydrogen bonds. The relative rates of these reactions for some olefins are shown in Table I. These data refer to pressures sufficient for complete collisional deactivation, and have been corrected for the statistical weight of each bond type.

TABLE I

RELATIVE RATES OF ADDITION AND INSERTION REACTIONS OF METHYLENE (23)

| Olefin | :$CH_2$ source (photolysis) | Addition $\diagdown C{=}C\diagup$ | Insertion Allyl-H | Insertion Vinyl-H | Ref. |
|---|---|---|---|---|---|
| Ethylene | $CH_2N_2$ 4358 Å | 1.00 | — | 0.079 | 132 |
| | $CH_2CO$ 3130 Å | 1.00 | — | 0.036 | 126 |
| Propylene | $CH_2N_2$ unfilt. | 1.00 | 0.11 | 0.091 | 113 |
| | $CH_2CO$ 3130 Å | 1.00 | 0.060 | 0.03 | 113 |
| | $CH_2CO$ 2600 Å | 1.00 | 0.091 | 0.064 | 113 |
| Isobutene | $CH_2N_2$ unfilt. | 1.00 | 0.11 | 0.091 | 133 |
| | $CH_2CO$ 3130 A | 1.00 | 0.053 | 0.063 | 113 |
| trans-2-Butene | $CH_2N_2$ 4358 A | 1.00 | 0.15 | 0.11 | 127 |
| Allene | $CH_2N_2$ 4358 Å | 1.00 | — | 0.11 | 134 |
| 1,3-Butadiene | $CH_2N_2$ 4358 Å | 1.00 | — | $0.085^a$ | 135 |
| | $CH_2CO$ 3130 Å | 1.00 | — | $0.048^a$ | 135 |

[a] Mean values for both carbon-hydrogen bonds.

The data of Table I refer to singlet methylene. Triplet methylene produced either by spin inversion resulting from many collisions, or by sensitized photolysis, affords only minor amounts of insertion products.

Tetrafluoroethylene accepts methylene (produced by photolysis of ketene) with exclusive addition to the double bond. A tetrafluoropropene (presumably 1,1,3,3-tetrafluoropropene) obtained in the gas phase reaction was shown to arise by isomerization of excited tetrafluorocyclopropane (135a).

b. *Catalytic Reactions.* In the synthesis of cyclopropanes, the formation of complex product mixtures from the competitive addition and insertion of methylene is undesirable. The insertion reaction may be suppressed by "catalytic" decomposition of diazomethane. Dialkylaluminum halides (57), zinc halides (64–66), and cuprous halides (61, 62) are suitable catalysts. Organometallic compounds such as $R_2AlCH_2I$ (57) have been detected as intermediates in these catalytic decompositions. Iodomethylzinc iodide ($ICH_2ZnI$) is accessible not only from diazomethane and zinc iodide (64, 66), but also from methylene iodide and zinc-copper couple (90, 91). Cyclopropane formation is thought to proceed via addition of the organometallic compound to the olefin and subsequent elimination of metal halide (57):

$$M{-}CH_2X + \diagup C{=}C\diagdown \rightarrow \underset{\underset{M}{|}}{-}C\underset{\underset{CH_2X}{|}}{-}C{-} \rightarrow MX + \underset{CH_2}{-C{-}{-}{-}C{-}} \tag{40}$$

Since the cyclopropane formation is stereospecific, this mechanism implies a well-defined stereochemistry in both the addition and the elimination steps, as well as configurational stability of the organometallic intermediate. Neither of these requirements has been reasonably substantiated. Alternatively, a three-center reaction involving a one-step displacement of MX from $M-CH_2-X$ by the olefin has been considered (66, 90, 136):

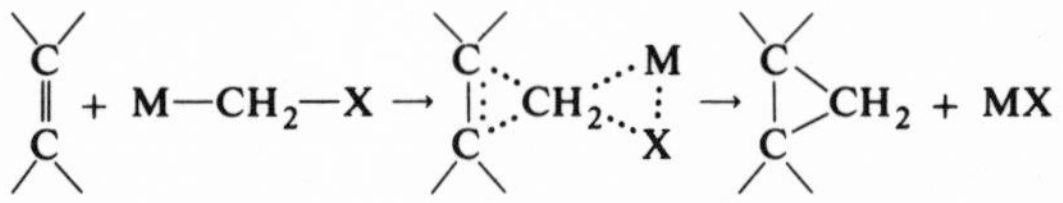

$$\underset{/C\backslash}{\overset{\backslash C/}{\|}} + M-CH_2-X \rightarrow \underset{/C\backslash}{\overset{\backslash C/}{[\overset{\cdots M}{:}CH_2\overset{\cdots}{:}]}}X \rightarrow \underset{/C\backslash}{\overset{\backslash C/}{|}}CH_2 + MX \qquad (41)$$

The role of $M-CH_2-X$ in Eq. (41) is, of course, more "methylene-like" than in Eq. (40). Notwithstanding the unresolved mechanistic problems, many useful applications in synthesis have been reported (137–139f). Some examples may demonstrate the scope and limitations of the reaction. Yields are generally higher with olefins carrying electron-donating groups. p-Methoxystyrene afforded a cyclopropane derivative in 70% yield, styrene 32%, vinyl acetate 31%, methyl crotonate 9% (90). Twofold addition to dienes occurs easily even if an excess of the olefin is used. The double bond carrying the higher number of alkyl groups is preferentially attacked in monoaddition:

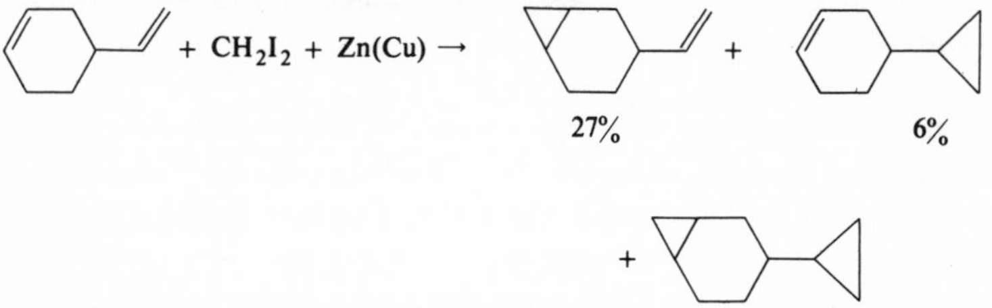

$$+ CH_2I_2 + Zn(Cu) \rightarrow \qquad + \qquad \qquad (42)$$

27%                                    6%

$$+$$

67%            (138)

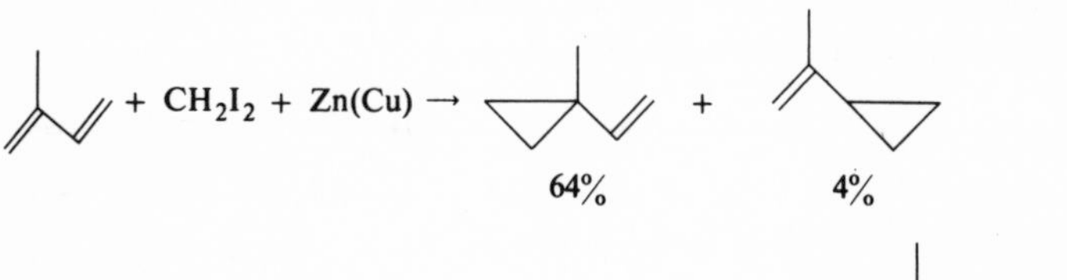

$$+ CH_2I_2 + Zn(Cu) \rightarrow \qquad + \qquad \qquad (43)$$

64%                    4%

$$+$$

32%      (139)

These findings indicate that the $ICH_2ZnI$ intermediate behaves as an electrophilic reagent. Successful application in the synthesis of dicyclopropylmercury from divinylmercury has been reported (*139a*). Various allyl- and vinylsilanes and -germanes $(R_3M—CH_2H=CH_2, R_3M—CH=CH_2; M=Si,Ge; R=Me, Et)$ have been converted to the corresponding cyclopropanes (*139c*). Hydroxyl groups do not interfere with the cyclopropane synthesis by means of methylene iodide and zinc-copper couple (*137*):

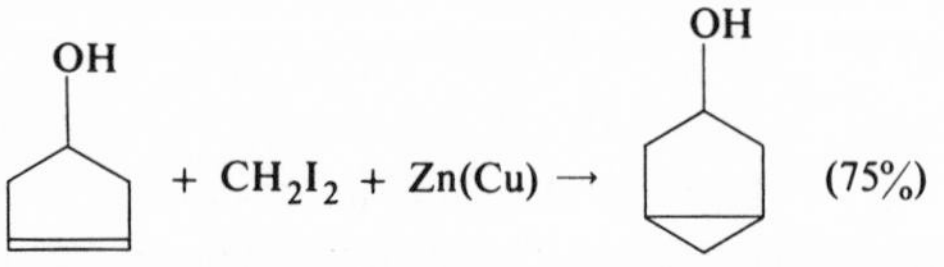

$$\text{(equation 44)} \qquad (75\%) \qquad (44)$$

A wide variety of cyclic allyl alcohols, all possessing a flexible ring system, have been converted to cyclic cyclopropylcarbinols in good yields (*139b*). The reaction was found to be stereospecific: the presence of a free hydroxyl group, or an alkoxy group, directs the introduction of the cyclopropane ring in a *cis* manner.

In addition, the hydroxyl groups also strongly facilitate the reaction, as was shown by competition experiments. The formation of a complex has been suggested as the first stage. In contrast, the related esters (allyl acetates) were attacked from the less hindered side and formed product in low yield.

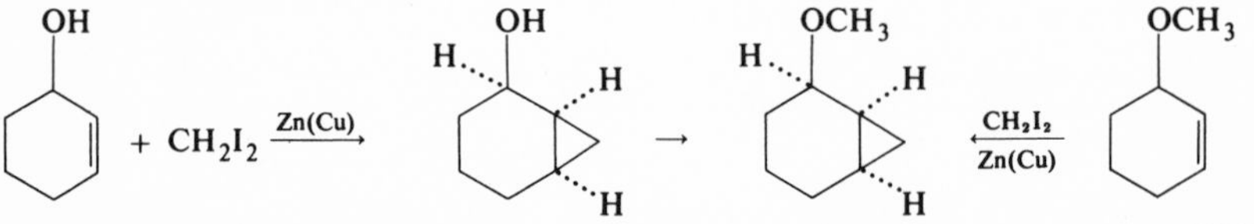

$$(44a)$$

The accelerating and directing effect of hydroxyl groups has been utilized in the synthesis of the bicyclic alcohols IVa (*139d*) and IVb (*139e*), in the course of homoaromaticity studies.

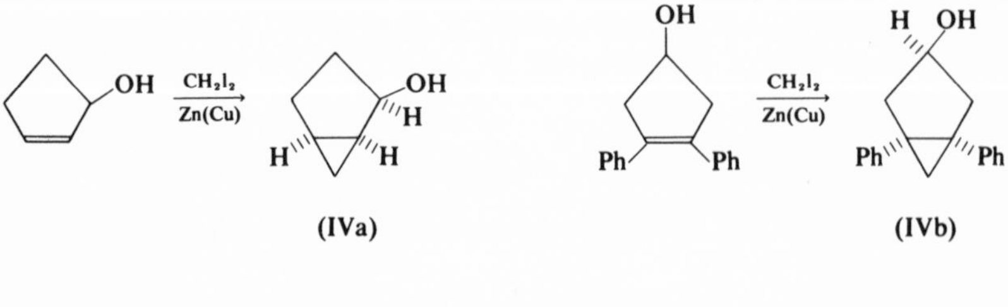

(IVa)                                              (IVb)

The total synthesis of $(\pm)$ = thujopsene (IVc), a tricyclic sesquiter-pene, has been achieved by the same method (*139f*):

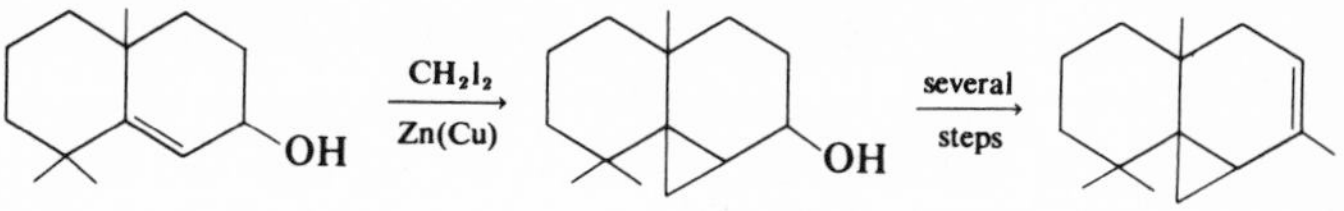

(IVc)

*c. Reversibility.* Obviously the addition of methylene to olefins cannot be reversed. One example of such a reversal ("extrusion" of methylene from cyclopropanes to give olefins) had been reported to account for some minor products in the pyrolysis of thujone (*140*). The underlying assignment of structure to these compounds, however, turned out to be incorrect (*141*).

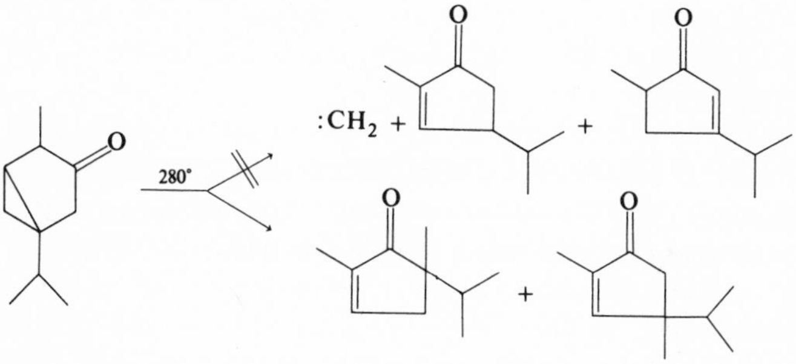

## 2. Dienes

Methylenecyclopropane has been obtained in 60–70% yield from the addition of methylene to allene (*134, 142*). Derivatives of methylene-cyclopropane and of spiropentane were produced from the allene V, methylene iodide, and zinc-copper couple (*143*).

Application of the Simmons-Smith reaction to an allene is also involved in a recent synthesis of hypoglycine A (Va) (*143a*).

$$CH_2=C=CH-CH_2-CO_2R + CH_2I_2 + Zn(Cu)$$

(V)

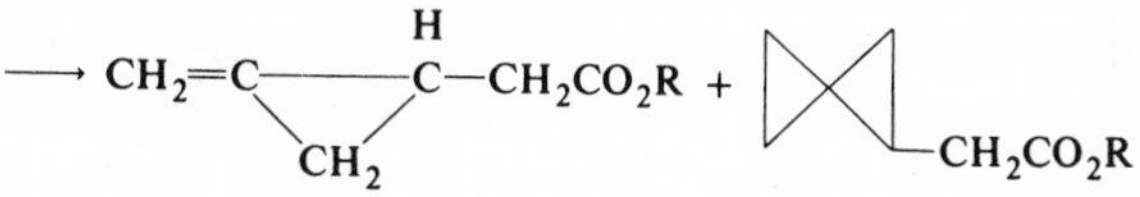

$$CH_2=C=CH-CH_2\underset{\underset{NH-CHO}{|}}{C}(CO_2Et)_2 \xrightarrow{\underset{Zn(Cu)}{CH_2I_2}} CH_2=C\overset{\overset{CH_2}{\diagup\diagdown}}{\phantom{m}}CH-CH_2\underset{\underset{NH-CHO}{|}}{C}(CO_2Et)_2$$

$$\rightarrow CH_2=C\overset{\overset{CH_2}{\diagup\diagdown}}{\phantom{m}}CH-CH_2-\underset{\underset{NH_2}{|}}{C}H-CO_2H \qquad (Va)$$

The reaction between methylene and butadiene appears to proceed by 1,2- rather than 1,4-addition. Vinylcyclopropane is the major product (*144*). The formation of some cyclopentene has been attributed to 1,4-addition by Franzen (*145*), and to the isomerization of activated vinylcyclopropane by Frey (*146*) and Flowers.

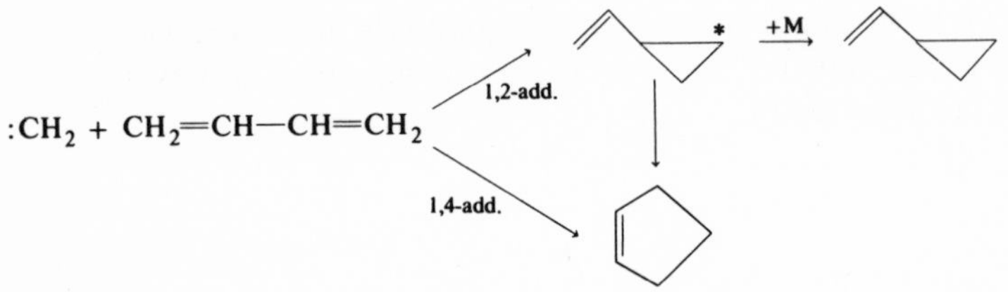

$$:CH_2 + CH_2=CH-CH=CH_2 \qquad\qquad (47)$$

Careful studies of the thermal isomerization of vinylcyclopropane (*147*) have revealed two distinct mechanisms. One proceeds with a particularly small energy of activation to give cyclopentene. The other is comparable to the isomerization of alkylcyclopropanes and affords a mixture of pentadienes. In view of the work of Flowers and Frey it appears improbable that complete collisional deactivation has been achieved under the conditions used by Franzen. On the other hand, Trotman-Dickenson *et al.* (*144*) state that some cyclopentene is formed even under high pressures. Although the possibility of 1,4-addition still awaits final elucidation, it is clear that it makes, at most, a minor contribution to the reaction between methylene and 1,3-butadiene.

Treatment of 1,3-dienes with methylene iodide and zinc-copper couple leads to mono- and diadducts of methylene (*139, 147a*) [cf. Eq. (43)]. Butadiene, with 0.5 (0.8) moles of methylene iodide at 60°, afforded 26 (26)% of vinylcyclopropane and 7 (23)% of dicyclopropyl (*147a*).

The catalyzed reaction of diazomethane with various polyenes has been studied. Passing gaseous diazomethane, carried by a stream of nitrogen, into a suspension of copper powder or cuprous chloride in the olefin appears to be the most effective method ("Gaspar-Roth recipe")

(*147b*).   *cis*-Hexa-1,3,5-triene afforded all possible cyclopropanation products [Eq. (47a)] except *cis*-1,2-divinylcyclopropane.   Instead cyclohepta-1,4-diene (formed by Cope rearrangement of *cis*-1,2-divinylcyclopropane) and products of its further cyclopropanation were isolated (*147b*).

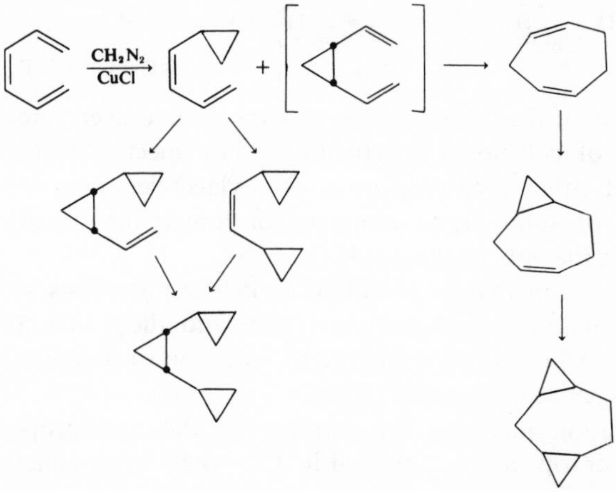

(47a)

   *trans*-1,2-Divinylcyclopropane was obtained, among other products, from *trans*-1,3,5-hexatriene (*147b*).   Application of the same method to cycloheptatriene afforded bicyclo[5.1.0]octa-2,4-diene (Vb) and bicyclo-[5.1.0]octa-2,5-diene ("homotropilidene") (Vc).   Vc undergoes a rapidly reversible, degenerate Cope rearrangement (*147b*).

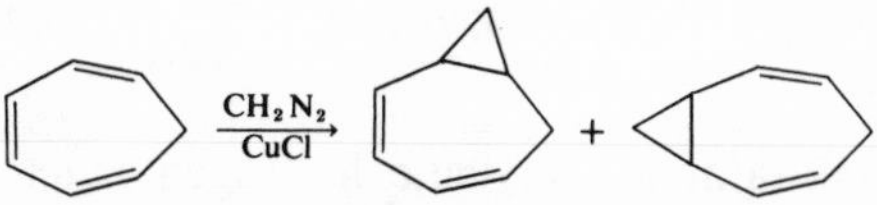

(Vb)               (Vc)

Similarly, cyclooctatetraene reacted to give bicyclo[6.1.0]nona-2,4,6-triene (Vd).   Rearrangement of Vd at 90° produced mainly *cis*-bicyclo-[4.3.0]nona-2,4,7-triene (Ve) (*156*).

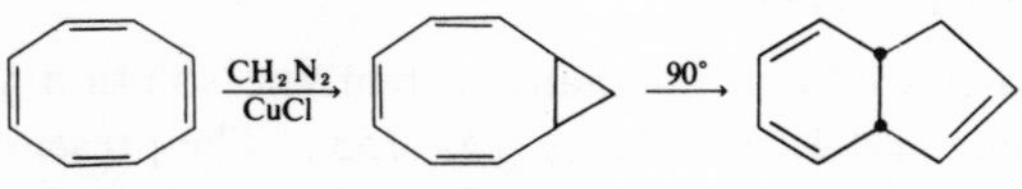

(Vd)               (Ve)

### 3. Acetylenes

The photolysis of diazomethane in the presence of acetylene gives allene and propyne instead of the expected cyclopropene. The formation of allene-1,1-$d_2$ from acetylene-1,2-$d_2$ indicates that the allene arises by way of a cyclopropene intermediate (148).

$$D-C\equiv C-D + :CH_2 \rightarrow \left[ \begin{array}{c} D-C{=\!\!=}C-D \\ \diagdown \diagup \\ CH_2 \end{array} \right] \rightarrow \begin{array}{l} CH_2{=}C{=}CD_2 \\ + CH_2D-C\equiv C-D \end{array} \tag{48}$$

Trapping of the cyclopropene was impossible even under favorable conditions of collisional deactivation. No spectral evidence for the presence of either cyclopropene or methylacetylene was obtained after photolysis of solid argon–acetylene–diazomethane deposits at 4°K., allene being the only product (148a).

Reaction of methylene produced by ketene photolysis with acetylene in the gas phase afforded methylacetylene and allene in a constant ratio of 1.5 ± 0.3 which was not affected by variation of pressure, or by addition of oxygen or nitric oxide (148b).

Substitution increases the stability of the cyclopropenes: 1,2-dimethylcyclopropene was obtained in 17% yield from dimethylacetylene and diazomethane (149).

The synthesis of sterculic acid (VI) was accomplished by reacting stearolic acid with methylene iodide and zinc-copper couple (150). The product was contaminated, however, with isomers containing exocyclic double bonds.

$$\begin{array}{l} CH_3(CH_2)_7C\equiv C(CH_2)_7CO_2H + CH_2I_2 \rightarrow CH_3(CH_2)_7C{=\!\!=}C(CH_2)_7CO_2H \\ \qquad\qquad\qquad + Zn(Cu) \qquad\qquad\qquad\qquad\qquad \diagdown\diagup \\ \qquad\qquad\qquad\qquad\qquad\qquad (VI) \qquad\qquad CH_2 \qquad\qquad\qquad (49) \end{array}$$

Compounds containing acetylenic hydrogen react with methylene iodide and zinc-copper couple to give the corresponding methylacetylenes. If double bonds are present within the same molecule, competitive or exclusive cyclopropane formation at the olefinic site takes place (151).

### 4. Aromatic Compounds

The photolysis of diazomethane in benzene solution yields 32% of cycloheptatriene and 9% of toluene (152, 153). The presence of norcaradiene in the product mixture, observed by Meerwein et al. (154), has not been confirmed by other authors (*153, 155*). The "valence tautomers," cycloheptatriene and norcaradiene, are apparently not separable. Spectroscopic studies on compounds having a norcaradiene-like structure, such as (VII), indicate that norcaradiene contributes little to the cycloheptatriene⇌norcaradiene equilibrium (*156*).

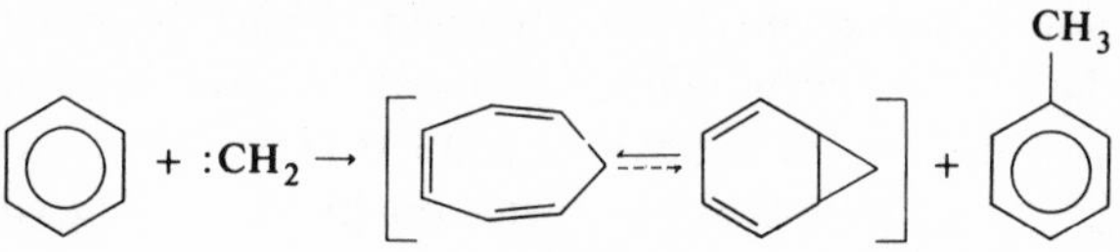

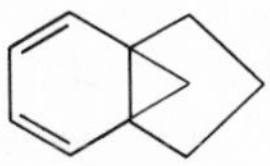

(VII)

(50)

The relative amounts of cycloheptatriene and toluene formed by attack of methylene on benzene were found to depend on the solvent. The ratio of cycloheptatriene/toluene increased from 3.3 (vapor phase) to 3.7 (2 $M$ solution of benzene in cyclohexane), 4.8 (pure benzene = 11.4 $M$), and 7.0 (2 $M$ solution of benzene in *tert*-butyl-naphthalene). The obvious effect of aromatic solvents has been discussed in terms of $\pi$-complexes of methylene (*156a*).

Toluene formed from benzene and $C^{14}H_2N_2$ contains all of the $C^{14}$ in the methyl group. We may conclude that the excess energy introduced by methylene is not sufficient to effect a profound reorganization of the carbon atoms. Such a reorganization, leading to the incorporation of $C^{14}$ in the aromatic nucleus, has been observed in the formation of toluene from benzene and recoiling $C^{14}$ atoms (*157*).

Cycloheptatriene not contaminated with toluene has been obtained from the catalyzed reaction of diazomethane with benzene. Cuprous chloride (yield of cycloheptatriene 85%, based on diazomethane), cuprous bromide (85%), and cupric chloride (80%) were the most efficient catalysts among 18 metals and metal salts employed (*62, 157a*).

The reaction of substituted benzenes with methylene has been reported (*153, 154*) but estimations of the isomer ratio are rare. Photolysis of diazomethane in anisole, and subsequent cleavage of the cresol ethers obtained, gave approximately equal amounts of *o*-, *m*-, and *p*-cresol (*154*). Treatment of pyridine under similar conditions yielded exclusively 2-methylpyridine (*158*).

The cuprous halide catalyzed reaction of diazomethane with various substituted benzenes afforded mixtures of 1-, 2-, and 3-substituted cycloheptatrienes (*157b*). The relative yields are governed by steric and electronic effects, in agreement with the concept of electrophilic attack on the benzene nucleus. Ring expansion with formation of an *A*-homo steroid has been achieved by treatment of β-estradiol dimethyl ether with diazomethane and cuprous halides (*157c*).

The crude product mixtures obtained from diazomethane and various indans have been dehydrogenated to give azulenes without previous separation of the methylene adducts (*159–163*). According to Treibs (*162, 163*), the formation of diazomethane *in situ* (from nitrosomethylurea) is advantageous. The azulenes made by this technique are listed in a review (*164*). The tricyclic hydrocarbon VII was detected among the products of the indan-diazomethane-cuprous chloride reaction (0.5–1% yield) (*156*). Cyclopropanation of furan and thiophene has been brought about, without competing insertion into C—H bonds, by both photochemical and catalytic decomposition of diazomethane (*157d*).

A surprisingly selective reaction of methylene was reported with phenylsilane, diphenylsilane, and diphenylgermane. Photolysis of diazomethane in the presence of these compounds led to exclusive insertion of methylene into the silicon-hydrogen and germanium-hydrogen bonds, respectively, with no detectable attack on the phenyl groups (*164a*).

## F. Reactions with Carbon-Oxygen Bonds

The first event attracting attention to the reactivity of methylene was the isolation of *n*-propyl ethyl ether and isopropyl ethyl ether from the photolysis of diazomethane in diethyl ether (*165*). This reaction is now recognized as an insertion of methylene into carbon-hydrogen bonds, but was previously thought to proceed by addition of methylene to the nonbonding electron pair of the oxygen, followed by rearrangement of the resulting ylide VIII (*166*):

$$R\!-\!O\!-\!CH_2CH_3 + :CH_2 \rightarrow \left[ \overset{\oplus}{\underset{\ominus CH_2}{R\!-\!O}}\!-\!CH_2CH_3 \right] \rightarrow R\!-\!O\!-\!CH_2CH_2CH_3$$

$$\downarrow \text{(VIII)} \tag{51}$$

$$\left[ \overset{\oplus}{R}\!-\!\overset{\ominus}{O}\!-\!\underset{CH_3}{CH}\!-\!CH_3 \right] \rightarrow R\!-\!O\!-\!\underset{CH_3}{CH}\!-\!CH_3$$

Since Eq. (51) would involve reaction of the carbon-oxygen bond, arguments against the "ylide mechanism," which have been obtained on the basis of $C^{14}$-labeling (*167*), should be summarized here. Diethyl ether and $C^{14}H_2$ (from $C^{14}H_2N_2$) afforded ethyl *n*-propyl ether carrying $C^{14}$ only in the terminal position, and not adjacent to the oxygen as required by the ylide mechanism. $C^{14}H_3$—O—$CH_2CH_2CH_2CH_3$ and :$CH_2$ afforded

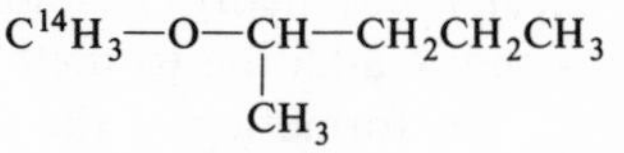

$$C^{14}H_3-O-\underset{\underset{CH_3}{|}}{CH}-CH_2CH_2CH_3$$

whereas 50% of

$$CH_3O-\underset{\underset{C^{14}H_3}{|}}{CH}-CH_2CH_2CH_3$$

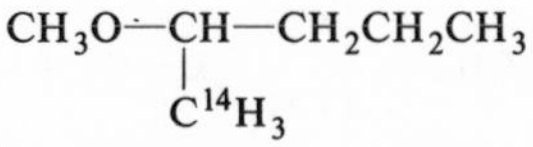

should be expected from the ylide

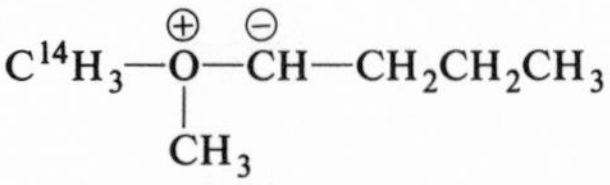

$$C^{14}H_3-\overset{\oplus}{O}-\underset{\underset{CH_3}{|}}{\overset{\ominus}{CH}}-CH_2CH_2CH_3$$

where both methyl groups attached to oxygen are equivalent.

The ylide mechanism has been retained, however, to account for the formation of methyl ethers and olefins in addition to the insertion products mentioned above (*167*). This view is supported by analogy with some special cases of the Hofmann elimination ($\alpha'$-$\beta$ type) where the intermediacy of an ylide has been demonstrated (*168*, *169*).

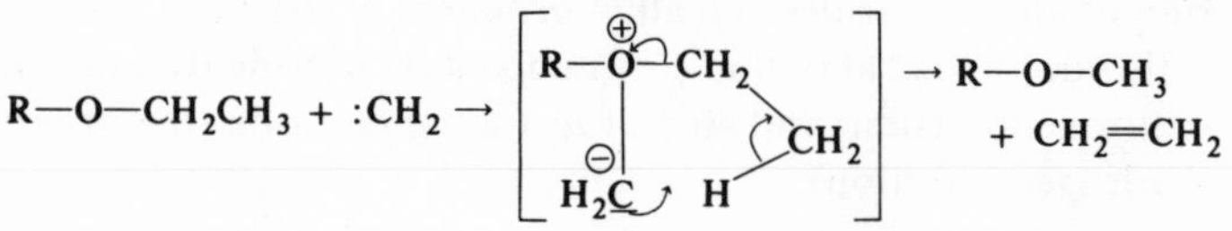

$$R-O-CH_2CH_3 + :CH_2 \rightarrow \left[ \begin{array}{c} R-\overset{\oplus}{O}\frown CH_2 \\ \overset{\ominus}{\underset{H_2C}{|}} \underset{\,H}{\overset{}{\frown}} CH_2 \end{array} \right] \rightarrow \begin{array}{c} R-O-CH_3 \\ + CH_2{=}CH_2 \end{array} \qquad (52)$$

The photolysis of diazomethane in ketones or esters gave products identical with those obtained by Lewis acid-catalysis in the dark (*154*):

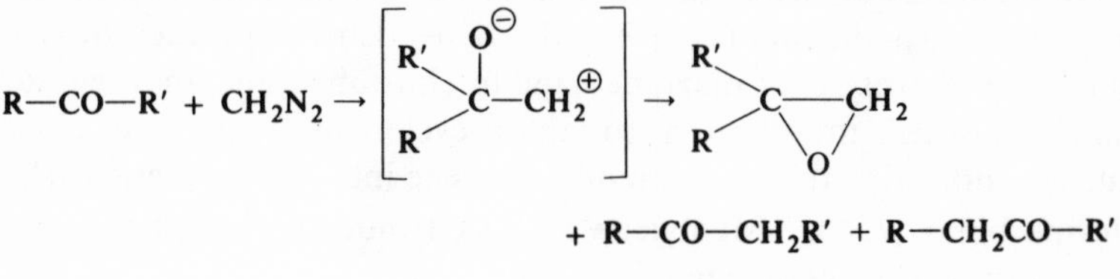

$$R-CO-R' + CH_2N_2 \rightarrow \left[ \begin{array}{c} R' \overset{\overset{O^{\ominus}}{|}}{\underset{R}{\diagup}} C-CH_2^{\oplus} \end{array} \right] \rightarrow \begin{array}{c} R' \\ \underset{R}{\diagup} C \overset{}{\underset{O}{\diagdown}} CH_2 \end{array} \qquad (53)$$

$$+ R-CO-CH_2R' + R-CH_2CO-R'$$

The formation of these compounds clearly involves nucleophilic attack on the carbonyl carbon atom. The reactant, therefore, is probably not methylene but rather diazomethane itself.

In a recent reinvestigation of the acetone-diazomethane reaction (*169a*), attack of an excited acetone molecule on ground state diazomethane was assumed for the UV region < 3200 Å. With light of wavelength > 3200 Å, diazomethane was believed to be the absorbing species. Under these conditions, 2,2,4,4-tetramethyl-1,3-dioxolane (IX) and 2-methoxypropene were obtained in addition to methyl ethyl ketone and 1,2-epoxy-2-methylpropane. The formation of the former products was explained in terms of a dipolar intermediate (VIIIa).

$$CH_3-C-CH_3 + :CH_2 \rightarrow \left[\begin{matrix} CH_3 \\ \phantom{}\\ CH_3 \end{matrix} \overset{\oplus}{>}C-O-\overset{\ominus}{\underline{C}}H_2 \right] \quad (VIIIa)$$

$$\underset{\nearrow + CH_3COCH_3}{} \qquad \underset{\searrow \sim H}{} \qquad (53a)$$

$$(CH_3)_2C-CH_2 \qquad\qquad CH_2=C-O-CH_3$$

(IX), with bridging $O$, $O$, $C$, $CH_3$, $CH_3$ and $CH_3$ group on the methoxypropene.

## G.  Reactions with Carbon-Halogen Bonds

In the case of alkyl fluorides, methylene inserts only into the carbon-hydrogen bonds, the carbon-fluorine bond being inert (*120, 135a*). On the other hand, there is a strong preference for insertion into the carbon-halogen bond of alkyl chlorides and alkyl bromides (*170*). For instance, *tert*-butyl chloride yielded about 60% of neopentyl chloride (the product of carbon-chlorine insertion) and 40% of *tert*-amyl chloride (the product of carbon-hydrogen insertion):

$$(CH_3)_3C-Cl + :CH_2 \rightarrow (CH_3)_3C-CH_2Cl + CH_3CH_2\underset{\underset{Cl}{|}}{C}(CH_3)_2 \quad (54)$$

Different reactivities of various alkyl chlorides have been observed in competition experiments (*118*) but the dependence on structure is not clear. The photolysis of diazomethane in chlorobenzene afforded some benzyl chloride, in addition to chlorocycloheptatriene and chlorotoluenes, indicating the insertion of methylene into the aromatic carbon-chlorine bond (*154*). Methylene attacks trifluoroiodomethane exclusively at the carbon-iodine bond (*170a*):

$$F_3C \!-\! I + CH_2N_2 \xrightarrow[\substack{gas \\ phase}]{h\nu} F_3C \!-\! CH_2I + F_3C \!-\! CH_2CH_2I$$

The mechanism of methylene insertion into carbon-halogen bonds probably differs from that of insertion into carbon-hydrogen bonds. The insertion of methylene into the carbon-chlorine bond of optically active 2-chlorobutane proceeded with 90% racemization (10% retention) (*120*). Insertion into the carbon-chlorine bond of methallyl chloride-1-$C^{14}$ led to considerable "mixing" of the isotopic label (*120*). These results suggest that radical abstraction of halogen is the first step in the reaction of methylene with carbon-halogen bonds. In many cases the radicals formed will recombine (eventually within the solvent cage), leading to apparent insertion. With polyhalomethanes, however, recombination is delayed and methylene initiates a radical chain reaction (*171*):

$$:CH_2 + CCl_4 \rightarrow \cdot CH_2Cl + \cdot CCl_3$$

$$\cdot CCl_3 + CH_2N_2 \rightarrow N_2 + \cdot CH_2CCl_3 \rightarrow ClCH_2\overset{\cdot}{C}Cl_2 \qquad (55)$$

$$ClCH_2\overset{\cdot}{C}Cl_2 + CH_2N_2 \rightarrow N_2 + \cdot CH_2CCl_2 \rightarrow \underset{\underset{CH_2Cl}{|}}{(ClCH_2)_2\overset{\cdot}{C}Cl}$$

$$(ClCH_2)_2\overset{\cdot}{C}Cl + CH_2N_2 \rightarrow N_2 + \cdot CH_2C(CH_2Cl)_2 \rightarrow \underset{\underset{Cl}{|}}{(ClCH_2)_3\overset{\cdot}{C}\cdot}$$

$$(ClCH_2)_3C\cdot + CH_2N_2 \rightarrow N_2 + \cdot CH_2C(CH_2Cl)_3$$

$$(ClCH_2)_3C \!-\! CH_2\cdot + CCl_4 \rightarrow (ClCH_2)_4C + \cdot CCl_3$$

The fast migration of chlorine in the intermediate radicals is thought to prevent chain transfer at an early stage, and to make $C(CH_2Cl)_4$ the major product (60%). The high quantum yield and the inhibiting effect of radical scavengers support the chain mechanism. $BrCCl_3$, $HCCl_3$, and $Cl_3C \!-\! CO_2R$ react according to Eq. (55). Starting with $CBr_4$, $CBr_2Cl_2$, $CHBr_3$, and $CHI_3$ however, the intervening radicals will eliminate $Br\cdot$ (or $I\cdot$) rather than rearrange (*172*). Methylene bromide and 1,1-dibromoethylene were the major products obtained from carbon tetrabromide and diazomethane:

$$:CH_2 + CBr_4 \rightarrow \cdot CH_2Br + \cdot CBr_3$$

$$\cdot CBr_3 + CH_2N_2 \rightarrow N_2 + \cdot CH_2CBr_3 \rightarrow CH_2 \!=\! CBr_2 + Br\cdot \qquad (56)$$

$$Br\cdot + CH_2N_2 \rightarrow N_2 + BrCH_2\cdot$$

$$BrCH_2\cdot + CBr_4 \rightarrow CH_2Br_2 + \cdot CBr_3$$

## H.  Reactions with Organometallic Compounds

Attempts to produce methylene by $\alpha$-elimination invariably lead to products which may be derived by the addition of methylene to the organometallic compounds used as strong bases in the elimination reaction.  Equation (57) has been proposed to account for the formation of some ethylbenzene and traces of n-propylbenzene from methyl chloride and phenyl sodium (78).  Benzyl sodium, the postulated intermediate in this scheme, should not be formed from the metalation of toluene by phenyl sodium under the conditions used in this work.  Transmetalation can be definitely ruled out for the reaction of methyl chloride with amyl sodium, in which the formation of some n-heptane has been observed (79).

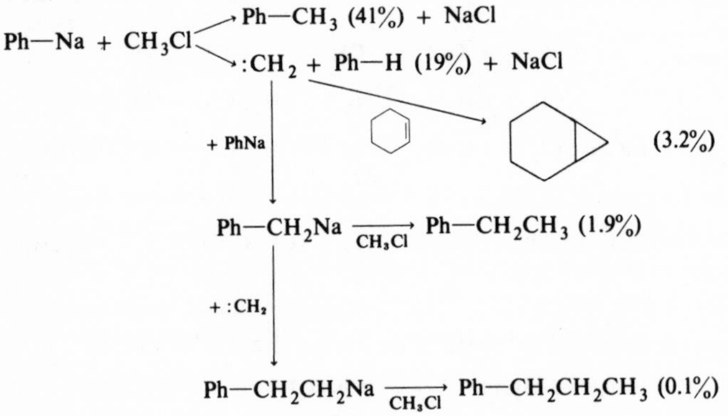

$$Ph-Na + CH_3Cl \begin{cases} \longrightarrow Ph-CH_3 \ (41\%) + NaCl \\ \longrightarrow :CH_2 + Ph-H \ (19\%) + NaCl \end{cases}$$

$$+ PhNa \downarrow \qquad \bigcirc \longrightarrow \bigtriangleup\!\!\!\bigcirc \quad (3.2\%) \qquad (57)$$

$$Ph-CH_2Na \xrightarrow[CH_3Cl]{} Ph-CH_2CH_3 \ (1.9\%)$$

$$+ :CH_2 \downarrow$$

$$Ph-CH_2CH_2Na \xrightarrow[CH_3Cl]{} Ph-CH_2CH_2CH_3 \ (0.1\%)$$

A variety of similar reactions is known.  A mixture of n-alkanes ($C_5$–$C_{10}$) has been obtained from dimethyl ether, or n-butyl methyl ether, and butyl lithium (173).  If methylene bromide reacts with lithium alkyls (aryls), bromine instead of hydrogen is transferred.  Methylene bromide and phenyl lithium afforded bromobenzene (25%), benzyl bromide (21%), and dibenzyl (37%) (174).  $S_N2$ displacement to give benzyl bromide cannot be ruled out with certainty in this case.  The formation of methyl bromide (5%), ethyl bromide (48%), and n-propyl bromide (13%) from methylene bromide and methyl lithium is not consistent, however, with a displacement mechanism (175).  Displacement would not account for the n-propyl bromide, and it does not even account for the ethyl bromide, as no ethyl chloride was obtained from bromochloromethane and methyl lithium (175).  It follows that the reactions discussed here can be represented in general form by Eq. (58).

$$2R\text{—}M + X\text{—}CH_2\text{—}Y \rightarrow R\text{—}CH_2\text{—}M + R\text{—}X + M\text{—}Y$$

X = H, Br
Y = Cl, Br, OCH$_3$

$$\downarrow X\text{—}CH_2\text{—}Y$$

$$R\text{—}CH_2CH_2\text{—}M + R\text{—}CH_2X + M\text{—}Y \qquad (58)$$

$$\downarrow X\text{—}CH_2\text{—}Y$$

$$R\text{—}CH_2CH_2CH_2\text{—}M + R\text{—}CH_2CH_2X + M\text{—}Y$$

$$\vdots$$

The individual steps of Eq. (58) are less clear. The elimination of X and Y from X—CH$_2$—Y may well be a two-step process, and R—CH$_2$—M may result either by addition of methylene to R—M, or by displacement at an intermediate M—CH$_2$—Y:

$$R\text{—}M + X\text{—}CH_2\text{—}Y \xrightarrow{-RX} M\text{—}CH_2\text{—}Y \xrightarrow[(S_N1)]{-MY} :C_2 \qquad (59)$$

$$\begin{array}{ccc} & +R\text{—}M \downarrow (S_N2) & \diagdown +R\text{—}M \\ & R\text{—}CH_2M + M\text{—}Y & R\text{—}CH_2M \end{array}$$

The formation of cyclopropanes from olefins in the methyl chloride–phenyl sodium (78), dimethyl ether–butyl lithium (57), and methylene bromide–methyl lithium (84) systems has been taken as evidence for the intervention of methylene. This evidence is not convincing, however, in view of the well-established capacity of stable M—CH$_2$—X structures (R$_2$AlCH$_2$X, IZnCH$_2$I) to convert olefins to cyclopropanes. Insertion of methylene into the carbon-hydrogen bonds of the solvent has not been observed in elimination reactions [for one possible exception see (89)]. To explain the result of such reactions, we are left, therefore, with the choice of either assuming a methylene of unusually low reactivity, or an organometallic compound, M—CH$_2$—Y, of unusually high reactivity.

Referring to the hypothetical intermediate, M—CH$_2$—Y, the two alternative mechanisms may be regarded as $S_N1$ and $S_N2$ processes, respectively. Since the conventional mechanistic criteria, such as reaction order, solvent effects, and Walden inversion, cannot be applied, it will be difficult to resolve the ambiguity indicated in Eq. (59).

## REFERENCES

1. J. E. Lennard-Jones, *Trans. Faraday Soc.* **30**, 70 (1934).
2. C. A. McDowell, *Discussions Faraday Soc.* **2**, 143 (1947).
3. K. J. Laidler and E. J. Casey, *J. Chem. Phys.* **17**, 213 (1949).

4. J. E. Lennard-Jones and J. A. Pople, *Discussions Faraday Soc.* **10**, 9 (1951).
5. A. D. Walsh, *J. Chem. Soc.* **1953**, 2260.
6. G. A. Gallup, *J. Chem. Phys.* **26**, 716 (1957).
7. J. M. Foster and S. F. Boys, *Rev. Mod. Phys.* **32**, 305 (1960).
8. G. Herzberg, *Astrophys. J.* **96**, 314 (1942); *Rev. Mod. Phys.* **14**, 195 (1942).
9. R. Herman, *Compt. rend.* **223**, 281 (1946).
10. P. Goldfinger, P. LeGoff, and M. Letort, *Compt. rend.* **227**, 632 (1948).
11. A. Monfils and B. Rosen, *Nature* **164**, 713 (1949).
12. A. E. Douglas, *Astrophys. J.* **114**, 406 (1951).
13. K. Clusius and A. E. Douglas, *Can. J. Phys.* **32**, 319 (1954).
14. D. A. Ramsay, *Ann. N. Y. Acad. Sci.* **67**, 485 (1957).
15. G. Herzberg and J. Shoosmith, *Nature* **183**, 1801 (1959).
16. G. Herzberg, *Proc. Roy. Soc.* **A262**, 291 (1961).
17. F. P. Lossing, K. U. Ingold, and I. H. S. Henderson, *J. Chem. Phys.* **22**, 621 (1954).
18. A. Langer, J. A. Hipple, and D. P. Stevenson, *J. Chem. Phys.* **22**, 1836 (1954).
19. F. P. Lossing, *Ann. N. Y. Acad. Sci.* **67**, 499 (1957).
20. R. I. Reed and W. Snedden, *Trans. Faraday Soc.* **55**, 876 (1959).
21. E. W. C. Clark and C. A. McDowell, *Proc. Chem. Soc.* **1960**, 69.
22. W. A. Chupka, D. J. Meschi, and J. Berkowitz, Paper presented at the 18th Intern. Congr. of Pure and Applied Chemistry, Montreal, Canada, 1961.
23. H. M. Frey *in* "Progress in Reaction Kinetics," Vol. II. Pergamon Press, New York. In press.
24. J. Schmidlin and M. Bergmann, *Ber. deut. chem. Ges.* **43**, 2821 (1910).
25. H. Staudinger and O. Kupfer, *Ber. deut. chem. Ges.* **45**, 501 (1912).
26. J. A. Müller and E. Peyral, *Compt. rend.* **196**, 279 (1933).
27. A. T. Williamson, *J. Am. Chem. Soc.* **56**, 2216 (1934).
28. A. N. Strachan and W. A. Noyes, *J. Am. Chem. Soc.* **76**, 3258 (1954).
29. W. A. Noyes, G. B. Porter, and I. E. Jolley, *Chem. Revs.* **56**, 49 (1956).
30. G. B. Porter, *J. Am. Chem. Soc.* **79**, 827 (1957).
31. G. B. Porter, *J. Am. Chem. Soc.* **79**, 1878 (1957).
32. G. B. Kistiakowsky and W. L. Marshall, *J. Am. Chem. Soc.* **74**, 88 (1952).
33. T. B. Wilson and G. B. Kistiakowsky, *J. Am. Chem. Soc.* **80**, 2934 (1958).
34. W. F. Ross and G. B. Kistiakowsky, *J. Am. Chem. Soc.* **56**, 1112 (1934).
35. R. G. W. Norrish, H. G. Crone, and O. Saltmarsh, *J. Chem. Soc.* **1933**, 1533; *J. Am. Chem. Soc.* **56**, 1644 (1934).
36. G. B. Kistiakowsky and N. W. Rosenberg, *J. Am. Chem. Soc.* **72**, 321 (1950).
37. G. B. Kistiakowsky and K. Sauer, *J. Am. Chem. Soc.* **78**, 5699 (1956); **80**, 1066 (1958).
38. T. G. Pearson, R. H. Purcell, and G. S. Saigh, *J. Chem. Soc.* **1938**, 409.
39. R. G. W. Norrish and G. B. Porter, *Discussions Faraday Soc.* **2**, 97 (1947).
40. G. B. Kistiakowsky and P. H. Kydd, *J. Am. Chem. Soc.* **79**, 4825 (1957).
41. K. H. Sauer, Ph.D. Thesis, Harvard University, 1957.
42. K. Knox, R. G. W. Norrish, and G. Porter, *J. Chem. Soc.* **1952**, 1477.
43. F. O. Rice and A. L. Glasebrook, *J. Am. Chem. Soc.* **55**, 4329 (1933); **56**, 2381 (1934).
44. B. S. Rabinovitch and D. W. Setser, *J. Am. Chem. Soc.* **83**, 750 (1961).
45. P. S. Shantarovitch, *Doklady Akad. Nauk S.S.S.R.* **116**, 255 (1957).

46. A. Hantzsch and M. Lehmann, *Ber. deut. chem. Ges.* **34**, 2522 (1901).
47. Th. Curtius, A. Darapsky, and E. Müller, *Ber. deut. chem. Ges.* **41**, 3168 (1908).
48. F. W. Kirkbridge and R. G. W. Norrish, *J. Chem. Soc.* **1933**, 119.
49. H. M. Frey, *J. Am. Chem. Soc.* **82**, 5947 (1960).
50. H. Meerwein, *Angew. Chem.* **60A**, 78 (1948).
51. G. D. Buckley and N. H. Ray, *J. Chem. Soc.* **1952**, 3701.
52. S. W. Cantor and R. C. Osthoff, *J. Am. Chem. Soc.* **75**, 931 (1953).
53. C. E. H. Bawn and T. B. Rhodes, *Trans. Faraday Soc.* **50**, 934 (1954).
54. J. Feltzin, A. J. Restanio, and R. B. Mesrobian, *J. Am. Chem. Soc.* **77**, 206 (1955).
55. A. G. Davies, D. G. Hare, O. R. Khan, and J. Sikora, *Proc. Chem. Soc.* **1961**, 172.
56. J. Goubeau and K. H. Rohwedder, *Ann.* **604**, 168 (1957).
57. H. Hoberg, *Angew. Chem.* **73**, 114 (1961); *Ann.* **656**, 1 (1962).
58. L. C. Leitch, E. Cagnon, and E. Cambron, *Can. J. Research* **28B**, 256 (1950).
59. G. D. Buckley, L. H. Cross and N. H. Ray, *J. Chem. Soc.* **1950**, 2714.
60. C. E. H. Bawn and A. Ledwith, *Chem. & Ind. (London)* **1957**, 1180.
61. M. F. Dull and P. G. Abend, *J. Am. Chem. Soc.* **81**, 2588 (1959).
62. E. Müller, H. Fricke, and W. Rundel, *Z. Naturforsch.* **15b**, 753 (1960); *Ann.* **661**, 38 (1963).
63. A. Ledwith, *Chem. & Ind. (London)* **1956**, 1310.
64. G. Wittig and K. Schwarzenbach, *Angew. Chem.* **71**, 652 (1959).
65. U. Schöllkopf and A. Lerch, *Angew. Chem.* **73**, 27 (1961).
66. G. Wittig and K. Schwarzenbach, *Ann.* **650**, 1 (1962).
67. E. Schmitz and R. Ohme, *Tetrahedron Letters* **1961**, 612.
67a. R. Ohme and E. Schmitz, *Chem. Ber.* **97**, 297 (1964).
68. W. H. Graham, *J. Am. Chem. Soc.* **84**, 1063 (1962).
69. L. Pierce and V. Dobyns, *J. Am. Chem. Soc.* **84**, 2651 (1962).
70. H. M. Frey and I. D. R. Stevens, *Proc. Chem. Soc.* **1962**, 79.
71. L. S. Kassel, *J. Am. Chem. Soc.* **54**, 3949 (1932); **57**, 833 (1935).
72. I. L. Knunyants, N. P. Gambarjan, and E. M. Rochlin, *Ucpecchi Khim.* **27**, 1361 (1958).
73. M. Letort and X. Duval, *Compt. rend.* **219**, 452 (1944).
74. H. Wiener and M. Burton, *J. Am. Chem. Soc.* **75**, 5815 (1953).
75. W. Groth and H. Laudenklos, *Naturwissenschaften* **24**, 796 (1936).
76. H. Okabe and J. R. McNesby, *J. Chem. Phys.* **34**, 668 (1961).
77. L. H. Gevantman and R. R. Williams, *J. Phys. Chem.* **56**, 569 (1952).
77a. A. P. Wolf, *Ann. Rev. Nucl. Chem.* **10**, 259 (1960).
77b. G. Stöcklin and A. P. Wolf, *J. Am. Chem. Soc.* **85**, 229 (1963).
78. L. Friedman and J. G. Berger, *J. Am. Chem. Soc.* **82**, 5758 (1960).
79. W. Kirmse, *Angew. Chem.* **73**, 540 (1961).
80. E. Warhurst, *Quart. Revs. (London)* **5**, 44 (1951).
81. C. E. H. Bawn and W. J. Dunning, *Trans. Faraday Soc.* **35**, 185 (1939).
82. C. E. H. Bawn and J. Milsted, *Trans. Faraday Soc.* **35**, 889 (1939).
83. C. E. H. Bawn and C. F. H. Tipper, *Discussions Faraday Soc.* **2**, 104 (1947).
84. W. T. Miller, Jr. and C. S. Y. Kim, *J. Am. Chem. Soc.* **81**, 5008 (1959).
85. M. Dennstedt and J. Zimmermann, *Ber. deut. chem. Ges.* **18**, 3316 (1885).

86. E. R. Alexander, A. B. Herrick, and Th. M. Roder, *J. Am. Chem. Soc.* **72**, 2760 (1950).
87. G. Emschwiler, *Compt. rend.* **183**, 666 (1926).
88. M. Faillebin, *Compt. rend.* **174**, 112 (1922).
89. O. M. Nefedov, A. A. Ivaschenko, M. I. Manakov, W. I. Sherjajev, and A. D. Petrov, *Izvest. Akad. Nauk S.S.S.R., Otdel. Khim. Nauk* **1962**, 367.
90. H. E. Simmons and R. D. Smith, *J. Am. Chem. Soc.* **80**, 5323 (1958).
91. R. S. Shank and H. Shechter, *J. Org. Chem.* **24**, 1825 (1959).
92. G. Wittig and R. Polster, *Ann.* **599**, 1 (1956).
93. V. Franzen and G. Wittig, *Angew. Chem.* **72**, 417 (1960).
94. E. J. Corey and M. Chaykovsky, *J. Am. Chem. Soc.* **84**, 866 (1962).
95. V. Franzen and H. E. Driessen, *Tetrahedron Letters* **1962**, 661; *Chem. Ber.* **96**, 1881 (1963).
96. E. J. Corey and M. Chaykovsky, *J. Am. Chem. Soc.* **84**, 3782 (1962); *Tetrahedron Letters* **1963**, 169.
97. C. Rosenblum, *J. Am. Chem. Soc.* **60**, 2819 (1938); **63**, 3322 (1941).
98. H. Gesser and E. W. R. Steacie, *Can. J. Chem.* **34**, 113 (1956).
99. J. Chanmugam and M. Burton, *Can. J. Chem.* **34**, 1021 (1956); *J. Am. Chem. Soc.* **78**, 509 (1956).
100. J. A. Bell and G. B. Kistiakowsky, *J. Am. Chem. Soc.* **84**, 3417 (1962).
101. W. B. DeMoore, H. O. Pritchard, and N. Davidson, *J. Am. Chem. Soc.* **81**, 5874 (1959).
102. R. A. Holroyd and W. A. Noyes, *J. Am. Chem. Soc.* **78**, 4831 (1956).
103. M. Burton, Th. W. Davis, A. Gordon, and H. A. Taylor, *J. Am. Chem. Soc.* **63**, 1956 (1941).
104. H. M. Frey, *Proc. Chem. Soc.* **1959**, 318.
105. H. M. Frey, *J. Am. Chem. Soc.* **82**, 5947 (1960).
106. W. v. E. Doering and H. Prinzbach, *Tetrahedron* **6**, 24 (1959).
107. W. v. E. Doering, R. G. Buttery, R. G. Laughlin, and N. Chaudhuri, *J. Am. Chem. Soc.* **78**, 3224 (1956).
108. D. B. Richardson, M. C. Simmons, and I. Dvoretzky, *J. Am. Chem. Soc.* **82**, 5001 (1960); **83**, 1934 (1961).
109. H. M. Frey, *J. Am. Chem. Soc.* **80**, 5005 (1958).
110. J. H. Knox and A. F. Trotman-Dickenson, *Chem. & Ind. (London)* **1957**, 731.
111. H. M. Frey and G. B. Kistiakowsky, *J. Am. Chem. Soc.* **79**, 6373 (1957).
112. J. H. Knox and A. F. Trotman-Dickenson, *Chem. & Ind. (London)* **1957**, 1039.
113. J. N. Butler and G. B. Kistiakowsky, *J. Am. Chem. Soc.* **82**, 759 (1960); **83**, 1324 (1961).
114. H. M. Frey, *Trans. Faraday Soc.* **56**, 1201 (1960).
115. M. Vanpee and F. Grard, *Bull. soc. chim. Belges* **60**, 208 (1951).
116. W. v. E. Doering, L. H. Knox, and M. Jones, Jr., *J. Org. Chem.* **24**, 136 (1959).
117. V. Franzen and H. Kuntze, *Ann.* **627**, 15 (1959).
118. J. N. Bradley and A. Ledwith, *J. Chem. Soc.* **1961**, 1495.
119. J. Chesick, *J. Am. Chem. Soc.* **84**, 2448 (1962).
119a. J. W. Simons and B. S. Rabinovitch, *J. Am. Chem. Soc.* **85**, 1023 (1963).
120. W. v. E. Doering *et al.*, unpublished results.
121. V. Franzen, *Abstr. of Papers 141st Meeting Am. Chem. Soc.*, p. 23-o.

122. J. R. Majer, B. Mile, and J. C. Robb, *Trans. Faraday Soc.* **57**, 1692 (1961).
123. D. McDuffie, Ph. D. Thesis, Yale University, 1960.
124. W. v. E. Doering and P. LaFlamme, *J. Am. Chem. Soc.* **78**, 5447 (1956).
125. P. S. Skell and R. C. Woodworth, *J. Am. Chem. Soc.* **78**, 4496 (1956); **81**, 3383 (1959).
126. B. S. Rabinovitch, E. Tschuikow-Roux, and E. W. Schlag, *J. Am. Chem. Soc.* **81**, 1081 (1959).
127. H. M. Frey, *Proc. Roy. Soc.* **A251**, 575 (1959).
128. F. A. L. Anet, R. F. W. Bader, and A. M. v. d. Auwera, *J. Am. Chem. Soc.* **82**, 3217 (1960).
129. H. M. Frey, *J. Am. Chem. Soc.* **82**, 5947 (1960).
130. K. R. Kopecky, G. S. Hammond, and P. Leermakers, *J. Am. Chem. Soc.* **83**, 2397 (1961); **84**, 1015 (1962).
131. F. J. Duncan and R. J. Cvetanovic, *J. Am. Chem. Soc.* **84**, 3539 (1962).
132. B. S. Rabinovitch, personal communication to H. M. Frey (*23*).
133. H. M. Frey, *Proc. Roy. Soc.* **A250**, 409 (1959).
134. H. M. Frey, *Trans. Faraday Soc.* **57**, 951 (1961).
135. H. M. Frey, *Trans. Faraday Soc.* **58**, 516 (1962).
135a. B. A. Grzybowska, J. H. Knox, and A. F. Trotman-Dickenson, *J. Chem. Soc.* **1963**, 746.
136. G. L. Closs and L. E. Closs, *Angew. Chem.* **74**, 431 (1962).
137. S. Winstein, J. Sonnenberg, and L. deVries, *J. Am. Chem. Soc.* **81**, 6523 (1959).
138. S. D. Koch, D. V. Lopiekes, R. M. Kliss, and R. J. Wineman, *J. Org. Chem.* **26**, 3122 (1961).
139. L. A. Nachapetjan, I. L. Safonova, and B. A. Kazanskij, *Izvest. Akad. Nauk S.S.S.R., Otdel. Khim. Nauk* **1962**, 902.
139a. E. Tobler and D. J. Foster, *Z. Naturforsch.* **17b**, 135 (1962).
139b. W. G. Dauben and G. H. Berezin, *J. Am. Chem. Soc.* **85**, 468 (1963).
139c. I. E. Dolgij, A. P. Mescerjakov, and G. K. Gajvoronskaja, *Izvest. Akad. Nauk S.S.S.R., Otdel, Khim. Nauk* **1963**, 1111.
139d. E. J. Corey and R. L. Dawson, *J. Am. Chem. Soc.* **85**, 1782 (1963).
139e. E. J. Corey and H. Uda, *J. Am. Chem. Soc.* **85**, 1788 (1963).
139f. W. G. Dauben and A. C. Ashcraft, *J. Am. Chem. Soc.* **85**, 3673 (1963).
140. R. E. Eastman and A. V. Winn, *J. Am. Chem. Soc.* **82**, 5908 (1960).
141. W. v. E. Doering, M. R. Willcott III, and M. Jones, Jr., *J. Am. Chem. Soc.* **84**, 1224 (1962).
142. A. T. Blomquist and D. J. Conolly, *Chem. & Ind. (London)* **1962**, 310.
143. E. F. Ullmann and W. J. Fanshawe, *J. Am. Chem. Soc.* **83**, 2379 (1961).
143a. D. K. Black and S. R. Landor, *Tetrahedron Letters* **1963**, 1065.
144. B. Grzybowska, J. H. Knox, and A. F. Trotman-Dickenson, *J. Chem. Soc.* **1961**, 4402; **1962**, 3826.
145. V. Franzen, *Chem. Ber.* **95**, 571 (1962).
146. H. M. Frey, *Trans. Faraday Soc.* **58**, 516 (1962).
147. M. C. Flowers and H. M. Frey, *J. Chem. Soc.* **1961**, 3547.
147a. C. G. Overberger and G. W. Haler, *J. Org. Chem.* **28**, 867 (1963).
147b. W. v. E. Doering and W. Roth, *Tetrahedron* **19**, 715 (1963).
148. H. M. Frey, *Chem. & Ind. (London)* **1960**, 1266.

148a. M. E. Jacox and D. E. Milligan, *J. Am. Chem. Soc.* **85**, 278 (1963).

148b. T. Terao, N. Sakai, and S. Shida, *J. Am. Chem. Soc.* **85**, 3919 (1963).

149. W. v. E. Doering and T. Mole, *Tetrahedron* **10**, 65 (1960).

150. N. T. Castellucci and C. E. Griffin, *J. Am. Chem. Soc.* **82**, 4107 (1960).

151. L. Vo-Quang, P. Cadiot, and A. Willemart, *Compt. rend.* **255**, 950 (1962).

152. W. v. E. Doering and L. H. Knox, *J. Am. Chem. Soc.* **72**, 2305 (1950).

153. W. v. E. Doering, L. H. Knox, and F. Detert, *J. Am. Chem. Soc.* **75**, 297 (1953).

154. H. Meerwein, H. Disselnkötter, F. Rappen, H. v. Rintelen, and H. van de Vloed, *Ann.* **604**, 151 (1957).

155. R. M. Lemmon and W. Strohmeier, *J. Am. Chem. Soc.* **81**, 106 (1959).

156. E. Vogel, *Angew. Chem.* **74**, 829 (1962); E. Vogel, W. Wiedemann, H. Kiefer, and W. F. Harrison, *Tetrahedron Letters* **1963**, 673.

156a. G. A. Russell and D. G. Hendry, *J. Org. Chem.* **28**, 1933 (1963).

157. A. P. Wolf, B. Gordon, and C. S. Redvanly, *Abstr. of Papers 131st Meeting Am. Chem. Soc.*, **1957**, p. 12-o.

157a. E. Müller and H. Fricke, *Ann.* **661**, 38 (1963).

157b. E. Müller, H. Fricke, and H. Kessler, *Tetrahedron Letters* **1963**, 1501.

157c. E. Müller, B. Zeeh, R. Heischkeil, H. Fricke, and H. Suhr, *Ann.* **662**, 38 (1963).

157d. E. Müller, H. Kessler, H. Fricke, and H. Suhr, *Tetrahedron Letters* **1963**, 1047.

158. R. Daniels and O. LeRoy Salerni, *Proc. Chem. Soc.* **1960**, 286.

159. W. v. E. Doering, J. R. Mayer, and C. H. DePuy, *J. Am. Chem. Soc.* **75**, 2386 (1953).

160. S. Dev, *J. Indian Chem. Soc.* **30**, 729 (1953).

161. K. Alder and P. Schmitz, *Chem. Ber.* **86**, 1539 (1953).

162. W. Treibs, *Angew. Chem.* **67**, 76 (1955); *Ann.* **603**, 145 (1957).

163. W. Treibs, M. Quarg, and E. J. Poppe, *Ann.* **598**, 32 (1956).

164. K. Hafner, *Angew Chem.* **70**, 419 (1958).

164a. K. A. W. Kramer and A. N. Wright, *J. Chem. Soc.* **1963**, 3604.

165. H. Meerwein, H. Rathjen, and H. Werner, *Ber. deut. chem. Ges.* **75**, 1610 (1942).

166. R. Huisgen, *Angew. Chem.* **67**, 459 (1955).

167. V. Franzen and L. Fikentscher, *Ann.* **617**, 1 (1958).

168. G. Ayrey, E. Buncel, and A. N. Bourns, *Proc. Chem. Soc.* **1961**, 458.

169. F. Weygand, H. Daniel, and H. Simon, *Ann.* **654**, 111 (1962).

169a. J. N. Bradley and A. Ledwith, *J. Chem. Soc.* **1963**, 3480.

170. V. Franzen, *Ann.* **627**, 22 (1960).

170a. M. Hudlický and J. König, *Coll. Czech. Chem. Communs.* **28**, 2824 (1963).

171. W. H. Urry and J. R. Eiszner, *J. Am. Chem. Soc.* **73**, 2977 (1951); **74**, 5822 (1952).

172. W. H. Urry, J. R. Eiszner, and J. W. Wilt, *J. Am. Chem. Soc.* **79**, 918 (1957).

173. K. Ziegler and H. G. Gellert, *Ann.* **567**, 185 (1950).

174. G. Wittig and H. Witt, *Ber. deut. chem. Ges.* **74**, 1474 (1941).

175. W. Kirmse and B. v. Wedel, *Ann.* **666**, 1 (1963).

# CHAPTER 3

# Alkyl- and Dialkylcarbenes

MOST OF THE METHODS used to produce alkyl- and dialkylcarbenes are closely analogous to those discussed in the preceding chapter, although some modifications are necessary to overcome the difficulties created by the instability of many alkylcarbene precursors, such as diazoalkanes. Alkyl- and dialkylcarbenes are distinguished from other classes of carbenes by the predominance of intramolecular reactions leading to olefins and cyclopropanes. As such products may arise by many possible routes, the nature of the intermediate deserves thorough investigation. In particular, carbonium ions as well as carbenes may intervene in the decomposition of diazoalkanes.

In reactions designed to produce methylene by elimination, distinguishing between elimination-addition and displacement mechanisms presents a largely unresolved problem. No such troubles are encountered in this chapter. In most cases elimination is quite obvious from the reaction products. The detailed mechanism, however, whether $\alpha$-, $\beta$-, or $\gamma$-elimination, concerted or stepwise, requires much scrutiny before the intermediacy of a carbene can be ascertained.

## I. FORMATION OF ALKYL- AND DIALKYLCARBENES

### A. Decomposition

The utilization of alkylketenes as carbene precursors is restricted by their strong tendency to polymerize. Methylketene (1) and dimethylketene (2, 3) have been photolyzed and pyrolyzed. Similarly, the instability of many diazoalkanes does not permit handling in substance. Diazoethane has been decomposed in the gas phase (4–7), but few pure diazo compounds larger than diazoethane have been studied (8–10).

47

Fortunately, there are various methods which produce diazoalkanes *in situ*. The oxidation of camphor hydrazone with mercuric oxide has long been known (*11*) and was recently reinvestigated (*12*). The alkaline cleavage of toluenesulfonyl (= tosyl) hydrazones [Eq. (1)] has been used more frequently.

$$\underset{R}{\overset{R'}{>}}C=N-NH-SO_2R'' \xrightarrow{B:\ominus} \underset{R}{\overset{R'}{>}}C=N-\overset{\ominus}{N}-SO_2R'' \rightarrow \underset{R}{\overset{R'}{>}}C=N_2 + {}^{\ominus}O_2S-R''$$

$$(1)$$

If applied to tosylhydrazones of aromatic ketones (*13*) and to monotosylhydrazones of diketones (*14*), the reaction affords diazo compounds in good yields. With tosylhydrazones of aliphatic aldehydes and ketones the reaction proceeds only under conditions (130°–150°) which lead to an immediate decomposition of the diazoalkane. Carbonium ions result from protonation of the diazoalkane in a proton-donating solvent (e.g., glycol) (*15, 16*), whereas carbenoid reactions predominate in aprotic solvents (e.g., diglyme) (*15, 17*). Camphor tosylhydrazone has been particularly useful in elucidating the two mechanisms. Here, the carbonium ion gives exclusively camphene (I) by Wagner-Meerwein rearrangement, whereas the carbene leads to tricyclene (II) by intramolecular insertion:

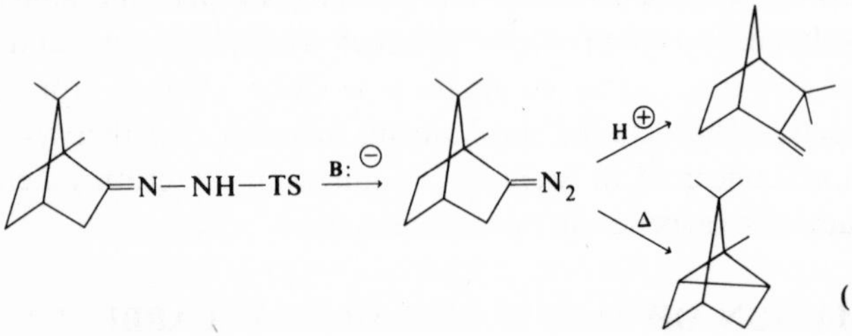

$$(2)$$

It should be noted, however, that most diazoalkanes are more sensitive toward protonation than diazocamphane. This can be shown by using solvents of "intermediate" protonating ability, e.g., acetamide. Whereas camphor tosylhydrazone gives 97–99% of tricyclene in this solvent (*15*), pinacolone tosylhydrazone shows about 50% carbonium ion rearrangement (*18*). Reactions run in acetamide and considered to be carbenoid on the basis of the camphor experiments (*19*) must be regarded with some suspicion.

Another point concerns the nature of the base. So far, only alkoxides were found to be useful. By abstracting the amide proton [Eq. (1)], the alkoxides give alcohols which are quite efficient in protonating diazoalkanes. Thus, even if diglyme or decalin are used as solvents, the system is never really aprotic. Best results are obtained at high (> 150°) temperatures where decomposition of the diazoalkanes is fast and the alcohols are rapidly removed from the reaction mixture. Nevertheless, a carbonium ion component of the tosylhydrazone cleavage can rarely be excluded with certainty, and may account for minor amounts of rearrangement products.

Attempts to avoid these difficulties by use of bases such as sodium hydride and sodium amide resulted in a completely different reaction mechanism (18).

Cleavage of tosylhydrazones may be effected by light, instead of heat, by irradiating the sodium salts in various solvents. Results with camphor tosylhydrazone agree well with those of the thermal reaction (20). Transient coloration supports the intermediacy of a diazoalkane. Some discrepancies noted between the cleavage of camphor tosylhydrazone and the mercuric oxide oxidation of camphor hydrazone (12) have now been resolved in terms of solvent effects (21).

The reaction of olefins with nitrous oxide (250°-300°, 100-500 atm.) (22, 23) appears to proceed in part according to Eq. (3). Products derived from diazoalkanes were found in several instances.

$$\begin{matrix} R' \\ \diagdown \\ R \diagup \end{matrix} C=C \begin{matrix} R' \\ \diagup \\ \diagdown R \end{matrix} + N_2O \rightarrow \begin{matrix} R' \\ \diagdown \\ R \diagup \end{matrix} C=O + \begin{matrix} R' \\ \diagdown \\ R \diagup \end{matrix} C=N_2 \qquad (3)$$

Dialkyldiazirines, the cyclic isomers of diazoalkanes, are readily prepared by oxidation of dialkyldiaziridines (24, 25). Various examples of thermal and photochemical decomposition have been reported (25-27b).

$$\begin{matrix} R' \\ \diagdown \\ R \diagup \end{matrix} C=O + \begin{matrix} NH_3 \\ \\ NH_2Cl \end{matrix} \rightarrow \begin{matrix} R' \\ \diagdown \\ R \diagup \end{matrix} C \begin{matrix} NH \\ | \\ NH \end{matrix} \xrightarrow{Ox.} \begin{matrix} R' \\ \diagdown \\ R \diagup \end{matrix} C \begin{matrix} N \\ \| \\ N \end{matrix} \qquad (4)$$

The formation of carbenes in the decomposition of azines is yet uncertain. Acetonitrile is the major product of acetaldazine photolysis (28), indicating rupture of the N—N bond rather than of the C—N bonds. The yield of nitrogen increases, however, above 100°; methane,

2-butene, and ethane are additional products, listed in the order of their importance.

The photolysis (1470 and 1295 Å, Xe resonance lines) of $CH_3CD_3$ gave hydrogen molecules derived predominantly from the same carbon atom ($H_2$ and $D_2$, little HD) (29). Methyl radicals were not involved as no $CD_3$—$CD_3$ was obtained. The primary process $CH_3$—$CH_3$ → $CH_3CH$: + $H_2$ offers a reasonable explanation of these observations.

Irradiation of hydrocarbons with a beam of $C^{11}$ ions in the M.e.v. energy range may also give rise to carbenes by "atomic insertion" (30). Many of the products, including considerable amounts of labeled acetylene, are not characteristic of a carbene reaction.

$$\begin{matrix} & & & & & & R\cdot\ +\ R'\ +\ HC{\equiv}C^{11}H \\ R'{\diagdown} & & & R'{\diagdown} & & {\nearrow} & \\ & CH_2\ +\ \dot{C}^{11} & \rightarrow & & CH{-}\dot{C}{-}H & {\rightarrow} & R{-}R'\ +\ HC{\equiv}C^{11}H \\ R{\diagup} & & & R{\diagup} & & {\searrow} & \\ & & & & & & R'{\diagdown} \\ & & & & & & {\quad}C{=}C^{11}H_2 \\ & & & & & & R{\diagup} \end{matrix} \quad (5)$$

Ethylene reacts with carbon atoms produced by nuclear transformations to give some allene (18%) and methylacetylene (4%), but the major product again is acetylene (31). This reaction may be compared to the photolysis of carbon suboxide in the presence of ethylene (32). The major products are allene (80%), methylacetylene (20%), and carbon monoxide. The $CO:C_3H_4$ ratio, extrapolated to infinite pressure, is 2.04. Energy considerations, based on the heat of formation of carbon suboxide, favor :C=C=O as the first formed intermediate, and rule out the possibility of a free carbon atom in the gas phase (32). Studies on the effect of added oxygen show that two distinct intermediates are involved, one of which reacts rapidly with oxygen and one which adds to ethylene even in the presence of excess oxygen. The two intermediates could be :C=C=O in different electronic states, but electronically excited carbon suboxide could also be involved (32).

The isotope distribution in allene derived from carbon suboxide-2-$C^{14}$ (33) indicates that most of the allene forms by way of a cyclic carbene intermediate.

$$O{=}C{=}\overset{14}{C}{=}C{=}O\ \rightarrow\ CO\ +\ :C{=}C{=}O\ \xrightarrow{\text{\scriptsize $>$C=C$<$}}\ O{=}C{=}\!\!<\!\!\triangleright$$

$$\rightarrow\ :\!\!<\!\!\triangleright\!\!\rightarrow\ H_2C{=}C{=}CH_2 \qquad (6)$$

$$\phantom{xxxxx}4\quad 92\quad 4\quad \%\quad C^{14}$$

In contrast, the ratio of $H_2C=C^{11}=CH_2$: $H_2C=C=C^{11}H_2$ produced by reaction of recoil $C^{11}$ atoms with ethylene varied from 2.0 (liquid ethylene) to 3.4 (neon-moderated gas phase reaction) (*33a*). Even under the conditions of a largely thermal reaction a considerable amount of allene appears to be formed by $C^{11}$ insertion into C—H bonds.

## B. Elimination

Previous evidence for $\alpha$-elimination of hydrogen bromide from octyl bromide by potassium amide (*34*) turned out to be erroneous (*35*). $\alpha$-Elimination of hydrogen chloride from primary alkyl chlorides does occur, however, under the action of sodium and potassium (not lithium) alkyls. The formation of substituted cyclopropanes from neopentyl chloride (*36, 37*) and neophyl chloride (*38*) had been observed by Whitmore *et al.*, but was interpreted in terms of a $\gamma$-elimination. The true course of this reaction has been elucidated but recently by means of deuterium- and tritium-labeled chlorides (*39–41*).

$$R—CH_2Cl + R'\,Na \rightarrow R'H + NaCl + R—CH: \tag{7}$$

Whereas the $\alpha$-elimination of hydrogen chloride fails with secondary alkyl halides (*39*), the elimination of bromine from *gem*-dibromoalkanes by means of lithium alkyls appears to be widely applicable (*42–44*).

$$\underset{R}{\overset{R'}{>}}C\underset{Br}{\overset{Br}{<}} + R''Li \rightarrow R''Br + \underset{R}{\overset{R'}{>}}C\underset{Br}{\overset{Li}{<}} \xrightarrow{-LiBr} \underset{R}{\overset{R'}{>}}C: \tag{8}$$

(III)

Reaction (8) is a two-step (rather than concerted) process which involves an organometallic intermediate, III. This has been shown by treating 1,1,3-trihalopropanes with methyl lithium (*44*). The halocyclopropanes formed contained the 1-, not the 3-halogen (e.g., bromocyclopropane from 1,1-dibromo-3-chloropropane, and chlorocyclopropane from 1,3-dibromo-1-chloropropane). The halocyclopropanes arise, therefore, by 1,3-elimination of lithium halide from the intermediate IV.

$$X—CH_2CH_2CH\underset{Z}{\overset{Y}{<}} + RLi \rightarrow X—CH_2CH_2CH\underset{Li}{\overset{Y}{<}} \xrightarrow{-LiX} \triangle\!\!-Y \tag{9}$$

$$\downarrow \text{(IV)} \ {-LiY}$$

$$X—CH_2CH_2CH: \rightarrow X—CH_2CH=CH_2$$

$$+ \ \triangle\!\!-X$$

Alkyldiphenylsulfonium salts undergo $\alpha$-elimination on treatment with trityl sodium [Eq. (10)] (45). A substantial amount of $\alpha$-elimination was observed even in the reaction of cyclodecene oxide with lithium diethylamide (46). Bicyclic products (cf. Section II, A) were formed from cyclodecene oxide-1,2-d with loss of 0.82–0.85 D atoms.

$$Ph_2\overset{\oplus}{S}-CH_2R \ \overset{\ominus}{X} + Ph_3C-Na \rightarrow Ph_3CH + NaX + Ph_2S + R-CH: \qquad (10)$$

An indirect method of $\alpha$-elimination consists of the interaction of chlorocarbenes with lithium alkyls. The second step of this reaction should be analogous to that of Eqs. (7) and (8).

$$R-\underset{..}{C}-Cl + R'Li \rightarrow \underset{R}{\overset{R'}{>}}C\underset{Cl}{\overset{Li}{<}} \rightarrow LiCl + R'-\underset{..}{C}-R \qquad (11)$$

In many instances the products are characteristic of a carbene intermediate (39, 47), but concerted reactions leading directly to olefins may also occur (18). The solvent and other variables often exert a profound influence on the product ratio. Furthermore, different combinations of chlorocarbene and lithium alkyl selected to produce the same carbene (e.g., $CH_3CH_2-\underset{..}{C}-Cl + CH_3Li$, $CH_3-\underset{..}{C}-Cl + CH_3CH_2Li$) give different product mixtures (18). This observation excludes any single common intermediate, whether organometallic or carbene. While reaction (11) is often satisfactory for qualitative studies, it should not be used for a quantitative comparison of carbene products.

## II. REACTIONS OF ALKYL- AND DIALKYLCARBENES

### A. Intramolecular Reactions

#### 1. Insertion

In alkyl- and dialkylcarbenes the divalent carbon atom inserts into the $\beta$- and $\gamma$-carbon-hydrogen bonds to give olefins and cyclopropanes, respectively:

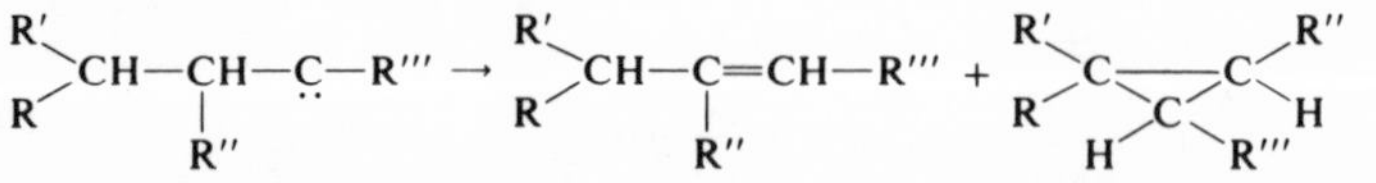

$$\underset{R}{\overset{R'}{>}}CH-CH-\underset{..}{C}-R''' \rightarrow \underset{R}{\overset{R'}{>}}CH-C=CH-R''' + \underset{R}{\overset{R'}{>}}C\underset{C}{=}C\overset{R''}{<_{R'''}^{H}} \qquad (12)$$

The reaction leading to olefins has been termed a "hydride shift" rather than insertion, but so far there is no evidence for a different mechanism.

The relative yields of cyclopropanes increase with increased branching of the alkyl groups (e.g., *n*-butyl < isobutyl < neopentyl) (*17, 39-41*), and appear to be governed by the proximity of suitable carbon-hydrogen bonds. This behavior may serve to distinguish a carbene intermediate from a carbonium ion where the yields of cyclopropanes *decrease* with increased branching (*48-50*). Not even a protonated cyclopropane intermediate has been detected by tracer techniques in the rearrangement of the neopentyl cation (*51, 52*).

The products obtained from intramolecular reactions of alkyl- and dialkylcarbenes are fairly independent of the way of formation, whether by decomposition or elimination. Results from some thoroughly investigated examples have been collected in Tables I–V to illustrate this statement.

TABLE I
PRODUCTS FROM *tert*-BUTYLCARBENE [(CH$_3$)$_3$C—CH:]
(Relative yields based on total C$_5$H$_{10}$ = 100)

| Carbene precursor | 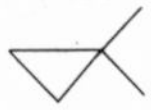 ▷ | 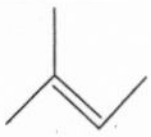 ⋀ | 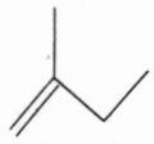 ⋀ |
|---|---|---|---|
| (CH$_3$)$_3$C—CH=N—NH—Ts + MeO$^\ominus$ (*17*) | 92 | 7 | 1 |
| (CH$_3$)$_3$C—CH$_2$Cl + PhNa (*40*) | 96 | 3.5 | — |
| (CH$_3$)$_3$C—CHI$_2$ + MeLi (*44*) | 95–97 | 3–5 | — |
| (CH$_3$)$_3$C—Li + CH$_2$Cl$_2$ (*47*) | 69 | 13 | 18 |
| (CH$_3$)$_3$C—CH⟨$^N_N$ (Pyrolysis) (*27a*) | 80 | 20 | — |

TABLE II
PRODUCTS FROM ISOPROPYLCARBENE [(CH$_3$)$_2$CH—CH:]

| Carbene precursor | 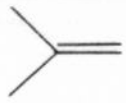 ⋗= | 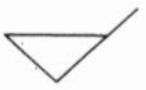 ▽ |
|---|---|---|
| (CH$_3$)$_2$CH—CHN$_2$ (pyrolysis) (*17*) | 67 | 33 |
| (CH$_3$)$_2$CH—CH=N—NH—Ts + MeO$^\ominus$ (*17*) | 62 | 38 |
| (CH$_3$)$_2$CH—CH$_2$Cl + Na (*39*) | 65 | 35 |
| (CH$_3$)$_2$CH—CH$_2$Cl + PhNa (*40*) | 66 | 34 |
| (CH$_3$)$_2$CH—Li + CH$_2$Cl$_2$ (pentane) (*18, 39*) | 75 | 25 |
| Ph$_2\overset{\oplus}{S}$—CH$_2$CH(CH$_3$)$_2$ + Ph$_3$CNa (*45*) | 75 | 25 |
| (CH$_3$)$_2$CH—CH⟨$^N_N$ (Pyrolysis) (*27a*) | 49 | 51 |

The deuterium isotope effect in the intramolecular insertion of *tert*-butylcarbene, $k_H/k_D = 1.71 \pm 0.06$, has been estimated by nuclear magnetic resonance (N.M.R.) analysis of the 1,1-dimethylcyclopropane obtained from $(CD_3)_2\underset{\underset{Li}{|}}{C}\!-\!CH_3$ and methylene chloride (*52a*).

TABLE III
PRODUCTS FROM *sec*-BUTYLCARBENE [$CH_3CH_2CH\!-\!CH:$]

| Carbene precursor | ![CH₃ branched] | ![] | ![] | ![] |
|---|---|---|---|---|
| $C_2H_5\underset{\underset{CH_3}{|}}{CH}\!-\!CH\!=\!N\!-\!NH\!-\!Ts + MeO$  (*47*) | 63 | 20 | 12 | 5 |
| $C_2H_5\underset{\underset{CH_3}{|}}{CH}\!-\!CH_2Cl + Na$ (*53*) | 53 | 21 | 26 | — |
| $C_2H_5\underset{\underset{CH_3}{|}}{CH}\!-\!Li + CH_2Cl_2$ (*47*) | 59 | 22 | 17 | 2 |

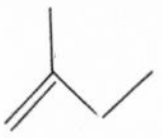

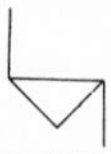

*sec*-Butylcarbene produced from optically active R(+)-isoamyl chloride afforded optically active (−)-*trans*-1,2-dimethyl-cyclopropane (*53*). This reaction permits assignment of absolute configuration in the series of *trans*-1,2-disubstituted cyclopropanes.

TABLE IV
PRODUCTS FROM *tert*-BUTYLMETHYLCARBENE [$(CH_3)_3C\!-\!\underset{..}{C}\!-\!CH_3$]

| Carbene precursor | 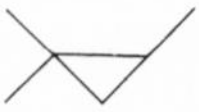 ![] |  ![] | 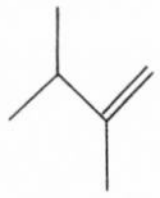 ![] | 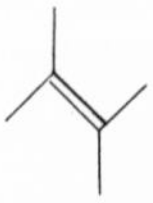 ![] |
|---|---|---|---|---|
| $(CH_3)_3C\!-\!\underset{\underset{CH_3}{|}}{C}\!=\!N\!-\!NH\!-\!Ts + MeO^{\ominus}$ (*17*) | 47 | 52 | Traces | |
| (*18*) | 52 | 41 | 4 | 3 |
| $(CH_3)_3C\!-\!CBr_2\!-\!CH_3 + MeLi$ (*44*) | 65 | 35 | — | — |
| $(CH_3)_3C\!-\!Li + Cl_2CH\!-\!CH_3$ (*18*) | 43 | 57 | — | — |

TABLE V
PRODUCTS FROM ETHYLMETHYLCARBENE [$CH_3CH_2$—$\overset{..}{C}$—$CH_3$]

| Carbene precursor | 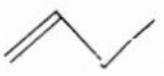 |  | 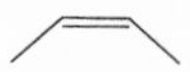 | 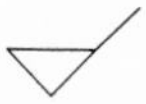 |
|---|---|---|---|---|
| $CH_3CH_2\overset{\displaystyle |}{\underset{\displaystyle CH_3}{C}}$=N—NH—Ts + MeO$^\ominus$ (17) | 5 | 67 | 28 | 0.5 |
| $CH_3CH_2$—C—$CH_3$ (pyrolysis) (26) | 3.6 | 66.5 | 29.5 | 0.4 |
| N=N    (photolysis) (26) | 23.4 | 38.6 | 35.6 | 2.4 |
| $CH_3CH_2CBr_2$—$CH_3$ + MeLi (44) | 1 | 74 | 25 | — |
| $CH_3CH_2CBrCl$—$CH_3$ + MeLi (44) | 2 | 74 | 23 | — |
| $CH_3CH_2Li$ + $Cl_2CH$—$CH_3$ (18) | 7 | 44 | 47 | — |

In the intramolecular insertion of *sec*-butylcarbene into $\gamma$-carbon-hydrogen bonds, reaction with secondary hydrogen is favored by a factor of 1.3–1.9 over reaction with primary hydrogen (cf. Table III). This result compares well with the discrimination displayed by methylene in the gas phase after collisional deactivation.

The "hydride shift" in dialkylcarbenes appears to be much more selective in favor of secondary hydrogen. Ratios of the relative rates (2°:1°) ranging from 20 to 150 may be deduced from Table V. Similar results have been obtained with methyl-*n*-propylcarbene, methyl-iso-propylcarbene, and other dialkylcarbenes. The only exception noted in Table V is the photolysis of ethylmethyldiazirine which affords results in striking contrast to those from the pyrolyses. These differences are most reasonably explained by postulating that the carbene produced photochemically is vibrationally excited (26).

Steric effects in intramolecular insertion reactions have received little

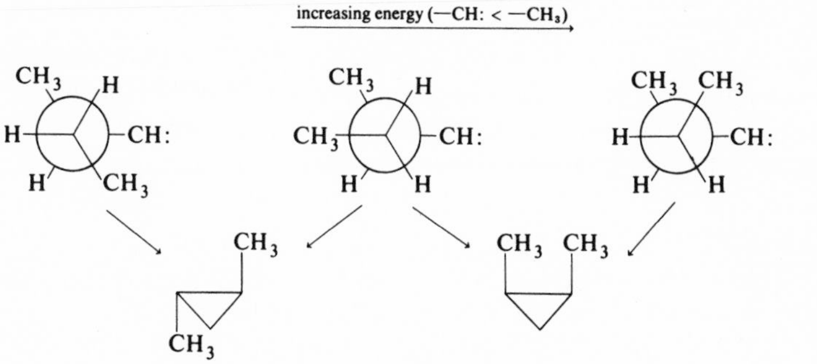

increasing energy (—CH: < —CH₃)

(13)

attention so far. As may be seen from Table III, *sec*-butylcarbene gives predominantly *trans*-1,2-dimethyl-cyclopropane with little of the *cis*-isomer. This result may reflect the higher thermodynamic stability of the *trans*-isomer (*53*), or may be attributed to conformational control (*47*).

Olefins arising by "hydride shift" are the only products obtained from carbenacyclopentane, carbenacyclohexane (*54*), and various carbenadecalins (*19*). Certain tricyclic carbenes derived from 3-diazotricyclo[6.2.1.0$^{2,7}$]undecane (*54a*) and 3-diazotricyclo[5.2.1.0$^{2,6}$] decane (*54b*) undergo exclusive shift of secondary hydrogen. The steric (or other) factors responsible for this unusual selectivity still await final elucidation.

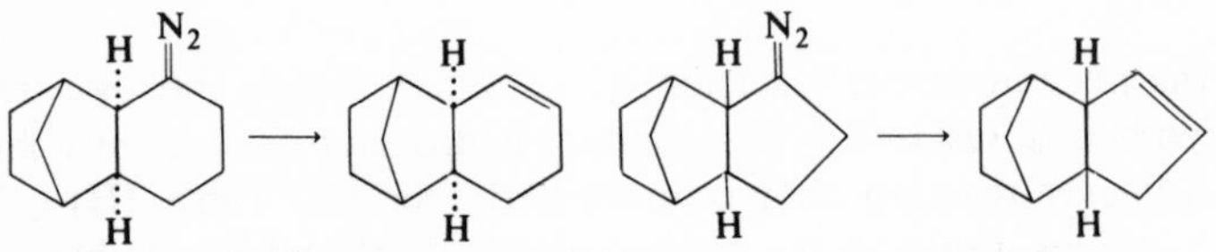

The well-known synthesis of (nor)tricyclene from (nor)camphor (*11, 12, 15*) has now been extended to the bicyclo[2.2.2]octane series (*54c*):

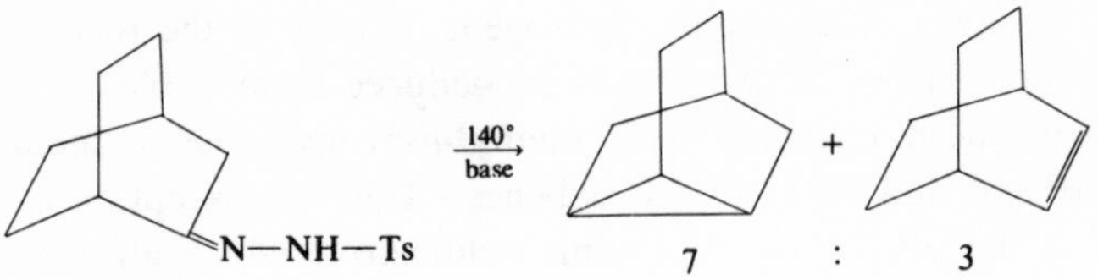

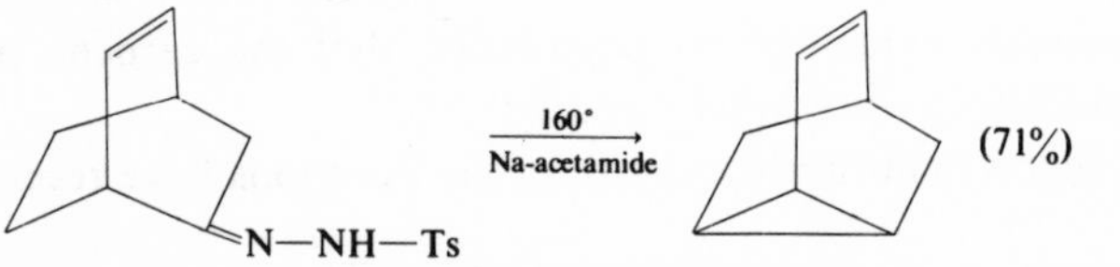

Insertion into the δ- and ε-carbon-hydrogen bonds occurs easily in medium-sized rings (*54*). The formation of larger than three-membered rings in transannular insertion reactions may be due to the proximity of the transannular hydrogen.

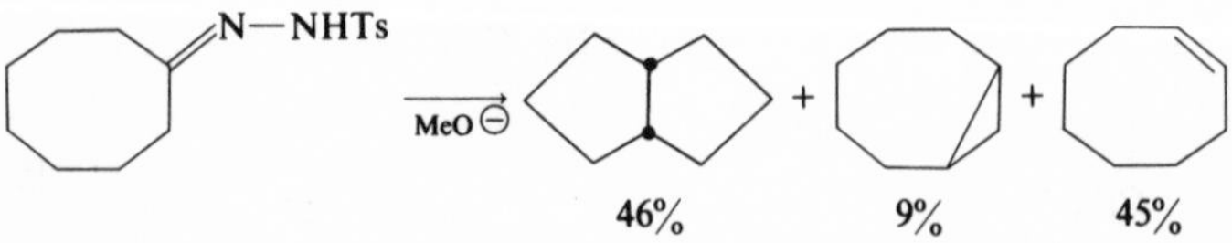

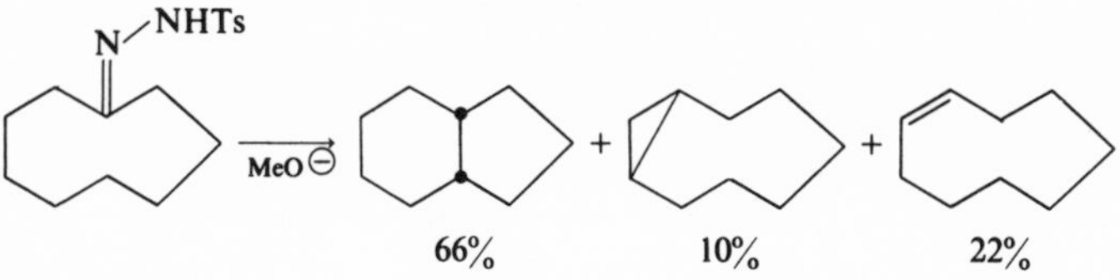

(15)

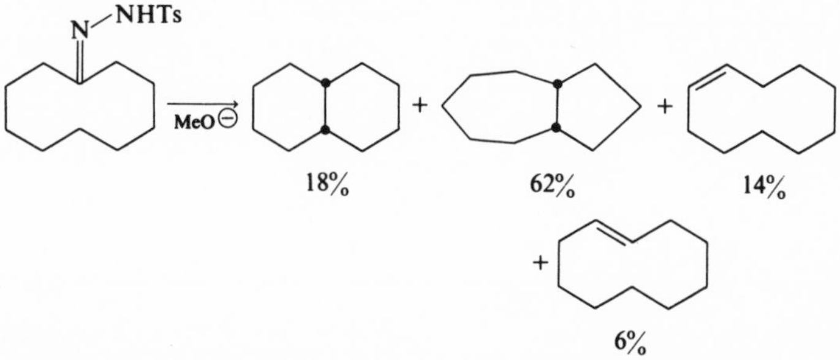

66%    10%    22%

18%    62%    14%    (16)

+

6%

The exclusive formation of *cis*-bicyclic systems indicates transfer of axial hydrogen and is consistent with the principle that insertions occur with retention of configuration.

Intramolecular insertion has also been found in the base-catalyzed ring opening of cyclic epoxides (46). The fate of the deuterium label in cyclodecene oxide-1,2-$d_2$, and in cyclooctene oxide-5,6-$d_2$, shows clearly that the reaction involves a carbene intermediate produced by $\alpha$-elimination.

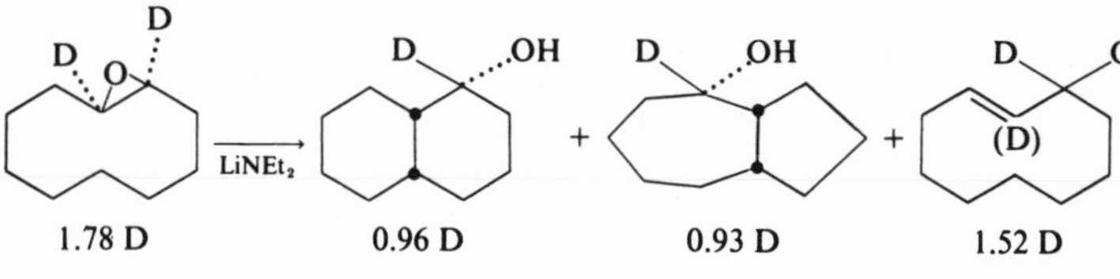

1.78 D    0.96 D    0.93 D    1.52 D    (17)

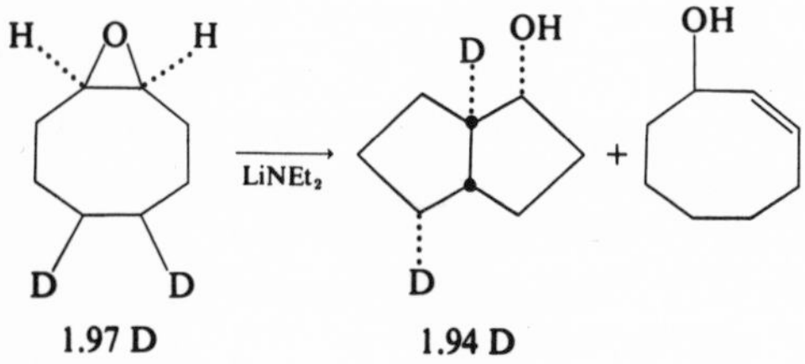

1.97 D    1.94 D    (18)

## 2. Rearrangement

A migration of alkyl groups does not occur easily in alkyl- and di-alkylcarbenes (cf. Tables I and IV). Carbenes of the neophyl type, and some carbenes containing small rings, are exceptions to this rule. The tosylhydrazones of cyclopropane carboxaldehyde, and of cyclopropyl methyl ketone, yield mainly cyclobutenes if treated with sodium methoxide in an aprotic solvent (55).

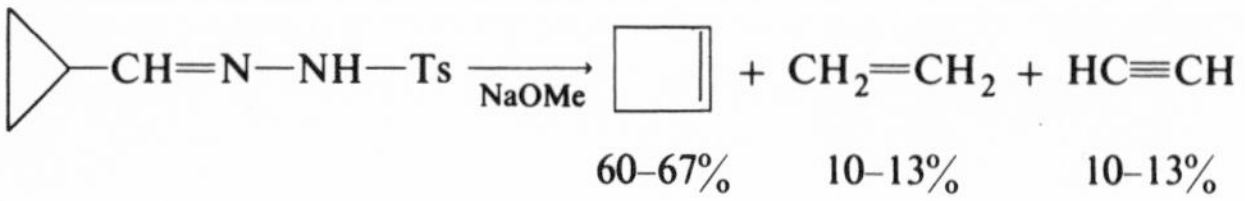

$$\triangleright\!\!-CH=N-NH-Ts \xrightarrow{\text{NaOMe}} \square + CH_2=CH_2 + HC\equiv CH \qquad (19)$$

$$\qquad\qquad\qquad\qquad \underset{60-67\%}{} \quad \underset{10-13\%}{} \quad \underset{10-13\%}{}$$

$$\triangleright\!\!-\underset{\underset{CH_3}{|}}{C}=N-NH-Ts \xrightarrow{\text{NaOMe}} \square^{CH_3} + \triangleright\!\!-\!\!\text{\textbackslash} + \text{\textbackslash} \qquad (20)$$

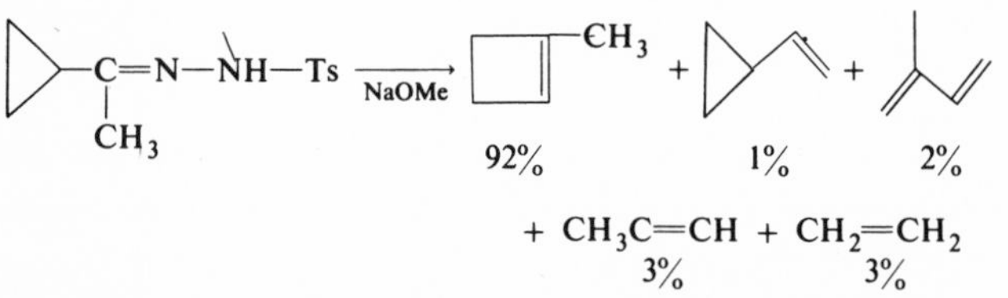

$$\qquad\qquad\qquad\qquad \underset{92\%}{} \qquad \underset{1\%}{} \quad \underset{2\%}{}$$

$$+ \underset{3\%}{CH_3C\equiv CH} + \underset{3\%}{CH_2=CH_2}$$

Intramolecular fragmentation to olefin and acetylene has been observed with the tricyclic carbene derived from nortricyclenone tosylhydrazone (IVa) (55a):

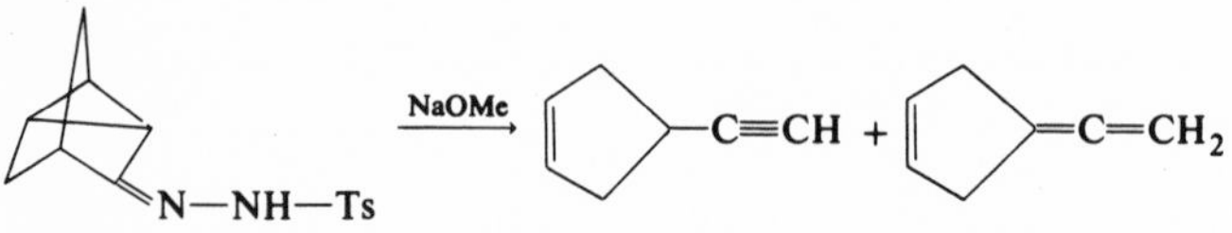

$$\underset{\text{(IVa)}}{\text{[structure]}\!\!-\!\!N-NH-Ts} \xrightarrow{\text{NaOMe}} \underset{\text{(IVb) (69\%)}}{\text{[structure]}-C\equiv CH} + \underset{\text{(IVc) (29\%)}}{\text{[structure]}=C=CH_2} \qquad (20a)$$

(19% yield of total hydrocarbon product)

The allene IVc is most probably formed by base-catalyzed isomerization of the acetylene IVb. Irradiation of the sodium salt of IVa produced exclusively IVb (42% yield). No comparable carbenoid reactions were observed on treatment of nortricyclyl chloride with sodium (55b).

Ring contraction leading to methylenecyclopropane is the major reaction of carbenacyclobutane (55). Some cyclobutene, formed by way of the familiar "hydride shift," is also obtained.

$$\boxed{=}\text{N—NH—Ts} \xrightarrow[\text{NaOMe}]{} \triangleright\!= + \square + \diagup\!\!\diagdown\!\!\diagup \qquad (21)$$

$$79\text{–}80\% \qquad 18\text{–}20\% \qquad 1\text{–}2\%$$

A mixture of cyclobutyl and cyclopropylcarbinyl ethyl ethers has been found after photolysis of diazocyclobutane in ethanol (9). The intervention of carbonium ions, formed by protonation of the diazalkane, is very likely under these reaction conditions.

The migration of phenyl groups appears to be more facile than that of alkyl groups. Pyrolysis of 2,2,2-triphenyldiazoethane afforded triphenylethylene in high yield (8). 2-Methyl-2-phenyldiazopropane (V) pyrolyzed with predominant phenyl shift, although some additional methyl migration has been reported (10) (the carbene intermediate is of the "neophyl" type).

$$\underset{\substack{| \\ \text{CH}_3 \\ (\text{V})}}{\overset{\substack{\text{CH}_3 \\ |}}{\text{Ph—C—CHN}_2}} \xrightarrow[60°]{} \underset{\text{CH}_3}{\overset{\text{CH}_3}{>}}\!\text{C}=\text{CH—Ph} + \underset{\text{CH}_3}{\overset{\text{Ph}}{>}}\!\text{C}=\text{CH—CH}_3 + \text{Ph}\!-\!\!\overset{\text{CH}_3}{\triangle} \qquad (22)$$

$$\qquad\qquad\qquad 50\% \qquad\qquad 9\% \qquad\qquad 41\%$$

The partial formation of rearranged olefins from β-phenylethyl halides under the action of alkali amides (56) may involve a carbene produced by α-elimination. Alternatively, a carbanion rearrangement may also explain the products of reaction (23). Carbanion rearrangements have been clearly demonstrated with 2,2,2-triphenylethyllithium and potassium (57).

$$\underset{\substack{| \\ R}}{\text{Ph—CH—CH}_2\text{Br}} \xrightarrow[\substack{\text{xylene,} \\ \text{reflux}}]{\text{KNH}_2} \underset{\substack{| \\ R}}{\text{Ph—C}=\text{CH}_2} + \text{R—CH}=\text{CH—Ph} \qquad (23)$$

Migration of fluorine has been observed in trifluoromethylcarbene produced by the photolysis of the corresponding diazoalkane (58):

$$\text{CF}_3\text{—CHN}_2 \xrightarrow[\text{0.1 atm.}]{h\nu} \text{CF}_3\text{—CH:} \rightarrow \text{CF}_2=\text{CHF}$$
$$\qquad\qquad\qquad\qquad\quad \downarrow + \text{CF}_3\text{CHN}_2 \qquad (30\%) \qquad\qquad (24)$$
$$\text{CF}_3\text{CH}=\text{CH—CF}_3 \quad (cis\text{- and } trans\text{-})$$
$$(50\%)$$

The high relative yield of hexafluorobutene-2 indicates that the migration of fluorine is slow as compared to the "hydride shift." In the photolysis of diazoethane, the ratio of 2-butene:ethylene is approximately 0.1 at 200 mm. (6, 7). In perfluoropropylcarbene, migration of a perfluoro-alkyl group, rather than of fluorine, takes place (58):

$$C_3F_7-CHN_2 \xrightarrow{h\nu} C_3F_7-CH: \rightarrow CF_2=CH-CF_2CF_3$$

$$\Big\downarrow + C_3F_7CHN_2 \qquad (40\%) \qquad\qquad (25)$$

$$C_3F_7CH=CH-C_3F_7$$
$$(50\%)$$

## B. Intermolecular Reactions

### 1. Methylcarbene and Dimethylcarbene

The ease of intramolecular stabilization leaves only a slight chance for intermolecular reactions of alkyl- and dialkylcarbenes. Since primary hydrogen undergoes "hydride shift" less readily than secondary and tertiary hydrogen (cf. Section II,A,1), a moderate stability of methylcarbene and dimethylcarbene can be expected.

In fact, some 2-butene was obtained (in addition to ethylene) in the pyrolysis of methylketene (1) and diazoethane (6, 7). The butene is probably formed by attack of methylcarbene on excess methylketene and diazoethane, respectively. The increase in the ratio of 2-butene:ethylene with increasing pressure (7) is in accord with this assumption. Attempts to trap methylcarbene by combination with carbon monoxide failed (4), but addition (in low yield) to propene (7) and cyclohexene (45) [but not 2-butene (7)] with the formation of cyclopropanes, has been reported. "Insertion" of methylcarbene into the silicon-hydrogen bond has been observed. The photolysis of diazoethane in the presence of phenylsilane afforded 5% of phenylethylsilane (59). It was shown that phenylethyl-silane was not formed from phenylsilane and ethylene.

When methylcarbene was produced by interaction of chlorocarbene and methyllithium, considerable amounts of propane and traces of propene were obtained in addition to ethylene (18). The presence of isopropyllithium in this system was demonstrated by reaction with methyl iodide to give isobutane. It appears, therefore, that methylcarbene has been trapped by addition to excess methyllithium. Displacement at an intermediate organometallic compound (VI) (cf. Chapter 2, Section II,H) is considered less likely as no comparable reaction has been achieved with ethylcarbene (propene was the only product). Replacement of methyl by ethyl should not affect the reactivity of the organometallic intermediate, but greatly facilitates "hydride shift" at the carbene stage.

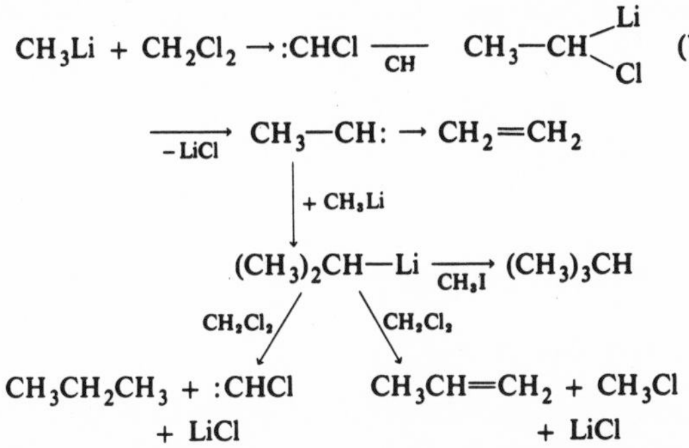

$$CH_3Li + CH_2Cl_2 \rightarrow :CHCl \xrightarrow{CH} CH_3-CH\begin{subarray}{l} Li \\ \diagdown Cl \end{subarray} \quad (VI)$$

$$\xrightarrow{-LiCl} CH_3-CH: \rightarrow CH_2=CH_2$$

$$\downarrow + CH_3Li$$

$$(CH_3)_2CH-Li \xrightarrow{CH_3I} (CH_3)_3CH$$

$$\overset{CH_3Cl_2}{\diagup} \qquad \overset{CH_3Cl_3}{\diagdown}$$

$$CH_3CH_2CH_3 + :CHCl \qquad CH_3CH=CH_2 + CH_3Cl$$
$$+ LiCl \qquad\qquad\qquad + LiCl$$

(26)

An analogous reaction of dimethylcarbene (from methyllithium and 1,1-dichloroethane) with methyllithium afforded isobutane and isobutene, but the ratio of $C_4:C_3$ products was small (18). The observation of some 2,3-dimethyl-2-butene in the pyrolysis (2) and photolysis (3) of dimethylketene also indicates some ability of dimethylcarbene for intermolecular reaction. No $C_6$-hydrocarbons were obtained in the pyrolysis and photolysis of dimethyldiazirine (27, 27b).

"Catalytic" decomposition of 2-diazopropane by zinc iodide (60) afforded some 2,3-dimethyl-2-butene, but no propene. It appears unlikely, therefore, that this reaction proceeds via a carbene intermediate. No (formal) addition of dimethylcarbene to olefins could be achieved by the zinc iodide procedure.

### 2. Carbenacyclopropanes

Incorporation of the divalent carbon atom in a cyclopropane ring virtually eliminates the "hydride shift." 2,2-Diphenylcarbenacyclopropane (VII), produced from the corresponding diazo compound, adds stereospecifically to cis- and trans-2-butene (61). The reactivity of various olefins toward VII has been estimated in competition experiments (61a). The data reveal a dominating steric effect when the two phenyl groups of VII are opposed to one or two alkyl groups. In addition to the olefin adducts, 1,1-diphenylallene (IX) is formed. A kinetic investigation has been made to relate the origin of the various products (62). If the sole source of the allene IX is the carbene VII, then the ratio of spiropentane VIII to allene IX should be proportional to the olefin concentration. This was not observed, nor was the ratio VIII:IX independent of the concentration of the olefin. It must be concluded that there are (at least) two different precursors of IX.

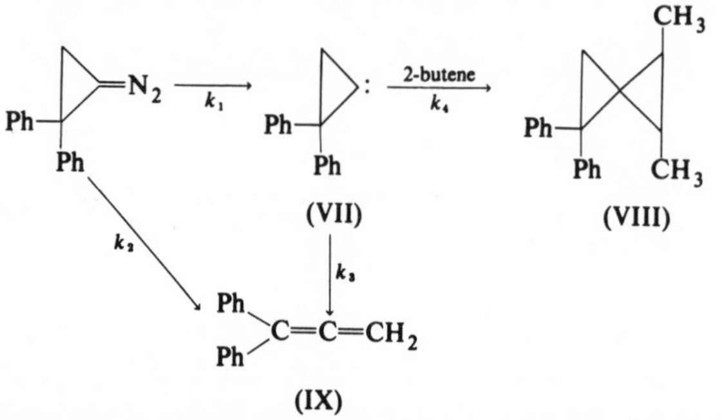

$$(27)$$

The reaction of optically active $N$-nitroso-$N$-($trans$-2,3-diphenylcyclopropyl)-urea with base affords 1,3-diphenylallene which exhibits a high degree of rotation (62a). This result excludes a carbene intermediate with free rotation about the $-\underset{\cdot\cdot}{C}-C$ bonds.

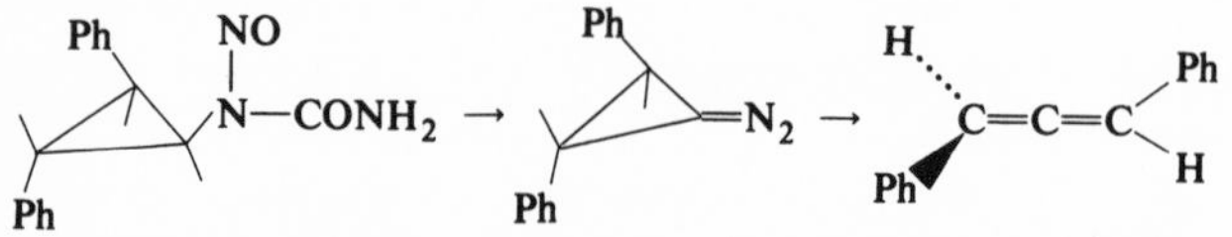

A carbene intermediate may be involved in the conversion of 1,1-dihalocyclopropanes to allenes by various reagents, such as magnesium (in ether) (63, 64), sodium on alumina (63), and lithium alkyls (42, 65).

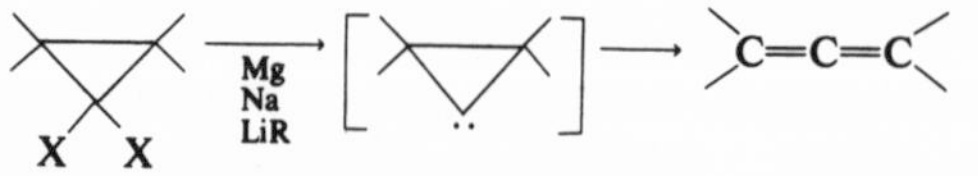

$$(28)$$

All attempts to trap the hypothetical carbene intermediate by intermolecular reactions have failed (64, 65), but interesting experiments aimed at the intramolecular addition of carbenacyclopropanes to double bonds have been reported (66). 1,1-Dibromo-2-(buten-3-yl)cyclopropane (X), on treatment with methyllithium at $-30°$, afforded 84% of the allene (XI) and 16% of the spirane (XII). The two products were formed in approximately equal amounts at $-78°$. One might suspect that the species adding to the double bond is an organometallic intermediate rather than a carbene.

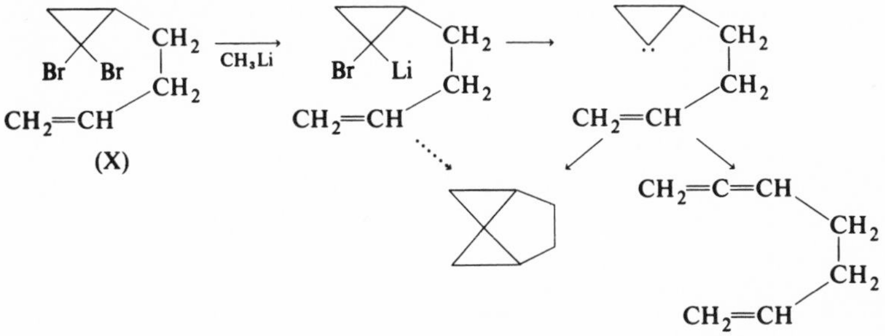

$$(29)$$

Allenes were the only products obtained from the dibromopentenyl- and -propenylcyclopropanes (XIII, XIV) related to X, whereas the vinyl compound XV afforded 1,2-dimethyl-cyclopentadiene as the major product (66).

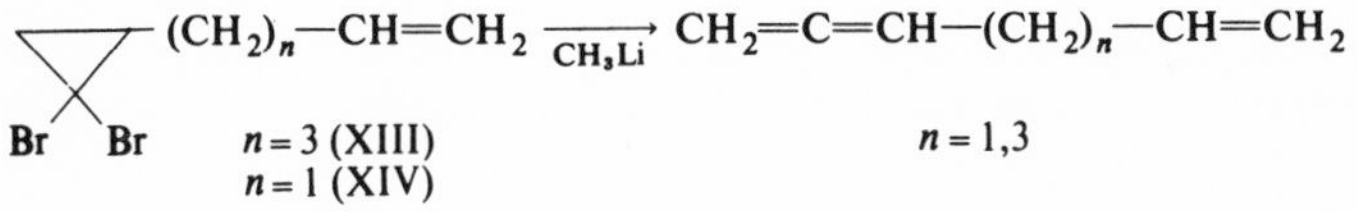

$$(30)$$

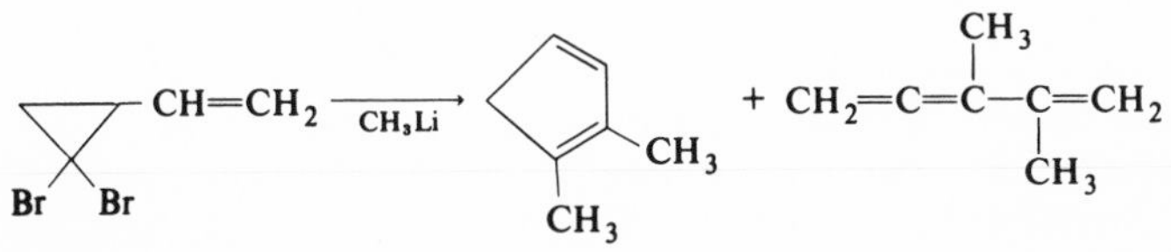

$$(31)$$

7,7-Dibromonorcarane is obviously incapable of forming an allene. Treatment with methyl lithium leads to products of intramolecular insertion (XVI, XVII), attack on the solvent (ether) with insertion into the carbon-hydrogen bonds (XVIII), addition to cyclohexene (XIX), and formation of an apparent dimer (XX) (42, 43). These reactions indicate a fairly indiscriminate intermediate. Intermolecular insertion is quite exceptional with carbenes produced by $\alpha$-elimination.

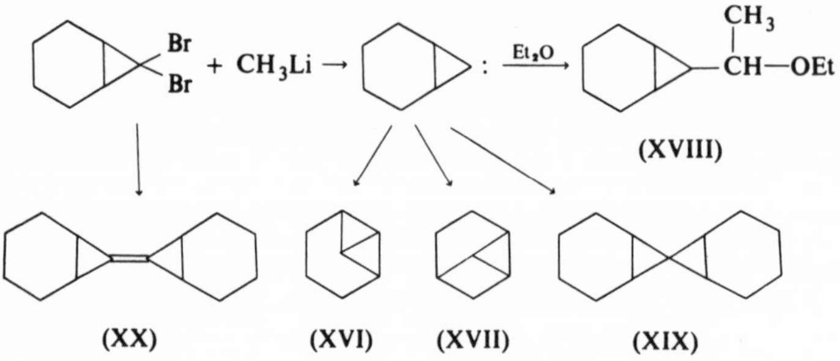

(32)

(XX)          (XVI)     (XVII)        (XIX)

Dibromobicyclo [3.1.0]hexane (XXI) under similar conditions affords 2-bromo-3-methycyclohexene (XXII) as the only product (67). XXII may result from the facile rearrangement of XXI to 2,3-dibromocyclohexene (68) (cf. Chapter 8, Section I,B,2c).

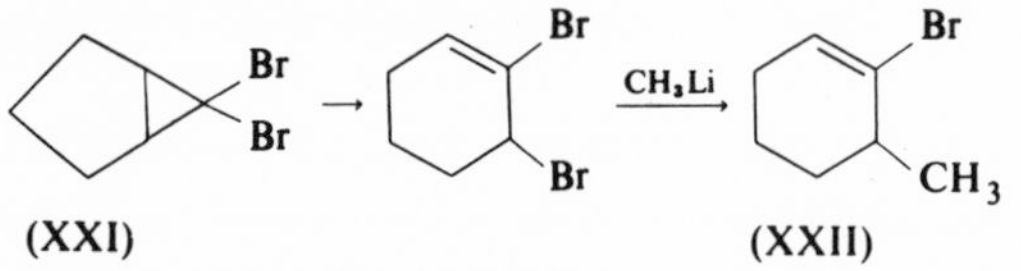

(33)

(XXI)                                 (XXII)

## REFERENCES

1. G. B. Kistiakowsky and B. H. Mahan, *J. Am. Chem. Soc.* **79**, 2412 (1957).
2. H. Staudinger and R. Endle, *Ber. deut. chem. Ges.* **46**, 1437 (1913).
3. R. A. Holroyd and F. E. Blacet, *J. Am. Chem. Soc.* **79**, 4830 (1957).
4. F. O. Rice and A. L. Glasebrook, *J. Am. Chem. Soc.* **56**, 741 (1934).
5. D. H. Volman, P. A. Leighton, F. E. Blacet, and R. K. Brinton, *J. Chem. Phys.* **18**, 203 (1950).
6. R. K. Brinton and D. H. Volman, *J. Chem. Phys.* **19**, 1394 (1951).
7. H. M. Frey, *Chem. & Ind. (London)* **1962**, 218; *J. Chem. Soc.* **1962**, 2293.
8. L. Hellerman and R. L. Garner, *J. Am. Chem. Soc.* **57**, 139 (1935).
9. D. E. Applequist and D. E. McGreer, *J. Am. Chem. Soc.* **82**, 1965 (1960).
10. H. Philip and J. Keating, *Tetrahedron Letters* **1961**, 523.
11. H. Meerwein and K. van Emster, *Ber. deut. chem. Ges.* **53**, 1815 (1920).
12. W. Reusch, M. W. DiCarlo, and L. Traynor, *J. Org. Chem.* **26**, 1711 (1961).
13. W. R. Bamford and T. S. Stevens, *J. Chem. Soc.* **1952**, 4735. D. G. Farnum, *J. Org. Chem.* **28**, 870 (1963).
14. M. P. Cava, R. L. Litle, and D. R. Napier, *J. Am. Chem. Soc.* **80**, 2257 (1958).
15. J. W. Powell and M. C. Whiting, *Tetrahedron* **7**, 305 (1959).
16. C. H. DePuy and D. H. Froemsdorf, *J. Am. Chem. Soc.* **82**, 634 (1960).
17. L. Friedman and H. Shechter, *J. Am. Chem. Soc.* **81**, 5512 (1959).
18. W. Kirmse and B. v. Bülow, *Chem. Ber.* **96**, 3316, 3323 (1963).
19. J. W. Powell and M. C. Whiting, *Tetrahedron* **12**, 168 (1961).

20. W. G. Dauben and F. G. Willey, *J. Am. Chem. Soc.* **84**, 1497 (1962).

21. P. Clarke, M. C. Whiting, G. Papenmeier, and W. Reusch, *J. Org. Chem.* **27**, 3356 (1962).

22. F. S. Bridson-Jones, G. D. Buckley, L. H. Cross, and A. P. Driver, *J. Chem. Soc.* **1951**, 2999.

23. F. S. Bridson-Jones and G. D. Buckley, *J. Chem. Soc.* **1951**, 3009.

24. S. R. Paulsen, *Angew. Chem.* **72**, 781 (1960).

25. E. Schmitz and R. Ohme, *Tetrahedron Letters* **1961**, 612; *Chem. Ber.* **94**, 2166 (1961).

26. H. M. Frey and I. D. R. Stevens, *J. Am. Chem. Soc.* **84**, 2647 (1962).

27a. E. Schmitz, D. Habisch, and A. Stark, *Angew. Chem.* **75**, 723 (1963).

27b. H. M. Frey and I. D. R. Stevens, *J. Chem. Soc.* **1963**, 3514.

28. R. K. Brinton, *J. Am. Chem. Soc.* **77**, 842 (1955).

29. H. Okabe and J. R. McNesby, *J. Chem. Phys.* **34**, 668 (1961).

30. C. MacKay and R. Wolfgang, *J. Am. Chem. Soc.* **83**, 2399 (1961).

31. C. MacKay, P. Pollak, H. E. Rosenberg, and R. Wolfgang, *J. Am. Chem. Soc.* **84**, 308 (1962).

32. K. Bayes, *J. Am. Chem. Soc.* **83**, 3712 (1961); **84**, 4077 (1962); **85**, 1730 (1963).

33. R. T. Mullen and A. P. Wolf, *J. Am. Chem. Soc.* **84**, 3214 (1962).

33a. M. Marshall, R. Wolfgang, and C. MacKay, *Tetrahedron Letters* **1963**, 2033.

34. D. G. Hill, W. A. Judge, P. S. Skell, S. W. Kantor, and Ch. R. Hauser, *J. Am. Chem. Soc.* **74**, 5599 (1952).

35. S. M. Luck, D. G. Hill, A. T. Stewart, and Ch. R. Hauser, *J. Am. Chem. Soc.* **81**, 2784 (1959).

36. F. C. Whitmore, A. H. Popkin, H. I. Bernstein, and J. P. Wilkins, *J. Am. Chem. Soc.* **63**, 124 (1941).

37. F. C. Whitmore and H. D. Zook, *J. Am. Chem. Soc.* **64**, 1783 (1942).

38. F. C. Whitmore, C. A. Weisgerber, and A. C. Shabica, Jr., *J. Am. Chem. Soc.* **65**, 1469 (1943).

39. W. Kirmse and W. v. E. Doering, *Tetrahedron* **11**, 266 (1960).

40. L. Friedman and J. G. Berger, *J. Am. Chem. Soc.* **83**, 492, 500 (1961).

41. P. S. Skell and A. P. Krapcho, *J. Am. Chem. Soc.* **83**, 754 (1961).

42. W. R. Moore and H. R. Ward, *J. Org. Chem.* **25**, 2073 (1960); **27**, 4179 (1962).

43. W. R. Moore, H. R. Ward, and R. F. Merritt, *J. Am. Chem. Soc.* **83**, 2019 (1961).

44. W. Kirmse and B. v. Wedel, *Ann.* **666**, 1 (1963).

45. V. Franzen, H. J. Schmidt, and Ch. Merz, *Chem. Ber.* **94**, 2942 (1961).

46. A. C. Cope, G. A. Berchtold, P. E. Peterson, and S. H. Sharman, *J. Am. Chem. Soc.* **82**, 6370 (1960).

47. G. L. Closs, *J. Am. Chem. Soc.* **84**, 809 (1962).

48. P. S. Skell and J. Starer, *J. Am. Chem. Soc.* **82**, 2971 (1960).

49. M. S. Silver, *J. Am. Chem. Soc.* **82**, 2971 (1960).

50. O. E. Edwards and M. Lesage, *Chem. & Ind. (London)* **1960**, 1107.

51. P. S. Skell, J. Starer, and A. P. Krapcho, *J. Am. Chem. Soc.* **82**, 5257 (1960).

52. G. J. Karabatsos and J. D. Graham, *J. Am. Chem. Soc.* **82**, 5250 (1960).

52a. M. J. Goldstein and S. J. Baum, *J. Am. Chem. Soc.* **85**, 1885 (1963).

53. W. v. E. Doering and W. Kirmse, *Tetrahedron* **11**, 272 (1960).

54. L. Friedman and H. Shechter, *J. Am. Chem. Soc.* **83**, 3159 (1961).

54a. C. Swithenbank and M. C. Whiting, *J. Chem. Soc.* **1963**, 4573.

54b. R. W. Alder and M. C. Whiting, *J. Chem. Soc.* **1963**, 4595.
54c. C. A. Grob and J. Hostynek, *Helv. Chim. Acta* **46**, 1676 (1963).
55. L. Friedman and H. Shechter, *J. Am. Chem. Soc.* **82**, 1002 (1960).
55a. S. J. Cristol and J. K. Harrington, *J. Org. Chem.* **28**, 1413 (1963).
55b. P. K. Freeman, D. E. George, and V. N. M. Rao, *J. Org. Chem.* **28**, 3234 (1963).
56. Ch. R. Hauser, *J. Am. Chem. Soc.* **62**, 933 (1940).
57. E. Grovenstein, Jr., and L. P. Williams, Jr., *J. Am. Chem. Soc.* **83**, 412 (1961).
58. R. Fields and R. N. Haszeldine, *Proc. Chem. Soc.* **1960**, 22.
59. K. A. W. Kramer and A. N. Wright, *Tetrahedron Letters* **1962**, 1095.
60. D. E. Applequist and H. Babad, *J. Org. Chem.* **27**, 288 (1962).
61. W. M. Jones, *J. Am. Chem. Soc.* **82**, 6200 (1960).
61a. W. M. Jones, M. H. Grasley, and W. S. Brey, Jr., *J. Am. Chem. Soc.* **85**, 2754 (1963).
62. W. M. Jones and M. H. Grasley, *Tetrahedron Letters* **1962**, 927.
62a. W. M. Jones, J. W. Wilson, Jr., and F. B. Tutwiler, *J. Am. Chem. Soc.* **85**, 3309 (1963).
63. W. v. E. Doering and P. LaFlamme, *Tetrahedron* **2**, 75 (1958).
64. T. J. Logan, *Tetrahedron Letters* **1961**, 173.
65. L. Skatteböl, *Tetrahedron Letters* **1961**, 167.
66. L. Skatteböl, *Chem. & Ind. (London)* **1962**, 2146.
67. W. R. Moore and H. R. Ward, *Chem. & Ind. (London)* **1961**, 594.
68. J. Sonnenberg and S. Winstein, *J. Org. Chem.* **27**, 748 (1962).

# CHAPTER 4

# Olefinic and Acetylenic Carbenes

## I. ALKENYLCARBENES

VARIOUS METHODS which were found useful in the production of alkyl-
and dialkylcarbenes have been successfully applied to generate alkenylcarbenes. Substituted vinyllithium compounds react with methylene
chloride to give chlorocarbene which adds to excess organometallic
reagent with formation of an alkenylcarbene $(1, 3)$:

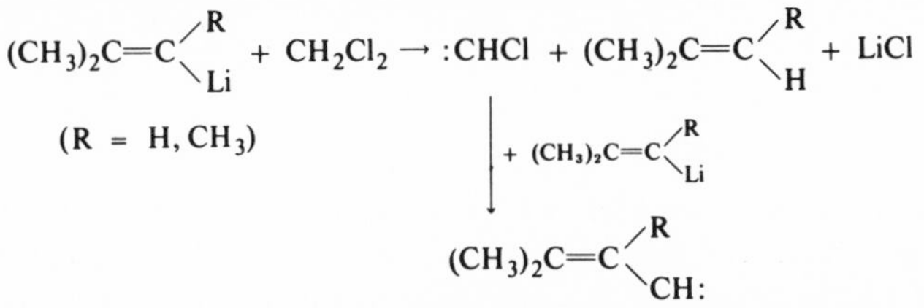

$$(CH_3)_2C=C\overset{R}{\underset{Li}{\diagup}} + CH_2Cl_2 \rightarrow \;:CHCl + (CH_3)_2C=C\overset{R}{\underset{H}{\diagup}} + LiCl$$

$$(R = H, CH_3) \qquad \Bigg\downarrow\; + (CH_3)_2C=C\overset{R}{\underset{Li}{\diagup}} \qquad\qquad (1)$$

$$(CH_3)_2C=C\overset{R}{\underset{CH:}{\diagup}}$$

$\alpha$-Elimination of hydrogen chloride from 2,3,3-trimethylallyl chloride
(I) has been brought about in low yield by lithium alkyls [Eq. (2)] $(2, 3)$.
Halogen-metal interchange on 1,1-dibromo-2,3-dimethyl-2-butene (II)
proved to be a more effective route to the carbene intermediate [Eq. (2)]
$(3)$. The tosylhydrazone of 2,3-dimethylcrotonaldehyde, when treated
with sodium methoxide in aprotic solvents, also gave rise to the same
alkenylcarbene [Eq. (3)] $(2)$.

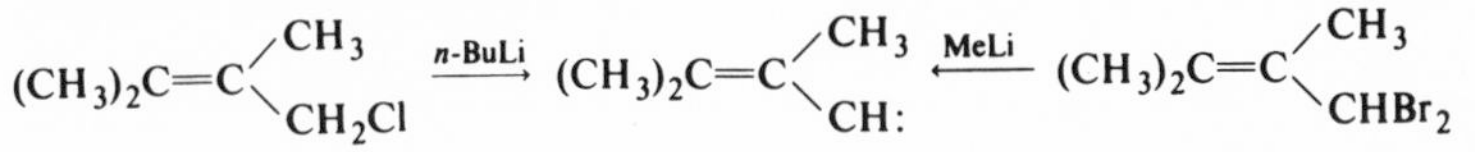

$$(CH_3)_2C=C\overset{CH_3}{\underset{CH_2Cl}{\diagup}} \xrightarrow{n\text{-BuLi}} (CH_3)_2C=C\overset{CH_3}{\underset{CH:}{\diagup}} \xleftarrow{\text{MeLi}} (CH_3)_2C=C\overset{CH_3}{\underset{CHBr_2}{\diagup}} \qquad (2)$$

$$\text{(I)} \qquad\qquad\qquad\qquad\qquad\qquad\qquad\qquad \text{(II)}$$

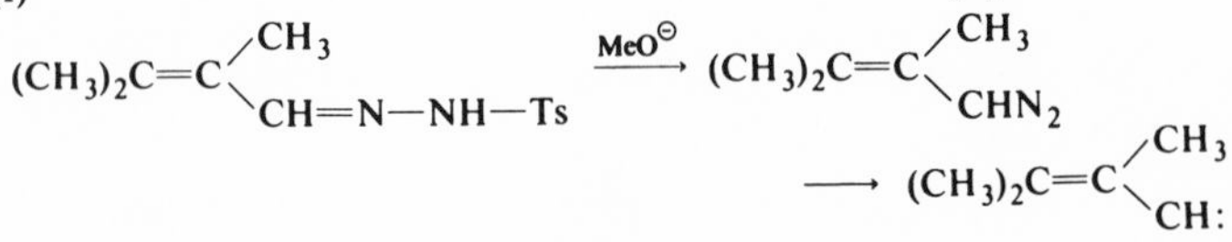

$$(CH_3)_2C=C\overset{CH_3}{\underset{CH=N-NH-Ts}{\diagup}} \xrightarrow{MeO^{\ominus}} (CH_3)_2C=C\overset{CH_3}{\underset{CHN_2}{\diagup}}$$

$$\longrightarrow (CH_3)_2C=C\overset{CH_3}{\underset{CH:}{\diagup}} \quad (3)$$

The only products obtained so far from these alkenylcarbenes are substituted cyclopropenes, formed by intramolecular addition [Eq. (4)] (*1–3*). The transition state of this unusual ring closure has been discussed in detail (*3*), and it was concluded that $\beta$- and $\gamma$-methyl groups lower the activation barrier. The vinyl hydrogen of the cyclopropenes undergoes hydrogen-lithium exchange under the conditions of reactions (1) and (2). Carboxylation affords cyclopropenecarboxylic acids, and an additional methyl group is introduced by treatment with methyl iodide.

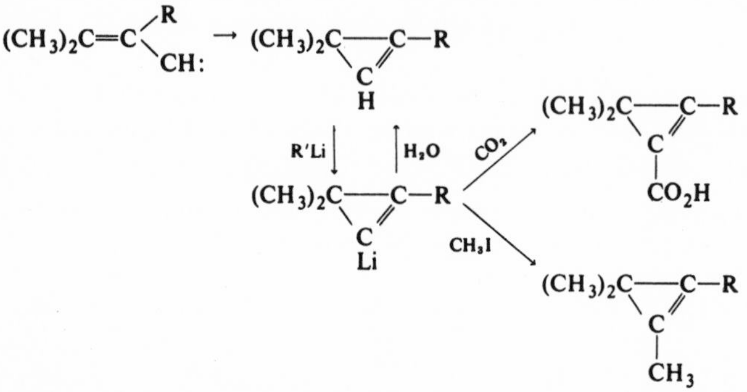

$$(CH_3)_2C{=}C\begin{smallmatrix}R\\CH:\end{smallmatrix} \rightarrow (CH_3)_2\underset{\underset{H}{\overset{|}{C}}}{C}{-}\overset{\diagup}{C}{-}R \tag{4}$$

Cyclopropenes have also been obtained by photolysis of pyrazolenines (*3a*). However, a careful study of the tosylhydrazone decomposition [Eq. (3)] has ruled out pyrazolenines as immediate precursors of the cyclopropenes (*3b*). 1-Diazo-2,3-dimethyl-2-butene and 4-diazo-2-methyl-2-pentene have been isolated and could be converted to cyclopropenes by photolysis *and* pyrolysis, whereas the conversion of pyrazolenines was effected only by light. The latter reaction may well proceed by way of a diazoalkene (*3c*).

Photolysis of the resonance-stabilized diazocyclopentadiene (*4*) produces a cyclic alkenylcarbene which inserts into the carbon-hydrogen bonds of the solvent, e.g., cyclohexane (*5*). The structure of the products is probably III, but the location of the double bonds has not been ascertained.

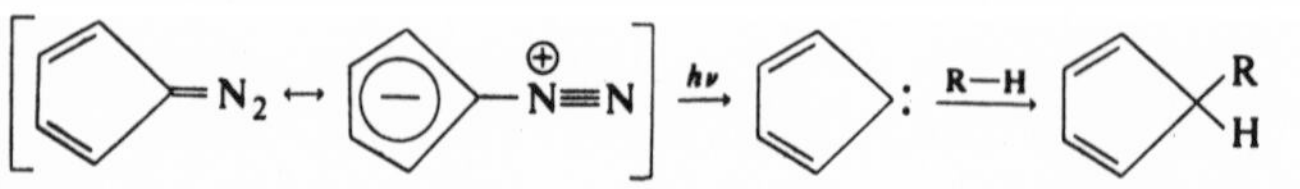

$$\left[ \bigcirc{=}N_2 \leftrightarrow \ominus\bigcirc{-}\overset{\oplus}{N}{\equiv}N \right] \overset{h\nu}{\to} \bigcirc: \overset{R-H}{\to} \bigcirc\begin{smallmatrix}R\\H\end{smallmatrix} \tag{5}$$

(III)

Allylcarbene (generated by photolysis of allyldiazomethane) undergoes hydrogen shift to give butadiene, and intramolecular addition with formation of the highly strained bicyclobutane (5a).

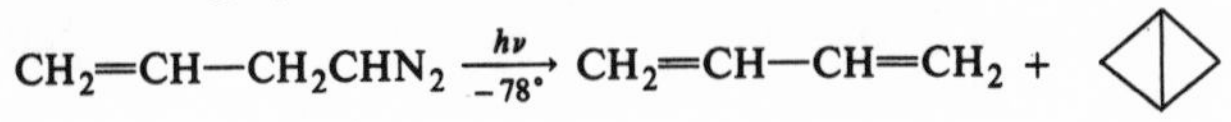

$$CH_2\!=\!CH\!-\!CH_2CHN_2 \xrightarrow[-78°]{h\nu} CH_2\!=\!CH\!-\!CH\!=\!CH_2 + \text{◁▷}$$

$$5 \qquad\qquad\qquad\qquad\qquad 1$$

## II. ALKYNYLCARBENES

Ethynylcarbene ("propargylene"), generated in the photolysis of diazopropyne, does not insert into carbon-hydrogen bonds and adds to olefins in a nonstereospecific manner (6). Results with trans- and cis-2-butene are shown in Eq. (6).

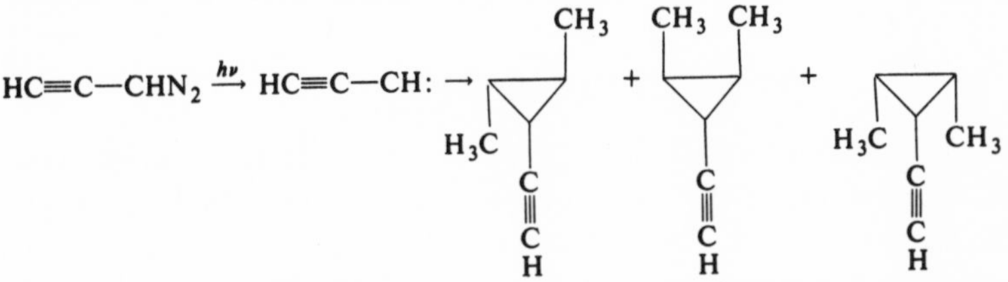

| | | | |
|---|---|---|---|
| trans-2-butene: | 95% | 3.5% | 1.5% |
| cis-2-butene: | 13% | 33% | 54% |

As with other nonstereospecifically reacting carbenes, the addition to trans-2-butene is more stereoselective than that to cis-2-butene. Propargylene was assumed to react in a low lying triplet state which has been rationalized by molecular orbital considerations (6).

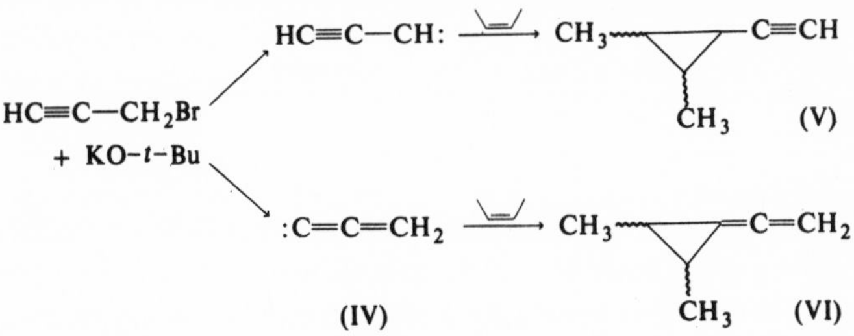

Unfortunately, attempts to produce propargylene by α-elimination from propargyl bromide have led to ambiguous results (7). In the presence of cis-2-butene a mixture of the acetylene V and the allene VI was obtained (stereochemistry unknown). The question remains unsettled whether the intermediate involved here was ethynylcarbene or ethenylidenecarbene (IV).

Propynylcarbene (VII) adds to olefins not only at C-1 but also at C-3 (8), indicating a "propargyl" resonance of carbenes which compares to the allyl resonance of carbonium ions.

$$[CH_3-C{\equiv}C-CH{:}\leftrightarrow CH_3-\overset{\cdot\cdot}{C}-C{\equiv}CH] + CH_3-CH{=}CH-CH_3$$

(VII)                                         (cis- or trans-)

$$\rightarrow CH_3-\overset{\diagup}{\underset{\diagdown}{C}H}\quad CH-CH_3 + CH_3-\overset{\diagup}{\underset{\diagdown}{C}H}\quad CH-CH_3 \qquad (8)$$

$$\underset{H}{}\overset{C}{\diagup}\diagdown C{\equiv}C-CH_3 \qquad \underset{H_3C}{}\overset{C}{\diagup}\diagdown C{\equiv}CH$$

(3 stereoisomers)                    (3 stereoisomers)

### III. ALKYLIDENECARBENES

cis-ω-Bromostyrene may undergo a concerted β-elimination (hydrogen and bromine are in the trans-position), and reacts with sodium hydroxide in isopropanol $2 \times 10^5$ times faster than the trans-isomer. With phenyllithium, however, the ratio $k_{cis}/k_{trans}$ is 0.5 (9, 10). To account for this difference, the reaction with phenyllithium was assumed to proceed by α-elimination (9). The migration of the phenyl group, as required by the α-elimination mechanism, was not confirmed, however, by $C^{14}$ experiments (10). Obviously no α-elimination is possible with the isomers of 1-chloro-1,2-diphenylethylene. Nevertheless the cis-isomer reacts with phenyllithium 22 times faster than the trans-isomer (11). This work indicates a preference of phenyllithium for cis-elimination which is probably due to some coordination of the attacking base and the departing chloride by the lithium cation. Thus α-elimination may be excluded for haloalkenes containing β-hydrogen.

$$Ph-C^{14}H{=}CHBr + BuLi \xrightarrow{\beta\text{-el.}} Ph-C^{14}{\equiv}CH$$

$$\searrow \alpha\text{-el.} \qquad\qquad\qquad\qquad (9)$$

$$Ph-\underset{H}{C^{14}}{=}C{:} \rightarrow Ph-C{\equiv}C^{14}H$$

On the other hand, α-elimination with subsequent (or simultaneous) migration of aryl groups is clearly established with 1-halo-2,2-diarylethylenes. These compounds afford diarylacetylenes when treated with alkoxides (*12–14*), hydroxides (*15*), and amides (*16*), of potassium or sodium. The action of lithium alkyls has been studied in recent years. Treatment of 1-bromo-2,2-diphenylethylene with butyllithium was reported to result in 57% of hydrogen-lithium exchange (leading to diphenylacetylene), and 34% of bromine-lithium exchange (*17*). Hydrogen-lithium exchange occurred exclusively with phenyllithium (*18*).

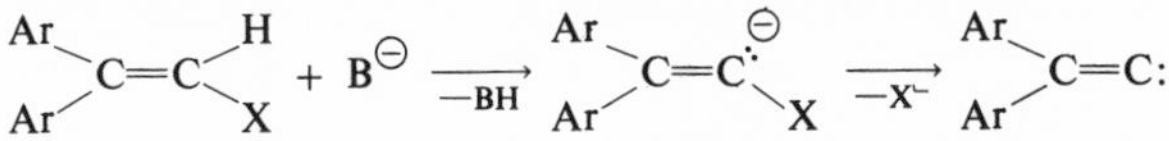

$$
\underset{Ar}{\overset{Ar}{>}}C=C\underset{X}{\overset{H}{<}} + B^{\ominus} \xrightarrow[-BH]{} \underset{Ar}{\overset{Ar}{>}}C=C\underset{X}{\overset{\ominus}{\cdot\cdot}} \xrightarrow{-X^-} \underset{Ar}{\overset{Ar}{>}}C=C:
$$

$$\text{(VIII)} \qquad\qquad \text{(IX)} \qquad\qquad (10)$$

$$\to Ar-C\equiv C-Ar$$

α-Elimination of halogen, instead of hydrogen halide, can be achieved by treating 1,1-dihalo-2,2-diarylethylenes with lithium (*19*), butyllithium (*17*), phenyllithium, or potassium triphenylmethide (*19a*).

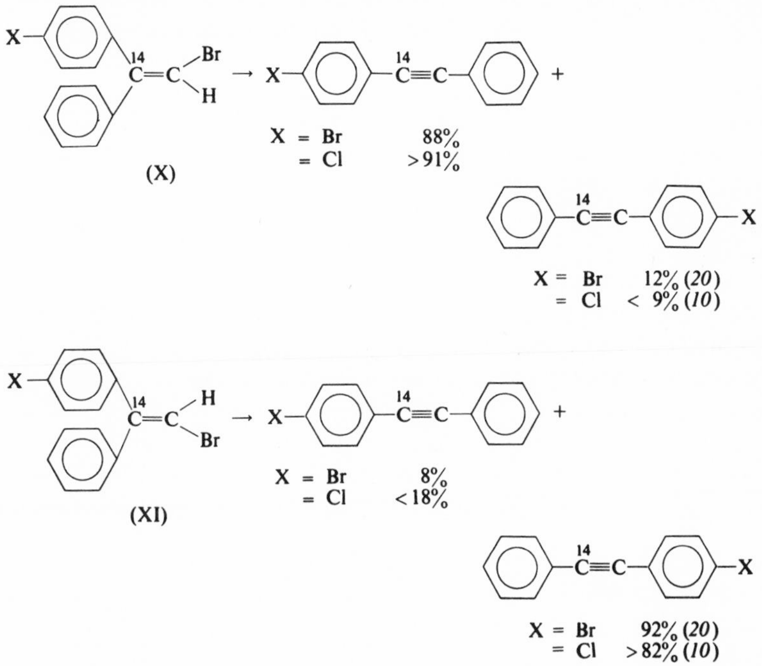

No final decision can be made as to whether reaction (10) involves a carbene intermediate (IX). The aryl migration was shown to be highly stereoselective by studying the $C^{14}$-labeled *cis-* and *trans*-isomers X and XI (*10, 20*). The aryl group *cis* to the hydrogen (*trans* to the halogen) was found to migrate preferentially. These observations require that the carbene intermediate IX, if involved, should retain the *cis-* and *trans* geometry. Such configurational stability does not appear very likely, but could be understood if the carbene carbon maintained its $sp^2$ character (with one $sp^2$ hybrid orbital occupied by an electron pair and the other unoccupied) (*11*). Most workers in this field explain reaction (10) in terms of a carbanion rearrangement or a completely concerted mechanism.

In contrast to the results with X and XI, predominant migration of the *p*-methoxyphenyl group has been observed with both isomers of 2-bromo-1-*p*-methoxyphenyl-1-phenyl-[2—$C^{14}$]ethylene (20a). The activation enthalpy is much smaller, however, for the rearrangement of the *trans*-isomer (*20b*).

Intermolecular reactions, such as apparent dimerization and substitution [Eq. (12)], occur with XII (rearrangement would lead to incorporation of the acetylenic bond in a six-membered ring) (*18*). Again, no clear distinction between carbene and carbanion intermediates can be made.

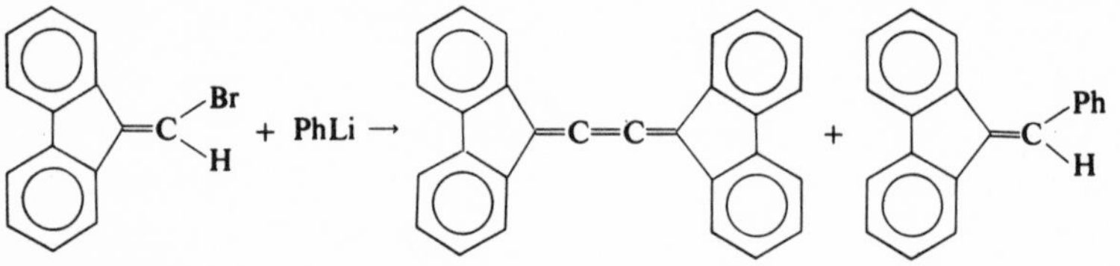

$$\text{(XII)} \hspace{7cm} \text{(12)}$$

An entirely different route to the hypothetical carbene intermediate IX is the reaction of diphenylketene with triethyl phosphite (*21*). The two reactants combine in an exothermic reaction to give an adduct which may be pyrolyzed at 215° with the formation of diphenylacetylene and triethyl phosphate. The intermediate in this reaction is considered to be a coordinated structure (XIII). A carbanion rearrangement appears improbable in this case, but a concerted mechanism cannot be excluded.

$$Ph_2C{=}C{=}O + P(OEt)_3 \rightarrow Ph_2C{=}\overset{\oplus}{C}{-}O{-}\overset{\ominus}{P}(OEt)_3 \rightarrow Ph{-}C{\equiv}C{-}Ph$$

$$\text{(XIII)} \hspace{4cm} + OP(OEt)_3$$

$$(13)$$

The generation of aliphatic alkylidenecarbenes has been attempted by treatment of appropriate vinyl halides with potassium *tert*-butoxide (*21a*) or phenyllithium (*21b*). The *tert*-butoxide procedure affordes moderate (8–20%) yields of cyclohexene adducts in addition to *tert*-butyl vinyl ethers.

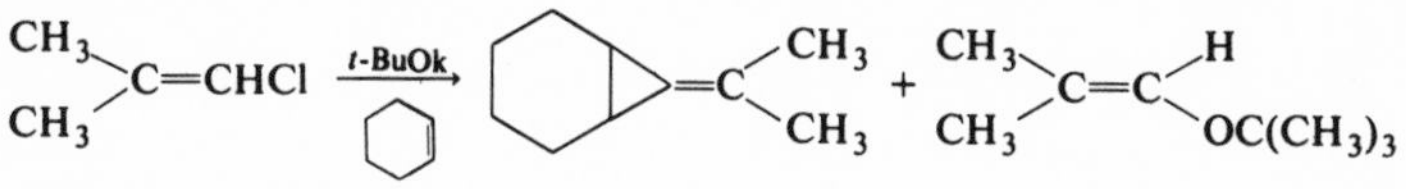

Similarly, displacement of chlorine occurred in the reaction of 1-chloro-methylenecyclohexane with phenyllithium (*21b*).

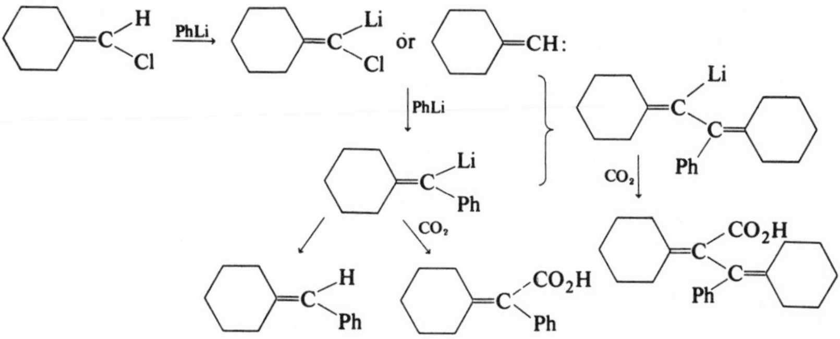

## IV. ALKENYLIDENECARBENES

The solvolysis of *tert*-ethynyl halides (e.g., XIV) is very slow as compared to *tert*-butyl halides, but is strongly accelerated by base. Under these conditions the kinetics are first order with respect to both halide (XIV) and base concentrations, and the reaction proceeds predominantly with displacement of the halogen (very little elimination of hydrogen halide) (*22–24*). Base catalysis was not observed when the acetylenic hydrogen was replaced by an alkyl group (*25*).

By solvolyzing XIV in 80% EtOD–20% $D_2O$ mixtures it was shown that the base-catalyzed exchange of the acetylenic protons is appreciably faster than base-promoted solvolysis (*26*). Thus the reaction involves a rapid equilibrium rather than rate-determining formation of the conjugate base. The conjugate base (XV) undergoes $S_N1$-ionization rather

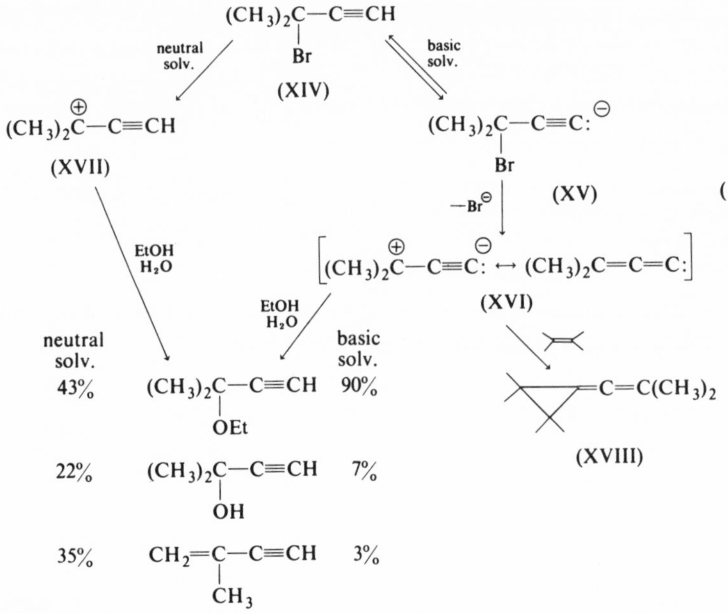

$$(CH_3)_2C-C\equiv CH$$

$$\text{(XIV)} \quad | \quad Br$$

neutral solv. / ... basic solv.

$$\overset{\oplus}{(CH_3)_2C}-C\equiv CH$$
(XVII)

$$(CH_3)_2C-C\equiv C:\overset{\ominus}{}$$
$$| \quad Br$$
(XV)          (14)

$$-Br^{\ominus} \Big|$$

$$\left[ (CH_3)_2\overset{\oplus}{C}-C\equiv C:\overset{\ominus}{} \leftrightarrow (CH_3)_2C=C=C: \right]$$
(XVI)

EtOH H₂O          EtOH H₂O / basic solv.

neutral solv.     basic solv.
43%               90%

$$(CH_3)_2C-C\equiv CH$$
$$| \quad OEt$$

22%               7%
$$(CH_3)_2C-C\equiv CH$$
$$| \quad OH$$

35%               3%
$$CH_2=C-C\equiv CH$$
$$| \quad CH_3$$

$$\rightleftharpoons C=C(CH_3)_2$$
(XVIII)

than $S_N2$-displacement, as was shown by the "mass-law" effect of added halide ion (26). The different product mixtures obtained in the neutral and basic solvolysis clearly indicate that different intermediates are involved in the product-determining step. The rate-determining steps are also different, as may be seen from the isotope effects of

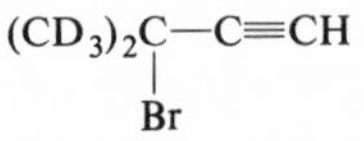

$$(CD_3)_2C-C\equiv CH \quad \text{(XIX)}$$
$$| \quad Br$$

XIX undergoes neutral solvolysis in 80% ethanol 1.84 times slower than the undeuterated compound, whereas the hydroxide-promoted solvolysis is slowed by a factor of only 1.31 (27). The intermediate in basic solvolysis is probably the zwitterion-carbene XVI. This ambident intermediate reacts with alcohols, amines, etc., mainly to give the propargylic products. In contrast, olefins are added at the terminal carbon with formation of alkenylidenencyclopropanes (XVIII) in 10–50% yield (7). In competition experiments the selectivity of XVI was shown to be comparable to that of dihalocarbenes (28) (Table I).

TABLE I

REACTIVITY OF OLEFINS TOWARD CARBENES $(-10°$ to $0°)$ $(28)$

| Olefin | $\log (k/k_0)$ | | | | |
|---|---|---|---|---|---|
| | $(CH_3)_2C{=}C{=}C{:}$ | $:CCl_2$ | $:CBr_2$ | $:CHCl$ | $:CH{-}CO_2R$ |
| 2,3-Dimethyl-2-butene | 1.3 | 1.73 | 0.84 | 0.67 | 0.21 |
| 2-Methyl-2-butene | 0.67 | 1.37 | 0.87 | 0.47 | 0.21 |
| 2-Methyl-1-butene | 0.70 | 0.74 | | | |
| Cyclohexene | 0.00 | 0.00 | 0.00 | 0.00 | 0.00 |
| 1-Hexene | $-0.60$ | $-0.73$ | $-0.71$ | | |
| 1-Pentene | | $-0.86$ | $-0.78$ | $-0.43$ | $-0.04$ |

Derivatives of diphenylethynylcarbinol (XXII) have also been studied (7). Addition of the intermediate·XXI, produced from the acetate XX with potassium *tert*-butoxide, to styrene has been achieved in 25% yield.

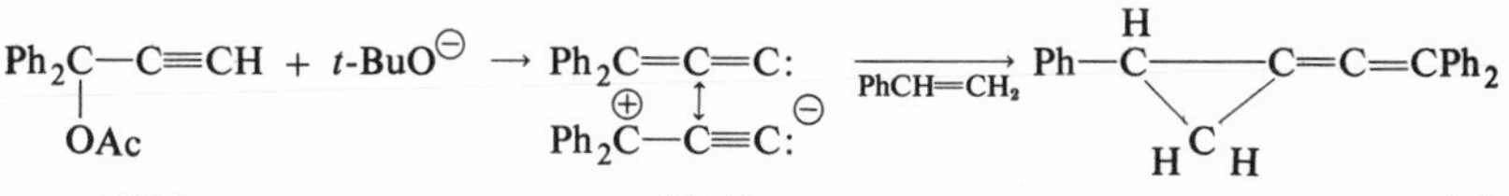

$$Ph_2C{-}C{\equiv}CH + t\text{-}BuO^{\ominus} \rightarrow Ph_2C{=}C{=}C{:} \xrightarrow{PhCH=CH_2} Ph{-}\overset{H}{C}{-----}C{=}C{=}CPh_2$$

(XX) (XXI) (15)

Treatment of the carbinol XXII with acetic anhydride and base has been reported to give tetraphenylhexapentaene (XXIII) (29). This reaction may be explained by assuming an attack of the carbene XXI on the conjugate base of the acetate XX (7):

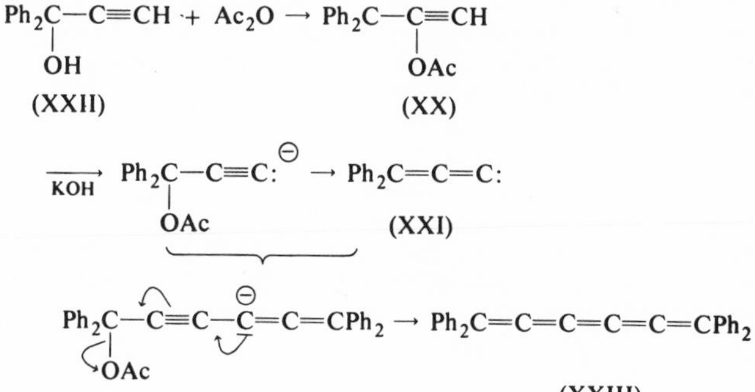

$$Ph_2C{-}C{\equiv}CH \dotplus Ac_2O \rightarrow Ph_2C{-}C{\equiv}CH$$

OH OAc
(XXII) (XX)

$$\xrightarrow{KOH} Ph_2C{-}C{\equiv}C{:}^{\ominus} \rightarrow Ph_2C{=}C{=}C{:}$$

OAc (XXI)

$$Ph_2C{-}C{\equiv}C{-}\overset{\ominus}{C}{=}C{=}CPh_2 \rightarrow Ph_2C{=}C{=}C{=}C{=}C{=}CPh_2$$

OAc (XXIII)

## REFERENCES

1. G. L. Closs and L. E. Closs, *J. Am. Chem. Soc.* **83,** 1003 (1961).
2. G. L. Closs and L. E. Closs, *J. Am. Chem. Soc.* **83,** 2015 (1961).

3. G. L. Closs and L. E. Closs, *J. Am. Chem. Soc.* **85**, 99 (1963).
3a. G. L. Closs and W. A. Böll, *Angew. Chem.* **75**, 640 (1963).
3b. G. L. Closs, L. E. Closs, and W. A. Böll, *J. Am. Chem. Soc.* **85**, 3796 (1963).
3c. G. L. Closs and W. A. Böll, *J. Am. Chem. Soc.* **85**, 3904 (1963).
4. W. v. E. Doering and C. H. DePuy, *J. Am. Chem. Soc.* **75**, 5955 (1953).
5. W. Kirmse, L. Horner, and H. Hoffmann, *Ann.* **614**, 19 (1958).
5a. D. M. Lemal, F. Menger, and G. W. Clark, *J. Am. Chem. Soc.* **85**, 2529 (1963).
6. P. S. Skell and J. Klebe, *J. Am. Chem. Soc.* **82**, 247 (1960).
7. H. D. Hartzler, *J. Am. Chem. Soc.* **81**, 2024 (1959); **83**, 4990 (1961).
8. P. S. Skell, Paper presented at the *137th Meeting Am. Chem. Soc., Cleveland, 1960.*
9. S. J. Cristol and R. F. Helmreich, *J. Am. Chem. Soc.* **77**, 5034 (1955).
10. D. Y. Curtin, E. W. Flynn, and R. F. Nystrom, *Chem. & Ind. (London)* **1957**, 1453; *J. Am. Chem. Soc.* **80**, 4599 (1958).
11. S. J. Cristol and R. S. Bly, Jr., *J. Am. Chem. Soc.* **83**, 4027 (1961).
12. P. Fritsche, *Ann.* **279**, 319 (1894).
13. W. P. Buttenberg, *Ann.* **279**, 324 (1894).
14. H. Wiechell, *Ann.* **279**, 337 (1894).
15. M. M. Tiffeneau, *Compt. rend.* **135**, 1374 (1902).
16. G. H. Coleman and R. D. Maxwell, *J. Am. Chem. Soc.* **56**, 132 (1934); **58**, 2310 (1936).
17. D. Y. Curtin and E. W. Flynn, *J. Am. Chem. Soc.* **81**, 4714 (1959).
18. D. Y. Curtin and W. H. Richardson, *J. Am. Chem. Soc.* **81**, 4719 (1959).
19. W. Schlenk and E. Bergmann, *Ann.* **463**, 71 (1928).
19a. F. B. Kirby, W. G. Kofron, and Ch. R. Hauser, *J. Org. Chem.* **28**, 2176 (1963).
20. A. A. Bothner-By, *J. Am. Chem. Soc.* **77**, 3293 (1955).
20a. W. Tadros, A. B. Sakla, M. S. Ishak, and E. R. Armanious, *J. Chem. Soc.* **1963**, 4218.
20b. W. M. Jones and R. Damico, *J. Am. Chem. Soc.* **85**, 2273 (1963).
21. T. Mikaiyama, H. Nambu, and M. Okamoto, *J. Org. Chem.* **27**, 3651 (1962).
21a. M. Tanabe and R. A. Walsh, *J. Am. Chem. Soc.* **85**, 3522 (1963).
21b. H. Günther and A. A. Bothner-By, *Chem. Ber.* **96**, 3112 (1963).
22. G. F. Hennion and D. E. Maloney, *J. Am. Chem. Soc.* **73**, 4735 (1951).
23. G. F. Hennion and E. G. Teach, *J. Am. Chem. Soc.* **75**, 1653 (1953).
24. G. F. Hennion and K. W. Nelson, *J. Am. Chem. Soc.* **79**, 2142 (1957).
25. A. Burawoy and E. Spinner, *J. Chem. Soc.* **1954**, 3752.
26. V. J. Shiner, Jr. and J. W. Wilson, *J. Am. Chem. Soc.* **84**, 2402 (1962).
27. V. J. Shiner, Jr., J. W. Wilson, G. Heinemann, and N. Solliday, *J. Am. Chem. Soc.* **84**, 2408 (1962).
28. H. D. Hartzler, *J. Am. Chem. Soc.* **83**, 4997 (1961).
29. P. Cadiot, *Ann. chim. (Paris)* [13] **1**, 214 (1956).

# CHAPTER 5

# Aryl- and Diarylcarbenes

THE GROUND STATE of aryl- and diarylcarbenes was shown to be a triplet state by observation of electron paramagnetic resonance (E.P.R.). Measurements have been made in dilute, single crystal solid solutions (*1*), and in dilute poly(chlorotrifluoroethylene) ("fluorolube") solutions cooled to 77°K. to form a rigid glass (*2, 3*). The carbene precursors included diphenyldiazomethane (*1, 2*), phenyldiazomethane (*3*), and 9-diazofluorene (*3*) which were decomposed by filtered UV light. Conclusions which may be drawn from the E.P.R. spectra are discussed in Chapter 12.

Methylene also possesses a triplet ground state, but reactions of singlet methylene initially produced from diazomethane are fast enough to exclude singlet → triplet transition under ordinary conditions. In contrast aryl- and diarylcarbenes appear to react from their triplet states. Nonsterospecific addition to double bonds, selective insertion and abstraction reactions, and facile oxidation by molecular oxygen support this statement. Several reasons may be envisioned for the different behavior of methylene and arylcarbenes, but no clear decision can be made so far (cf. Chapter 12).

## I. FORMATION OF ARYL- AND DIARYLCARBENES

### A. Decomposition

Photolysis and pyrolysis (*4*) of diazo compounds are the least ambiguous ways of producing aryl- and diarylcarbenes. The quantum yields of the UV photolysis of various diaryldiazomethanes range from 0.65 to 0.85 (*5*). Diazo precursors were used in most studies on aryl- and diarylcarbene reactions.

The gas phase pyrolysis of diphenylketene afforded fluorene (*6*). A comparable intramolecular shift of hydrogen has rarely been observed in diphenylcarbene chemistry. The reactions of this species, however, have usually been studied in solution where reactants for intermolecular reactions are readily available. The intermediacy of diphenylcarbene in the decomposition of diphenylketene is yet to be demonstrated.

Some tetraarylethylenes with angular distortion were assumed to dissociate at elevated temperatures with formation of diarylcarbenes (7). Thus tetra-α-naphthylethylene (I), on heating to 250°, gave 1,2-7,8-dibenzofluorene (II), bisdibenzofluorenyl (III), and di-α-naphthylmethane (IV). II was also obtained by pyrolysis, but not by photolysis, of di-α-naphthyldiazomethane. I afforded di-α-naphthylketone (V) in the presence of oxygen, and (di-α-naphthylmethyl) benzylamine (VI) in the presence of benzylamine. These products are reasonably explained in terms of a carbene intermediate (cf. Section II).

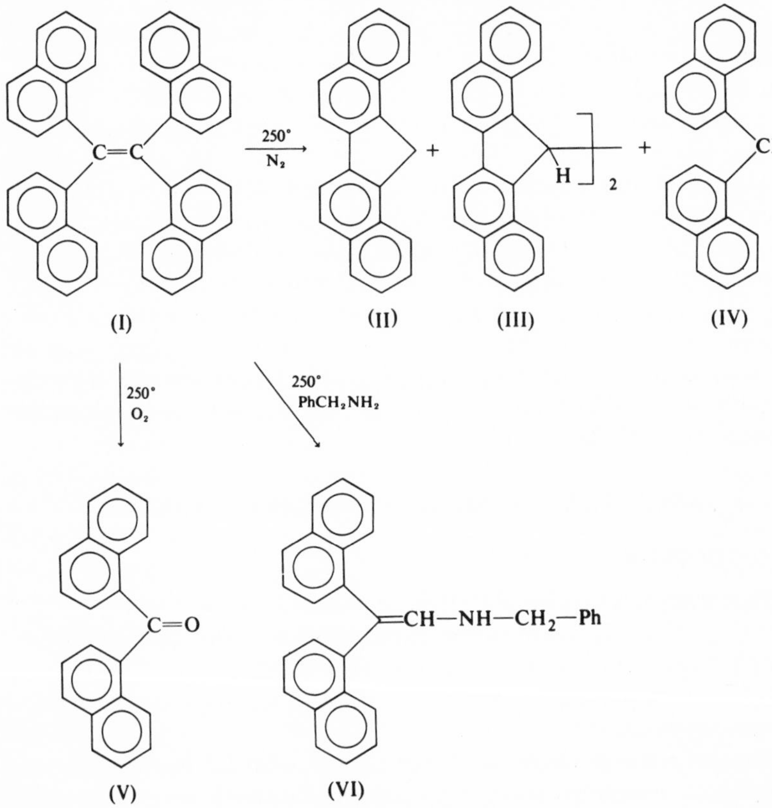

A carbene may be involved in the reaction of dixanthylene (VII) with sulfur to give xanthione (VIII) (8) since similar reactions of sulfur with diazo compounds have been reported (9) (cf. Section II,A).

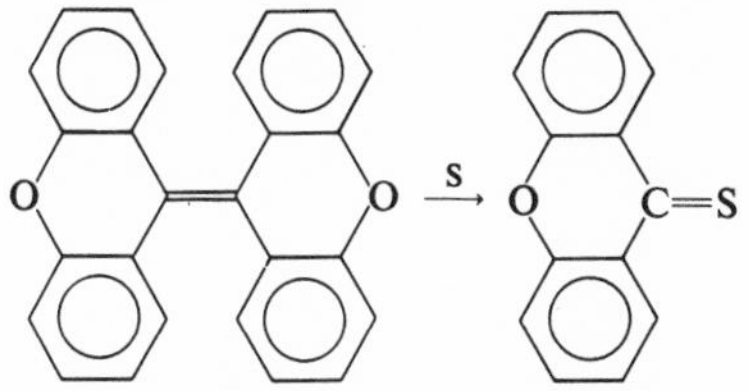

$$\text{(VII)} \xrightarrow{\text{S}} \text{(VIII)} \tag{2}$$

The spirane IX, accessible from acenaphthylene and diazofluorene, was found to decompose at 280° with formation of difluorenylidene (X) and acenaphthylene (10). This cyclopropane cleavage appears to be a reversal of the carbene addition to olefins, but the intermediacy of a carbene in reaction (3) has not been substantiated.

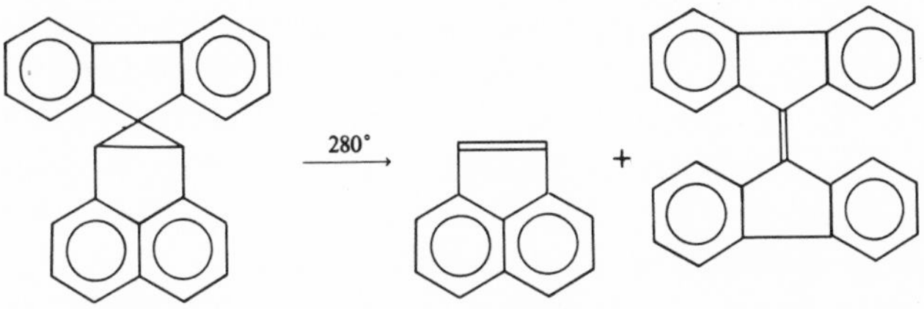

$$\text{(IX)} \xrightarrow{280°} + \text{(X)} \tag{3}$$

Trimethylammonium-9-fluorenylide (XI) was converted to 9-dimethylamino-9-benzylfluorene (XII) by heating with benzyldimethylamine (11). Reaction (4) obviously proceeds by way of an amine exchange followed by Stevens rearrangement. The amine exchange may be explained by an elimination (= carbene) mechanism, or by displacement.

The formation of tetraphenylethylene in the pyrolysis of diphenylchloromethane was observed as early as 1874 (12). More detailed studies of this reaction (4) were extended to benzyl chloride, benzal chloride (13, 14), and substituted diarylchloromethanes (15). The intervention of carbenes has been postulated but appears highly improbable. In view of our present knowledge apparent "dimerization" is rarely if ever due to carbenes. A radical mechanism has recently been proposed for the pyrolysis of diphenylchloromethane (16). Likewise, the pyrolysis of benzhydryl acetate did not afford diphenylcarbene (17).

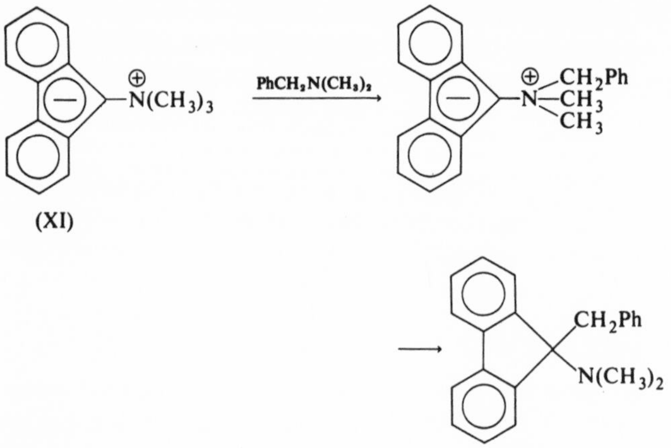

(XI)

$$(4)$$

(XII)

## B. Elimination

Elimination reactions may be regarded as "successful" if they produce an intermediate which adds to olefins with the formation of cyclopropanes. The question whether this intermediate is a free carbene, a carbene complex, or an organometallic compound, is discussed in Chapters 2 and 8. Few efforts have been made so far to distinguish between these possibilities in the arylcarbene series.

The elimination of bromine from gem-dibromides by means of lithium alkyls has been applied to dibromodiphenylmethane (18) and to various substituted benzal bromides (19). The intermediates obtained in these reactions were definitely different from those produced by photolysis of the related diazo compounds (cf. Section II,C).

Treatment of benzhydryl bromide with potassium amide in the presence of 1-octene resulted in the apparent addition of diphenylcarbene to the olefin (7% yield) (20). In contrast, no carbene adducts were obtained by dechlorination of dichlorodiphenylmethane with zinc, copper (17), and iron pentacarbonyl (21), and by dehydrochlorination of benzhydryl chloride with n-butyllithium (17).

Dehydrochlorination of benzyl chloride, however, in the presence of cyclohexene afforded 14% of 7-phenylnorcarane (XIII) among other products (22). A 20–25% yield of XIII was obtained in the related formation of phenylcarbene, or its equivalent, from phenyllithium and methylene chloride (23).

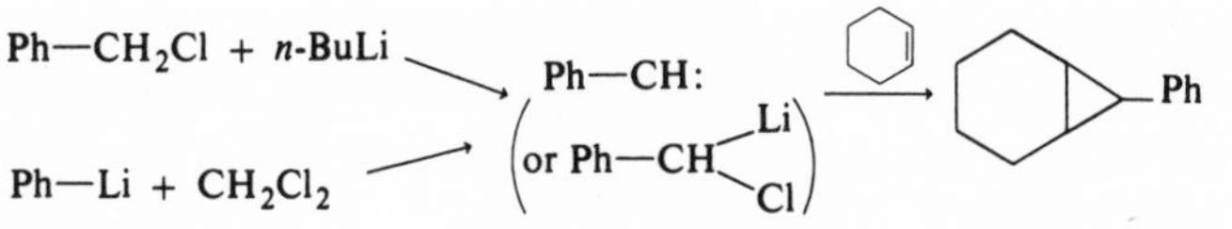

$$Ph—CH_2Cl + n\text{-BuLi} \searrow \qquad Ph—CH: \qquad \left( \begin{array}{c} \text{or } Ph—CH \overset{Li}{\underset{Cl}{\diagdown}} \end{array} \right) \longrightarrow \text{(structure)} —Ph \qquad (5)$$

$$Ph—Li + CH_2Cl_2 \nearrow$$

(XIII)

Phenylcarbene adducts of olefins have also been prepared from benzyl phenyl ether and n-butyllithium (24), and from benzyldiphenyl-sulfonium fluoborate and n-butyllithium (25).

The cyclopropanes formed in these reactions are frequently accompanied by apparent "dimers" of the hypothetical carbenes, e.g., stilbene and tetraphenylethylene. The synthesis of such olefins from suitable halides and base has long been known, the first reports concerning the formation of dinitrostilbenes from o- and p-nitrobenzyl chloride (26, 27), and of difluorenylidene (X) from 9-bromofluorene (28). Alkali amides in liquid ammonia gave excellent results (29, 30). Not only benzyl (31–33), allyl (34, 35), and phenacyl (36) halides have been converted to olefins under these conditions, but also halides containing β-hydrogen, such as α-phenylethyl chloride (37, 38).

The mechanism of this reaction has long been controversial. Nef (39) was the first to advocate a carbene intermediate, and he was supported by some later authors (40–42). Bergmann (41) realized that addition of the hypothetical carbene to olefins did not take place. He achieved addition to 1,2-diketones, but the products were recognized as epoxides, and their formation as a special case of the Darzens condensation (43).

The alternative mechanism, first advanced by Hahn (43) and Kleucker (44), involves alkylation of the intermediate carbanion XIV by excess starting halides, followed by dehydrohalogenation of the resulting halide XV:

$$\underset{}{>}CH—X + B \rightleftharpoons \overset{\ominus}{\underset{}{>}C}—X + BH^{\oplus} \qquad (6a)$$

$$\overset{\ominus}{\underset{}{>}C}—X + \underset{}{>}CH—X \rightarrow \underset{\underset{X}{|}}{>}C—CH\underset{}{<} + X^{\ominus} \qquad (6b)$$

(XIV)  (XV)

$$\underset{\underset{X}{|}}{>}C—CH\underset{}{<} + B \rightarrow \underset{}{>}C{=}C\underset{}{<} + BH^{\oplus} + X^{\ominus} \qquad (6c)$$

The sequence, Eq. (6), was substantiated by isolation, in good yield, of the halide XV under suitable conditions (30). Experiments with optically active $\alpha$-phenylethyl chloride indicated that the displacement step (6b) proceeds with Walden inversion (38). A recent kinetic study of the 9-bromofluorene–base system (45) gave additional support to Eq. (6). Exchange experiments on 9-bromo-9-deuterofluorene showed that conversion of 9-bromofluorene to difluorenylidene is much slower than hydrogen-deuterium exchange. The initial rate of formation of difluorenylidene was proportional to the square of the concentration of 9-bromofluorene, a result which indicates a rate-determining displacement of bromide ion from 9-bromofluorene by the rapidly formed 9-bromo-9-fluorenyl anion.

A modified carbene mechanism, however, has also been recently suggested. Disregarding the improbable dimerization of carbenes, there remains the possibility of reaction between the carbanion XIV and a carbene derived from XIV by elimination of halide ion:

$$>\!CH\!-\!X + B \underset{k_{-1}}{\overset{k_1}{\rightleftharpoons}} >\!\overset{\ominus}{C}\!-\!X + BH^{\oplus} \tag{7a}$$

$$>\!\overset{\ominus}{\underset{\sim}{C}}\!-\!X \underset{k_2}{\rightarrow} >\!C\!: + X^{\ominus} \tag{7b}$$

(XIV)

$$>\!C\!: + >\!\overset{\ominus}{\underset{\sim}{C}}\!-\!X \rightarrow >\!\overset{\ominus}{\underset{\sim}{C}}\!-\!\underset{\overset{|}{X}}{C}\!< \overset{-X^{\ominus}}{\longrightarrow} >\!C\!=\!C\!< \tag{7c}$$

The reaction of benzyl and 4-nitrobenzyl chloride in the presence of alkali has been shown to be of the first order in both halide and base concentrations (46). These kinetics would eliminate the carbanion displacement mechanism [Eq. (6)] if a rapid equilibrium (7a) were clearly established. Although deuterium was incorporated in recovered starting material after partial reaction in $D_2O$, the small but definite isotope effect observed with $\alpha$-$d$-4-nitrobenzyl chloride ($k_H/k_D = 1.28$) suggests that $k_{-1}$ is of similar magnitude as $k_2$ (46).

4-Nitrobenzyldimethylsulfonium ion in aqueous alkali followed the same second-order kinetics (47), and exchange of the methylene protons for deuterium was rapid as compared to stilbene formation (47a). It was noted, however, that the sulfur isotope effect ($k_{32}/k_{34} = 1.0066$) was not consistent with the slow formation of a carbene intermediate (7b), but rather with (7c) as the rate-determining step (47).

Without much supporting evidence, the mechanism, Eq. (7), has been suggested to explain the formation of stilbene from benzyltriphenylphosphonium bromide and sodium methoxide (*48*). In contrast, no 4,4'-dinitrostilbene has been obtained from 4-nitrobenzyltriphenylphosphonium bromide with sodium hydroxide in 50% ethanol (*47a*). Triphenylphosphine oxide and 4-nitrotoluene were the major products.

## II. REACTIONS OF ARYL- AND DIARYLCARBENES

When aryl- and diarylcarbenes are produced by photolysis or pyrolysis of the related diazo compounds, part of the carbene frequently reacts with excess diazoalkane:

$$R_2C: + R_2CN_2 \rightarrow R_2C=CR_2 + N_2 \qquad (8a)$$

$$\rightarrow R_2C=N-N=CR_2 \qquad (8b)$$

Whereas azines are the major products obtained from diaryldiazomethanes [Eq. (8b)], diazofluorene affords largely difluorenylidene [Eq. (8a)] (*4, 49*). The cause of this difference is not fully understood. It may reflect the relative electrophilic properties of the carbenes involved (cf. Section D). The terminal nitrogen appears to be the electrophilic site of a diazoalkane, as for example in the reaction with organometallic reagents to give (substituted) hydrazones (*50*). The carbon atom acts as the nucleophilic center of diazoalkanes, e.g., in protonation (*50*). Subsequent decomposition of azines to olefins may occur. Thus, di-*p*-anisyldiazomethane afforded an azine at 80°, but tetra-*p*-anisylethylene at 160° (*49*).

The rate of the thermal decomposition of diphenyldiazomethane was shown to be of the first order (*50a*). This result supports Eq. (8b) and eliminates a direct reaction of two diazo molecules to give azine and nitrogen.

## A. Reactions with Oxygen, Sulfur, and Carbon Monoxide

The different reactivities of methylene and diphenylcarbene, probably due to different spin states, are nicely demonstrated by reactions with oxygen and carbon monoxide. Whereas methylene adds easily to carbon monoxide and accepts oxygen only with difficulty (cf. Chapter 2, Sections II,B and C), diarylcarbenes behave inversely. Photolysis of diphenyldiazomethane in the presence of oxygen affords benzophenone (*51*), which may become the major product under suitable conditions $(52)$. The isolation of the cyclic peroxide XVI from the photooxidation of diphenyldiazomethane suggests a "carbonyl oxide" (XVa) as the primary product $(53)$.

$$Ph_2CN_2 \xrightarrow{h\nu} Ph_2C: \xrightarrow{O_2} \left[ Ph_2\overset{\oplus}{C}-O-\overset{\ominus}{O} \leftrightarrow Ph_2C=\overset{\oplus}{O}-\overset{\ominus}{O} \right] \qquad (9)$$

(XVa)

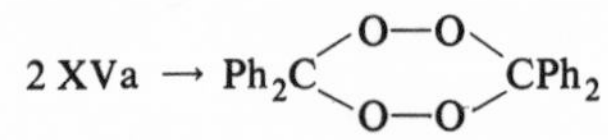

$$2\ XVa \rightarrow Ph_2C\underset{O-O}{\overset{O-O}{\diagdown}}CPh_2$$

(XVI)

Experiments with $^{36}O_2$ indicate that no decomposition of XVI (or a related polymeric peroxide), to give oxygen and benzophenone, occurred under the conditions of the photooxidation $(53)$. On the other hand, the formation of benzophenone on irradiation of diphenyldiazomethane in a solid air matrix at 20°K. has been reported $(54)$. A luminescent reaction occurred during the warm-up of rigid fluorocarbon glasses previously saturated with oxygen, and containing the products of diphenyldiazomethane photolysis. No emission was produced from a deoxygenated sample $(3)$.

The reaction of diaryldiazomethanes with sulfur to give thiiranes (XVII) has been interpreted in terms of Eq. (10) $(9)$. The observation that "the reaction is catalyzed by the action of sunlight" is the only evidence in favor of a carbene intermediate.

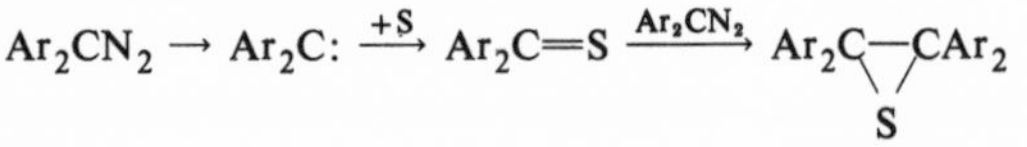

$$Ar_2CN_2 \rightarrow Ar_2C: \xrightarrow{+S} Ar_2C=S \xrightarrow{Ar_2CN_2} Ar_2\underset{S}{C-C}Ar_2 \qquad (10)$$

(XVII)

Diphenylcarbene does not react with carbon monoxide $(51)$. Attempts to force this reaction by decomposition of diphenyldiazomethane under high carbon monoxide pressures $(55)$, or in a solid, CO-containing matrix at 20°K. $(54)$ were unsuccessful. Carbonylation of diphenyldiazomethane has been achieved by nickel carbonyl $(55)$, but this is probably not a carbene reaction.

## B. Reactions with Carbon-Hydrogen Bonds

Phenylcarbene, produced by photolysis of phenyldiazomethane, inserted into the carbon-hydrogen bonds of aliphatic hydrocarbons, such as cyclohexane and *n*-pentane. In the latter case, the ratio of 2- and 3-benzylpentane to 1-phenylhexane, identical with the ratio of $2°:1°$ insertion, was 6.0 ± 0.3, indicating considerable discrimination in favor of secondary hydrogen (*56*). Irradiation of phenyldiazomethane in benzene solution led to ring expansion (cf. Section C), but did not afford diphenylmethane. Obviously, phenylcarbene does not insert into aromatic carbon-hydrogen bonds. Intramolecular reactions of this kind, however, are known (*57*):

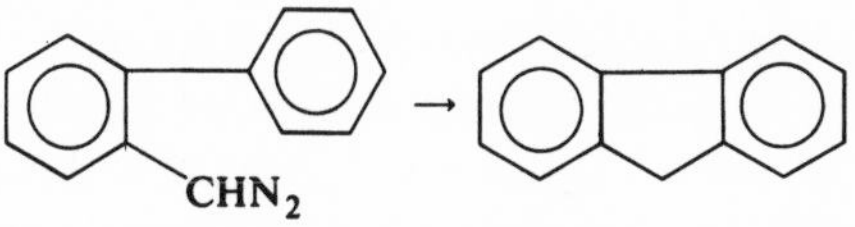

(11)

Intramolecular insertion of a phenylcarbene having an *ortho*-side chain was found to be fairly indiscriminate as to the location of the carbon-hydrogen bond (*56*). If the preference for secondary hydrogen is taken into account, attack on the β-, γ-, and δ-carbon-hydrogen bonds of 2-(*n*-butylphenyl)carbene from XVIII may be seen to occur almost randomly:

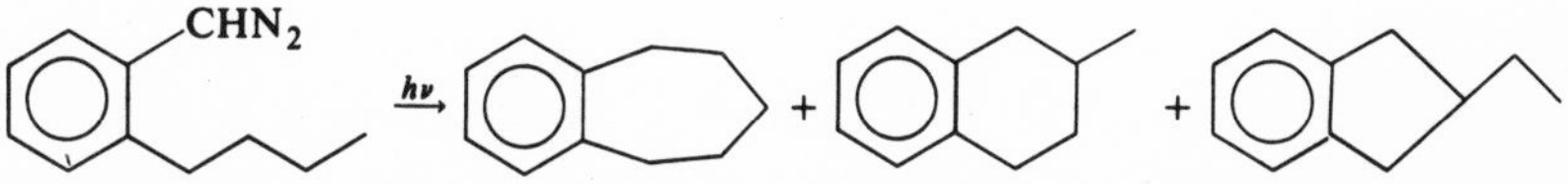

| (XVIII) | | found | 1 | : | 5 | : | 6 | (12) |
| | | corr. | 4 | : | 5 | : | 6 | |

This result is in contrast with the behavior of alkylcarbenes which rarely, if ever, produce larger than three-membered rings by intramolecular insertion. The preference for unstrained rings in reaction (12) may reflect the increased stability and lifetime of the (triplet?) phenylcarbene intermediate.

An apparently selective insertion of phenylcarbene into the allylic carbon-hydrogen bonds of cyclohexene has been observed when phenylcarbene was produced by α-elimination (*22, 24*). The origin of the 3-benzylcyclohexene is not yet fully elucidated.

A unique intramolecular abstraction reaction was found to occur in the photolysis of 2-(*n*-butylphenyl)diazomethane (XVIII). The olefin XIX was obtained in addition to the insertion products of Eq. (12), indicating the simultaneous abstraction of two neighboring hydrogen atoms (*56*):

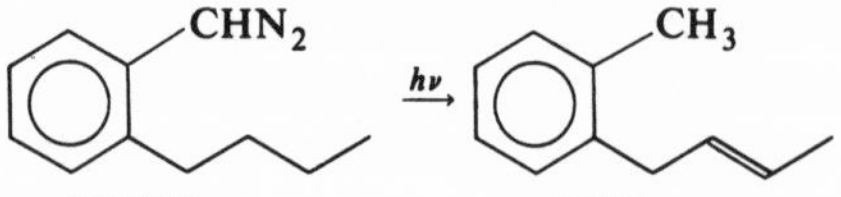

(XVIII)          (XIX)          (12a)

Most diarylcarbenes are incapable of "true" (three-center-type) insertion, rather they abstract hydrogen from suitable hydrocarbons. The benzhydryl radicals formed in this reaction are sufficiently stable to give dimers (tetraarylethanes) in fair yields (52). In favorable cases, dimers of the solvent radicals were also obtained. Thus 3,3'-dicyclohexenyl (XX) was detected after photolysis of diphenyldiazomethane in cyclohexene (7), and 1,2-diphenyl-1,2-dimethoxyethane (XXI) was formed in the pyrolysis of diphenyldiazomethane in benzyl methyl ether (57).

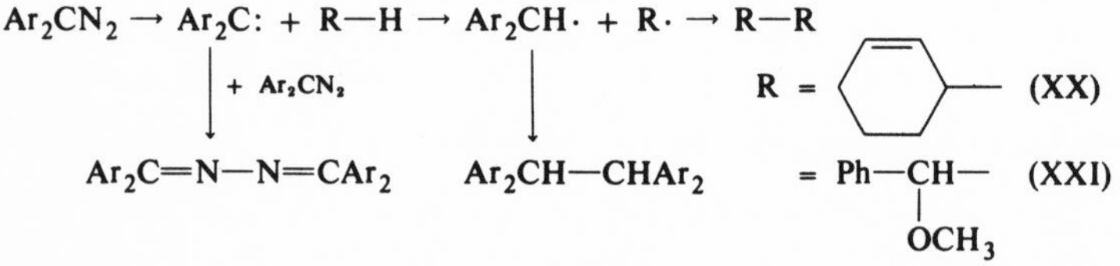

$Ar_2CN_2 \rightarrow Ar_2C: + R—H \rightarrow Ar_2CH\cdot + R\cdot \rightarrow R—R$

(13)

According to Eq. (13), the addition of diarylcarbene to excess diazo compound competes with hydrogen abstraction. The ratio of the two products, azine and tetraarylethane, depends on the hydrogen donor R—H. The azine was the major product in benzene whereas much tetraarylethane was obtained in toluene, cyclohexene, and isopropyl ether (52). No significant change in the product ratios was noticed when diphenyldiazomethane was compared to its 4-nitro and 4-chloro derivatives, but methoxy groups were found to eliminate the abstraction reaction completely. The azine was the only product obtained from 4-methoxy- and 4,4'-dimethoxydiphenyldiazomethane regardless of the solvent used in the photolysis (58).

If the solvent radical, R· in Eq. (13), is comparable in reactivity to the benzhydryl radical, apparent insertion products may form by an abstraction-recombination sequence. Thus 9-benzhydrylfluorene has been obtained by photolysis of diphenyldiazomethane in the presence of fluorene (52), and similar reactions with the allylic carbon-hydrogen bonds of olefins have been reported (18).

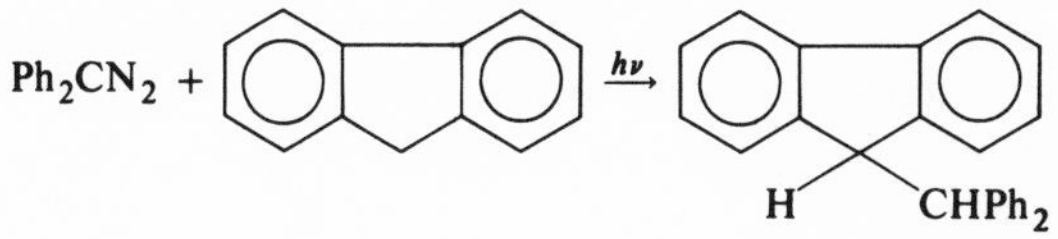

$$(14)$$

In contrast, 9-cyclohexylfluorene produced by photolysis of diazo-fluorene in cyclohexane solution (*52*) may be regarded to arise via "direct" insertion.

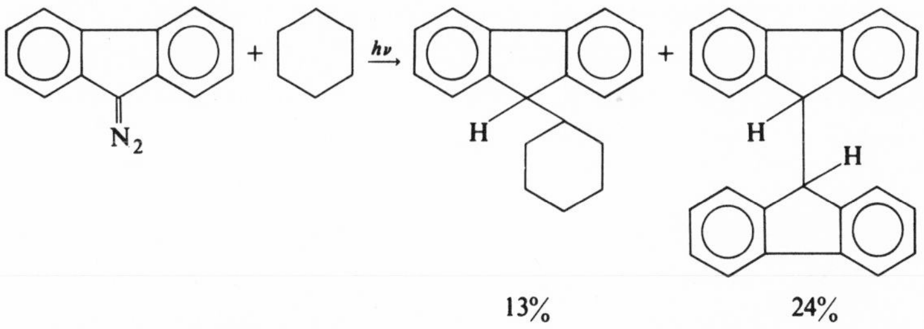

13%      24%

$$(15)$$

## C. Addition to Multiple Bonds

The addition of phenylcarbene to *cis*- and *trans*-2-butene is almost, but not entirely stereospecific. Approximately 3% of the "wrong" cyclopropane isomers were formed, both from *cis*- and *trans*-2-butene (*56*). An investigation of the *cis* addition with various substituted phenyl-carbenes and olefins revealed preferential formation of the more hindered products (*19*). Assignment of configuration to the stereoisomers

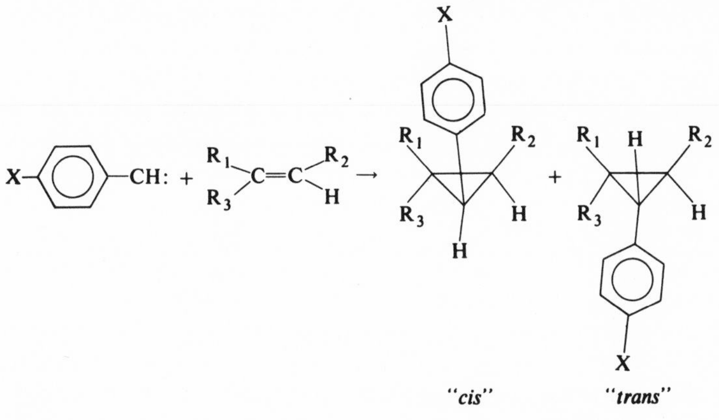

$$(16)$$

"cis"      "trans"

was made on the basis of the nuclear magnetic resonance (N.M.R.) spectra, and by independent synthesis of the minor adducts from *trans*-1-aryl-1-butenes via stereospecific reaction with methylene iodide and zinc-copper couple (*19*).

"cis":"trans" RATIO

| Olefin | X =<br>Carbene<br>precursor | —H | | —CH$_3$ | | —Cl | |
|---|---|---|---|---|---|---|---|
| | | —CHBr$_2$ | —CHN$_2$ | —CHBr$_2$ | —CHN$_2$ | —CHBr$_2$ | —CHN$_2$ |
| 1-Butene | | 2.1 | 1.0 | 2.8 | 1.3 | 2.1 | 1.1 |
| *cis*-2-Butene | | 2.4 | 1.1 | 4.5 | 1.4 | 3.4 | 1.2 |
| 2-Methyl-2-butene | | 1.3 | 1.1 | 1.4 | 1.3 | 1.4 | 1.1 |

The intermediate produced by α-elimination were more selective, but preference for the formation of the "*cis*"-isomer was also found in the diazo compound photolysis. "*cis*"-Orientation is considered, therefore, as a general phenomenon rather than a consequence of lithium halide participation. A transition state involving considerable charge separation may explain the observed stereochemistry (*19*).

Other olefins which have been converted to phenylcarbene adducts include cyclohexene (*22, 23*), isobutene (*24*), acenaphthylene (*25*), and ketene diethylacetal (*59*). 7-Phenylcycloheptatriene was obtained by photolysis of phenyldiazomethane in benzene solution (*56*).

Diphenylcarbene reacts with *cis*- and *trans*-2-butene to produce cyclopropanes by nonstereospecific reaction paths (photolysis of diphenyldiazomethane in solution). The originally reported product ratios (*60*) were probably erroneous because of incomplete separation from olefinic by-products. In a recent reinvestigation (*18*), 13% of *trans*-1,2-dimethyl-3,3-diphenylcyclopropane were obtained from *cis*-2-butene whereas the addition to *trans*-2-butene was even more selective.

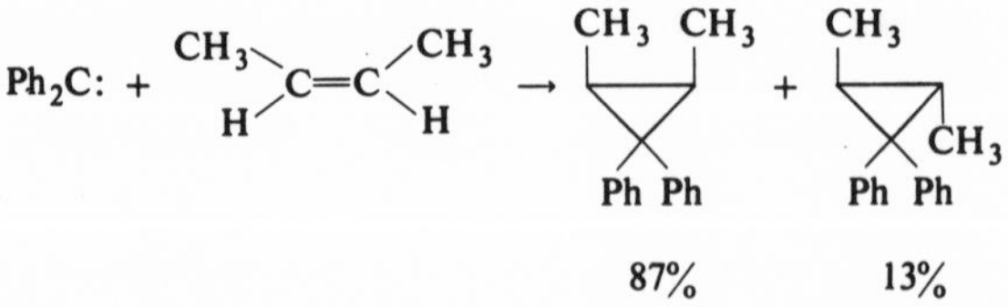

Ph$_2$C: +   (CH$_3$, H)C=C(CH$_3$, H)   →   [structure 87%]   +   [structure 13%]      (17)

If diphenylcarbene was produced from diphenyldibromomethane and methyllithium, the addition to *cis*- and *trans*-2-butene was entirely stereospecific, and no abstraction reactions occurred (*18*). This result has been explained in terms of a diphenylcarbene-lithium bromide complex.

Studies on the stereospecificity of 9-carbenafluorene (derived from 9-diazofluorene) were complicated by the light-induced interconversion of the adducts obtained with *cis*- and *trans*-2-butene (*60a*). Irradiation of both adducts led to identical photostationary states in which the *trans:cis* ratio was 1.74. Photoisomerization may affect the apparent stereochemistry of other carbene additions to olefins which give absorbing products.

Thus, photolysis of diazofluorene in the presence of either maleic or fumaric acid derivatives has been reported to give the *trans* adduct as the major product (*60b*).

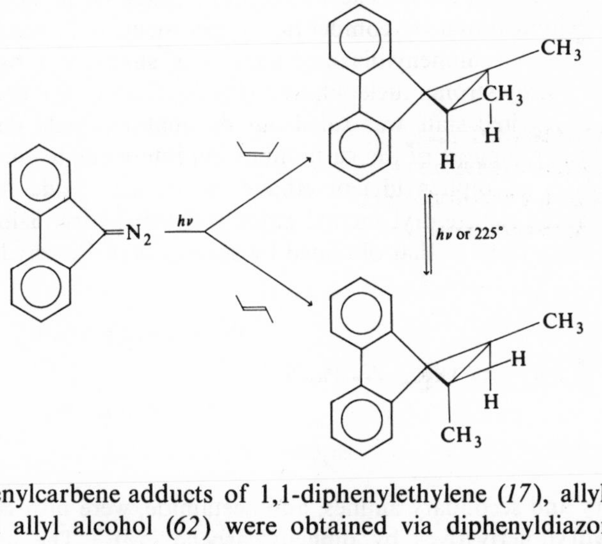
CH3
CH3
H
H
=N2
hν
hν or 225°
CH3
H
H
CH3

(17a)

Diphenylcarbene adducts of 1,1-diphenylethylene (*17*), allyl acetate (*61*), and allyl alcohol (*62*) were obtained via diphenyldiazomethane pyrolysis. Arylcarbene addition to diphenylacetylene was achieved by photolysis of phenyldiazoacetonitrile (XXII) (*63*) (for arylchlorocarbenes, see Chapter 8, Section III).

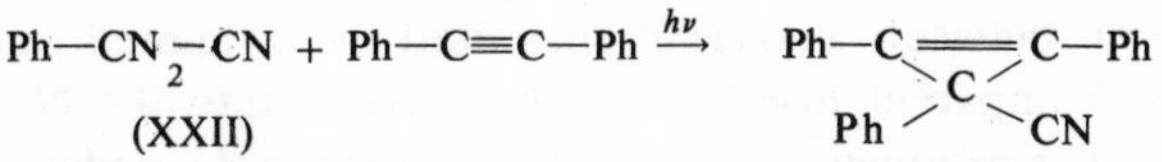
Ph—CN2—CN + Ph—C≡C—Ph
hν
Ph—C═C—Ph
C
Ph
CN
(XXII)

(18)

Diphenyldiazomethane and phenyl isocyanate react under the influence of UV light to afford 2,2-diphenylindoxyl, presumably via diphenylcarbene addition to the C=N bond and rearrangement of the $\alpha$-lactam intermediate (63a).

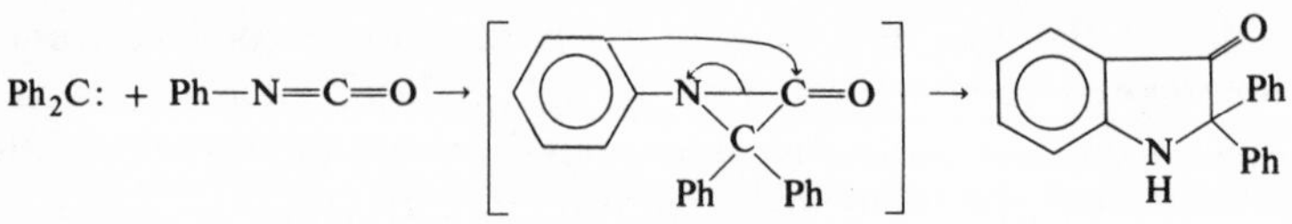

$$Ph_2C: + Ph-N=C=O \rightarrow$$

## D.  Reactions with Alcohols and Amines

Photolysis of diphenyldiazomethane in methanol afforded benzhydryl methyl ether in 70% yield (52). Diphenylcarbene was shown to behave in this reaction as a nucleophile which accepts a proton to give the diphenylcarbonium ion (64). The nucleophilic potential of diphenylcarbene was demonstrated by competition experiments with oxygen: the photooxidation of diphenyldiazomethane was suppressed by proton donors but not by strong nucleophiles. (Protonation of the diazo compound in an excited state was ruled out by quantum yield determinations.) Further support of the carbonium ion intermediate comes from the photolysis of diphenyldiazomethane in lithium azide–methanol, which produced benzhydryl methyl ether and benzhydryl azide in virtually the same ratio as that obtained by solvolysis of benzhydryl chloride.

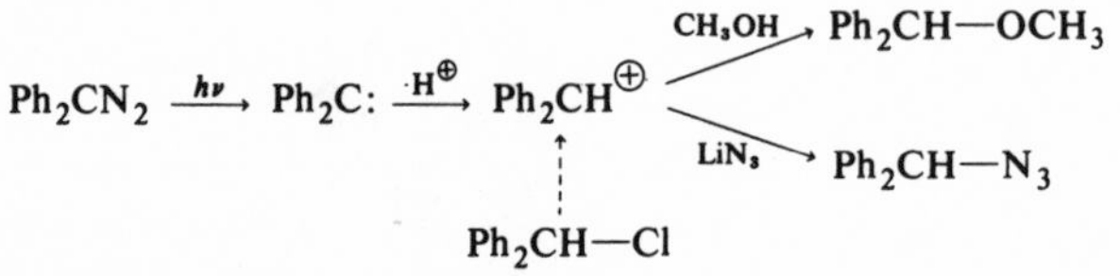

$$Ph_2CN_2 \xrightarrow{h\nu} Ph_2C: \xrightarrow{\cdot H^\oplus} Ph_2CH^\oplus \begin{array}{l} \xrightarrow{CH_3OH} Ph_2CH-OCH_3 \\ \xrightarrow{LiN_3} Ph_2CH-N_3 \end{array}$$

$$Ph_2CH-Cl$$

(19)

Primary and secondary amines, and acetamide, were also converted to benzhydryl derivatives by diphenylcarbene (52). The analogous reaction of di-$\alpha$-naphthyldiazomethane with benzylamine has been reported (7). The benzhydrylamines were accompanied by tetraaryl-ethanes, indicating radical abstraction processes.

Reaction between diarylcarbenes and benzyldimethylamine may proceed with apparent insertion of the carbene into the N—C(benzyl) bond (57). The products, e.g., XXIII, are reasonably explained in terms of an intermediate ylide which undergoes Stevens rearrangement.

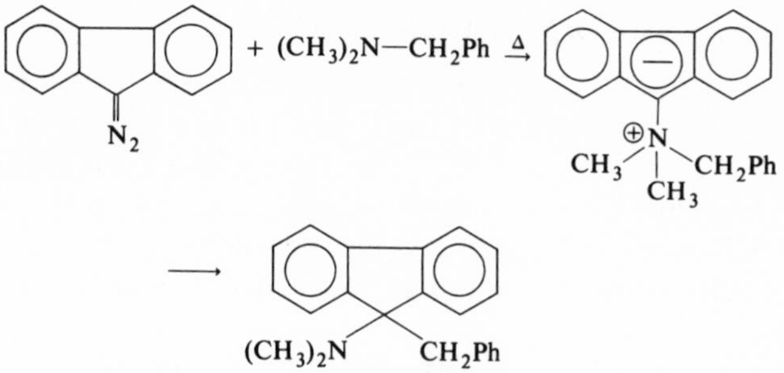

$$(20)$$

E. **Reactions with Halides**

The photolysis or pyrolysis of diphenyldiazomethane in the presence of bromotrichloromethane [Eq. (21)] led to various products among which halogenated tetraarylethylenes, such as **XXIV**, are unexpected. A radical abstraction mechanism has been proposed (*65*).

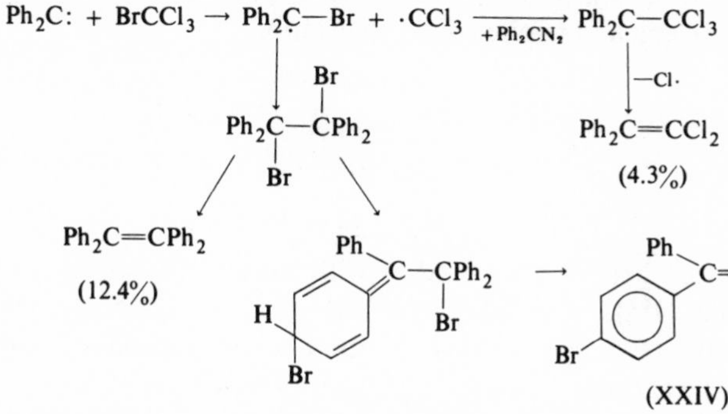

$$(21)$$

The photodecomposition of diazofluorene in *cis*- and *trans*-dichloroethylene afforded 9-chlorofluorene whereas 9,9-dichlorobisbiphenyleneethane (**XXV**) was obtained in carbon tetrachloride (*60b*).

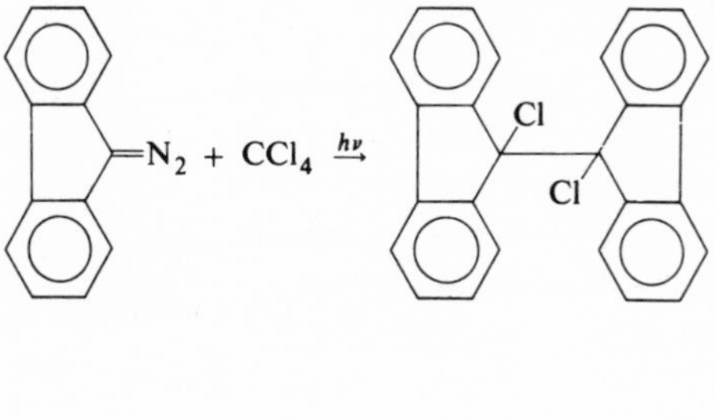

$$(XXV)$$

## F. Reactions with Organometallic Compounds

$\alpha$-Elimination at benzyl or benzhydryl halides by means of organo-lithium compounds may lead to further reaction of the intermediate involved with excess base. Thus 1,1,2-triphenylethane has been obtained from benzyl chloride and phenyllithium (66). As was pointed out previously (Chapter 2, Section II,H), such reactions can be interpreted in terms of addition to carbenes, or displacement at organometallic intermediates.

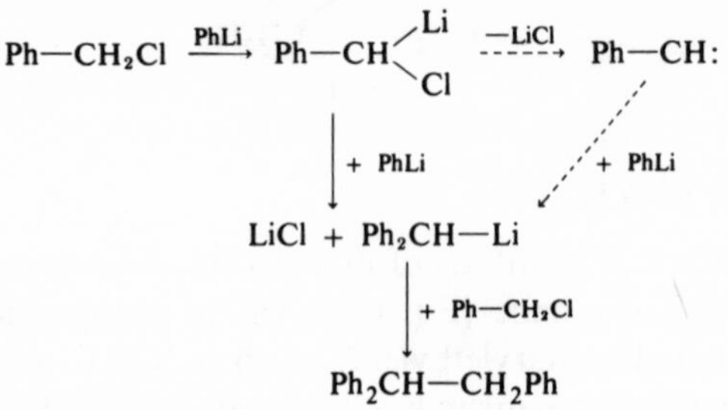

$$Ph-CH_2Cl \xrightarrow{PhLi} Ph-CH\begin{smallmatrix} Li \\ \\ Cl \end{smallmatrix} \xrightarrow{-LiCl} Ph-CH:$$

$$\downarrow + PhLi \qquad\qquad + PhLi$$

$$LiCl + Ph_2CH-Li \tag{22}$$

$$\downarrow + Ph-CH_2Cl$$

$$Ph_2CH-CH_2Ph$$

A similar reaction, starting with dichlorodiphenylmethane, led to tetraphenylethylene and triphenylmethane (66):

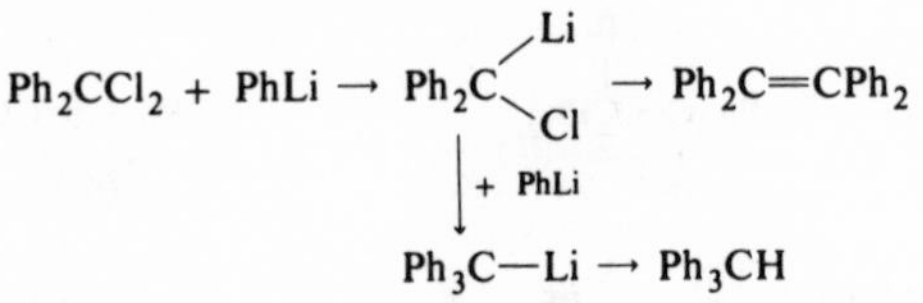

$$Ph_2CCl_2 + PhLi \rightarrow Ph_2C\begin{smallmatrix} Li \\ \\ Cl \end{smallmatrix} \rightarrow Ph_2C{=}CPh_2 \tag{23}$$

$$\downarrow + PhLi$$

$$Ph_3C-Li \rightarrow Ph_3CH$$

Treatment of benzyl phenyl ether with $n$-butyl lithium afforded 1-phenylpentane (1%), 1,6-diphenylhexane (3.4%), 1,2-diphenylhexane (14%), and stilbene (2.2%). The formation of these products has been explained in the carbene terminology as follows (24):

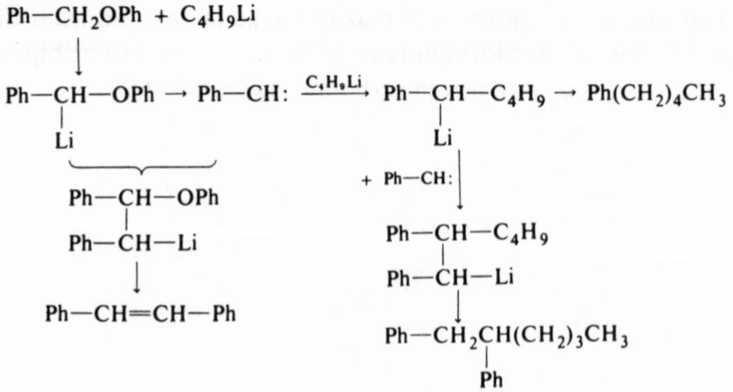

$$Ph-CH_2OPh + C_4H_9Li$$

$$\downarrow$$

$$Ph-\underset{\underset{Li}{|}}{CH}-OPh \rightarrow Ph-CH: \xrightarrow{C_4H_9Li} Ph-\underset{\underset{Li}{|}}{CH}-C_4H_9 \rightarrow Ph(CH_2)_4CH_3$$

$$\underbrace{\qquad\qquad}$$

$$Ph-CH-OPh \qquad\qquad + Ph-CH:$$
$$|$$
$$Ph-CH-Li \qquad\qquad Ph-CH-C_4H_9 \tag{24}$$
$$\downarrow \qquad\qquad\qquad |$$
$$Ph-CH{=}CH-Ph \qquad Ph-CH-Li$$
$$\downarrow$$
$$Ph-\underset{\underset{Ph}{|}}{CH_2}CH(CH_2)_3CH_3$$

## REFERENCES

1. R. W. Brandon, G. L. Closs, and C. A. Hutchison, *J. Chem. Phys.* **37**, 1878 (1962).
2. R. W. Murray, A. M. Trozzolo, E. Wasserman, and W. A. Yager, *J. Am. Chem. Soc.* **84**, 3213 (1962).
3. A. M. Trozzolo, R. W. Murray, and E. Wasserman, *J. Am. Chem. Soc.* **84**, 4990 (1962).
4. H. Staudinger and O. Kupfer, *Ber. deut. chem. Ges.* **44**, 2197 (1911).
5. W. Kirmse and L. Horner, *Ann.* **625**, 34 (1959).
6. H. Staudinger and R. Endle, *Ber. deut. chem. Ges.* **46**, 1437 (1913).
7. V. Franzen and H. I. Joschek, *Ann.* **633**, 7 (1960).
8. A. Schönberg and S. Nickel, *Ber. deut. chem. Ges.* **64**, 2323 (1931).
9. N. Latif and I. Fathy, *J. Org. Chem.* **27**, 1633 (1962).
10. A. Schönberg and N. Latif, *J. Am. Chem. Soc.* **75**, 2267 (1953).
11. V. Franzen, *Chem. Ber.* **93**, 557 (1960).
12. C. Engler and H. Bethge, *Ber. deut. chem. Ges.* **7**, 1125 (1874).
13. W. Löb, *Ber. deut. chem. Ges.* **36**, 3059 (1903).
14. H. Staudinger and O. Kupfer, *Ber. deut. chem. Ges.* **44**, 2194 (1911).
15. H. Gilman and B. F. Flick, *Rec. trav. chim.* **48**, 461 (1929).
16. S. G. Melkanovitskaya and I. P. Tsukervanik, *Zhur. Obshchei Khim.* **28**, 11 (1958).
17. J. E. Hodgkins and M. P. Hughes, *J. Org. Chem.* **27**, 4187 (1962).
18. G. L. Closs and L. E. Closs, *Angew. Chem.* **74**, 431 (1962).
19. G. L. Closs, R. A. Moss, and J. J. Coyle, *J. Am. Chem. Soc.* **84**, 4985 (1962).
20. A. Y. Garner, *Diss. Abstr.* **17**, 224 (1957).
21. C. E. Coffey, *J. Am. Chem. Soc.* **83**, 1623 (1961).
22. G. L. Closs and L. E. Closs, *Tetrahedron Letters No.* **24**, 26 (1960).
23. O. M. Nefedov, V. I. Sirjaev, and A. D. Petrov, *Zhur. Obshchei Khim.* **32**, 662 (1962).
24. U. Schöllkopf and M. Eisert, *Angew. Chem.* **72**, 349 (1960); *Ann.* **664**, 76 (1963).
25. V. J. Hruby and A. W. Johnson, *J. Am. Chem. Soc.* **84**, 3586 (1962).
26. C. A. Bischoff, *Ber. deut. chem. Ges.* **21**, 2071 (1888).
27. P. Walden and A. Kernbaum, *Ber. deut. chem. Ges.* **23**, 1958 (1890).
28. J. Thiele and A. Wanscheidt, *Ann.* **376**, 278 (1910).
29. L. A. Pinck and G. E. Hilbert, *J. Am. Chem. Soc.* **68**, 379 (1946).
30. Ch. R. Hauser, W. R. Brasen, P. S. Skell, S. W. Kantor, and A. E. Brodhag, *J. Am. Chem. Soc.* **78**, 1653 (1956).
31. F. W. Bergstrom and W. C. Fernelius, *Chem. Revs.* **20**, 435 (1937).
32. Ch. R. Hauser and W. J. Chambers, *J. Am. Chem. Soc.* **78**, 4942 (1956).
33. Ch. R. Hauser and P. J. Hamrick, *J. Am. Chem. Soc.* **79**, 3142 (1957).
34. M. S. Kharasch and E. Sternfeld, *J. Am. Chem. Soc.* **61**, 2318 (1939).
35. M. S. Kharasch, W. Nudenberg, and E. Sternfeld, *J. Am. Chem. Soc.* **62**, 2035 (1940).
36. M. S. Kharasch, W. Nudenberg, and E. K. Fields, *J. Am. Chem. Soc.* **66**, 1276 (1944).
37. M. S. Kharasch and M. Kleimann, *J. Am. Chem. Soc.* **65**, 11 (1943).
38. W. R. Brasen, S. W. Kantor, P. S. Skell, and Ch. R. Hauser, *J. Am. Chem. Soc.* **79**, 397 (1957).
39. J. U. Nef, *Ann.* **298**, 202 (1897).
40. A. Michael, *J. Am. Chem. Soc.* **42**, 820 (1920).
41. E. Bergmann and J. Hervey, *Ber. deut. chem. Ges.* **62**, 893 (1929).
42. C. K. Ingold and J. A. Jessop, *J. Chem. Soc.* **1930**, 709.

43. G. Hahn, *Ber. deut. chem. Ges.* **62,** 2485 (1929).
44. E. Kleucker, *Ber. deut. chem. Ges.* **62,** 2587 (1929).
45. D. Bethell, *J. Chem. Soc.* **1963,** 666.
46. S. B. Hanna, Y. Iskander, and Y. Riad, *J. Chem. Soc.* **1961,** 217.
47. C. G. Swain and E. R. Thornton, *J. Am. Chem. Soc.* **83,** 4033 (1961).
47a. I. Rothberg and E. R. Thornton, *J. Am. Chem. Soc.* **85,** 1704 (1963).
48. S. Trippett, *Proc. Chem. Soc.* **1963,** 19.
49. H. Staudinger and J. Goldstein, *Ber. deut. chem. Ges.* **49,** 1923 (1916).
50. R. Huisgen, *Angew Chem.* **67,** 439 (1955).
50a. H. Reimlinger, *Chem. Ber.* **97,** 339 (1964).
51. H. Staudinger, E. Anthes, and F. Pfenninger, *Ber. deut. chem. Ges.* **49,** 1928 (1916).
52. W. Kirmse, L. Horner, and H. Hoffmann, *Ann.* **614,** 19 (1958).
53. P. D. Bartlett and T. G. Traylor, *J. Am. Chem. Soc.* **84,** 3408 (1962).
54. W. B. De Moore, H. O. Pritchard, and N. Davidson, *J. Am. Chem. Soc.* **81,** 5874 (1959).
55. C. Rüchardt and G. N. Schrauzer, *Chem. Ber.* **93,** 1840 (1960).
56. C. D. Gutsche, G. L. Bachman, and R. S. Coffey, *Tetrahedron* **18,** 617 (1962).
57. W. R. Bamford and T. S. Stevens, *J. Chem. Soc.* **1952,** 4675.
58. L. Hockenberger, Dissertation, University of Mainz, 1961.
59. M. F. Dull and P. G. Abend, *J. Am. Chem. Soc.* **81,** 2588 (1959).
60. R. M. Etter, H. S. Skovronek, and P. S. Skell, *J. Am. Chem. Soc.* **81,** 1008 (1959).
60a. W. v. E. Doering and M. Jones, Jr., *Tetrahedron Letters* **1963,** 791.
60b. E. Funakubo, I. Moritani, T. Nagai, S. Nishida, and S. Murahashi, *Tetrahedron Letters* **1963,** 1069.
61. I. A. Dyakonov and O. V. Guseva, *Zhur. Obshchei Khim.* **22,** 1355 (1952).
62. I. A. Dyakonov, *Zhur. Obshchei Khim.* **21,** 1986 (1951).
63. R. Breslow and Ch. Yuan, *J. Am. Chem. Soc.* **80,** 5991 (1958).
63a. J. C. Sheehan and I. Lengyel, *J. Org. Chem.* **28,** 3252 (1963).
64. W. Kirmse, *Ann.* **666,** 9 (1963).
65. R. W. Murray and A. M. Trozzolo, *J. Org. Chem.* **27,** 3341 (1962).
66. G. Wittig and H. Witt, *Ber. deut. chem. Ges.* **74,** 1474 (1941).

# CHAPTER 6

# Carboalkoxycarbenes

ALTHOUGH CARBOALKOXY GROUPS have some effect on the reactivity of the divalent carbon atom, the general behavior of carboalkoxycarbenes resembles that of methylene rather than that of ketocarbenes. Intramolecular rearrangements predominate in ketocarbene chemistry whereas carboalkoxycarbenes readily undergo intermolecular reactions such as insertion and addition to olefins. The only common feature of carboalkoxycarbenes and ketocarbenes is a rather rare "abnormal" addition to multiple bonds in which these carbenes behave as 1,3-dipoles (cf. Section II,J).

## I. FORMATION OF CARBOALKOXYCARBENES

Only diazo esters have so far been utilized as carboalkoxycarbene precursors. Attempts to achieve $\alpha$-elimination of hydrogen halides from $\alpha$-halo esters resulted in condensation reactions of the intermediate carbanions rather than elimination of a halide ion. Treatment of ethyl diiodoacetate with zinc-copper couple led to the formal addition of carboethoxycarbene to olefins (1), but this reaction probably does not involve a true carbene intermediate (cf. Chapter 2, Sections I,B,2 and II,E,1,b).

The quantum yields of ethyl diazoacetate photolysis have been determined in various solvents, and with light of different wavelengths (2) (Table I). The quantum yields strongly decrease with increasing wavelength. Whereas light of 2600 Å appears to be more efficient in protic solvents than in hydrocarbons, the reverse efficiency holds for wavelengths greater than 3000 Å.

Temperatures above 150°C. are required for the thermal decomposition of ethyl diazoacetate. The presence of catalysts greatly facilitates the decomposition, 90°–100° being sufficient with copper powder, and

TABLE I

QUANTUM YIELDS OF ETHYL DIAZOACETATE PHOTOLYSIS (2)

(moles $N_2$ per quantum)

| Solvent | 2600 Å | 2804 Å | 3130 Å | 3650 Å | 4200 Å |
|---------|--------|--------|--------|--------|--------|
| Heptane | 1.11 | 1.02 | 0.54 | 0.31 | 0.20 |
| Ethanol | 1.35 | 1.1 | 0.34 | 0.15 | 0.12 |
| Methanol | 1.42 | 1.1 | 0.37 | 0.14 | 0.12 |
| Water | 2.8 | — | 0.36 | 0.12 | — |

considerable amounts of diethyl fumarate (3, 4). This apparent dimer of carboethoxycarbene is not produced by photolysis or (uncatalyzed) pyrolysis of ethyl diazoacetate, and formation by way of a carbene intermediate therefore appears unlikely. The reactivity of carboalkoxycarbenes is also affected by the presence of "catalysts." Carboethoxycarbene made by copper-catalyzed decomposition of ethyl diazoacetate does not insert into carbon-hydrogen bonds.

## II. REACTIONS OF CARBOALKOXYCARBENES

### A. Insertion into Carbon-Hydrogen Bonds

Carboalkoxycarbenes and bis(carboalkoxy)carbenes insert into the carbon-hydrogen bonds of alkanes, but introduction of the carboalkoxy groups renders the carbene increasingly selective (5, 6). The discrimination in favor of secondary and tertiary hydrogen is illustrated by the data of Table II.

TABLE II

RELATIVE RATES OF INSERTION INTO CARBON-HYDROGEN BONDS (6)

| Substrate | Ratio | $:CH_2$ | $:CH-CO_2Me$ | $:C(CO_2Et)_2$ |
|-----------|-------|---------|--------------|----------------|
| 2,3-Dimethylbutane | 3°/1° | 1.2 | 2.9 | 12.5 |
| Isobutane | 3°/1° | . . . | 3.1 | 21.0 |
| n-Pentane | 2°/1° | 1.0 | 2.3 | 8.4 |

The effect of carboalkoxy groups may be explained in terms of polar resonance structures which contribute to the transition state of the insertion reaction (6).

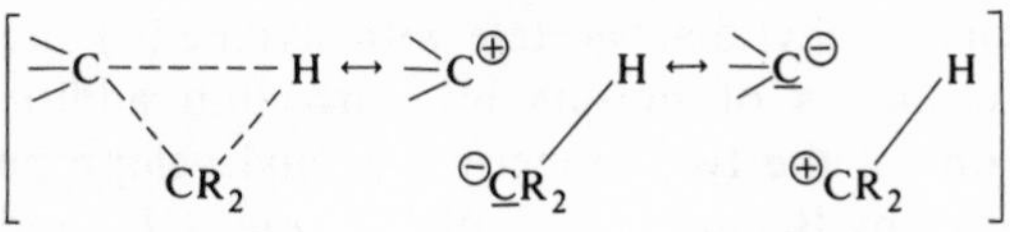

$$\left[ \ge C \text{-----} H \leftrightarrow \ge C^{\oplus} \quad H \leftrightarrow \ge \underline{C}^{\ominus} \quad H \right]$$

$$\quad\quad \overset{'}{C}R_2 \quad\quad\quad \overset{\ominus}{\underline{C}R_2} \quad\quad\quad \overset{\oplus}{C}R_2$$

(Ia)          (Ib)          (Ic)

Obviously, Ib contributes more to the resonance hybrid if $R = CO_2R$ than if $R = H$ because in the former case the negative charge may be dispersed over the carboalkoxy group(s). On the other hand, hyperconjugation stabilizes the positive charge in the order tertiary > secondary > primary carbon. Consequently, polarization of the transition state as expressed by Ib tends to increase the discrimination in favor of tertiary or secondary carbon-hydrogen bonds.

## B. Addition to Olefins

Diazo esters react with olefins by two distinct reaction paths to produce cyclopropanes. The diazo compound may lose nitrogen in the first step to give a carbene intermediate which adds to the olefin. This reaction [Eq. (1a)] is to be considered here. Alternatively, the diazo compound itself may add to the olefin with formation of a pyrazoline which, on thermal decomposition, gives rise to the same cyclopropane [Eq. (1b)].

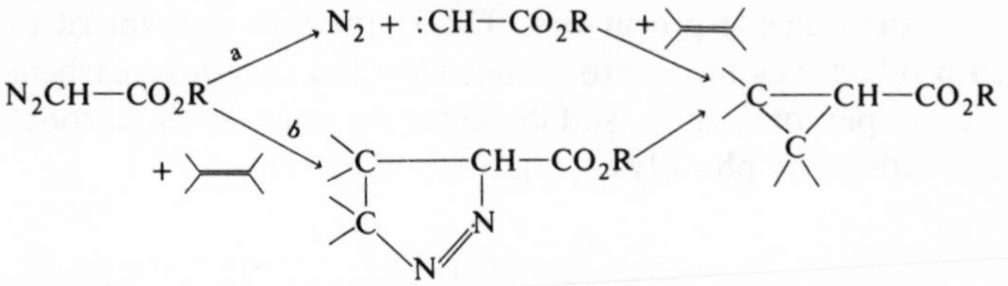

$$N_2CH-CO_2R \overset{a}{\underset{b}{\nearrow}} \begin{array}{c} N_2 + :CH-CO_2R + \rangle{=}\langle \\ \\ + \rangle{=}\langle \quad \ge C \text{------} CH-CO_2R \end{array} \ge C \text{------} CH-CO_2R \quad (1)$$

Pyrazoline intermediates are most likely to occur in thermal reactions of diazo esters with polar double bonds ($\alpha$, $\beta$-unsaturated ketones, esters, and nitriles). Kinetic measurements are indispensable to establish a carbenoid mechanism in such thermal reactions. Addition of the olefin in question should not affect the rate at which the diazo compound disappears. Nevertheless, UV irradiation of the reactants at low temperatures is better suited to the study of carboalkoxycarbene reactions [for a detailed discussion of the pyrazoline problem see (7)].

The reactions of ethyl diazoacetate with styrene (8) and cyclohexene (9) are early examples of presumably carbenoid addition processes. Whereas only one of the two isomeric 2-phenylcyclopropanecarboxylic acids was reported by Buchner (8), both the *trans*-(IIa) and the *cis*-(IIb) isomer were identified in later work (10). Structural assignment on the basis of oxidative degradation indicates (11, 12) that IIa is the major product.

$$Ph-CH=CH_2 + N_2CH-CO_2Et \xrightarrow{100-135°} \qquad + \qquad \qquad (2)$$

(IIa)        (IIb)

The addition of carbomethoxycarbene to *cis*- and *trans*-2-butene was shown to proceed stereospecifically *cis* [Eq. (3)] (13). The same result was obtained with *cis*- and *trans*-4-octene and stilbene (1).

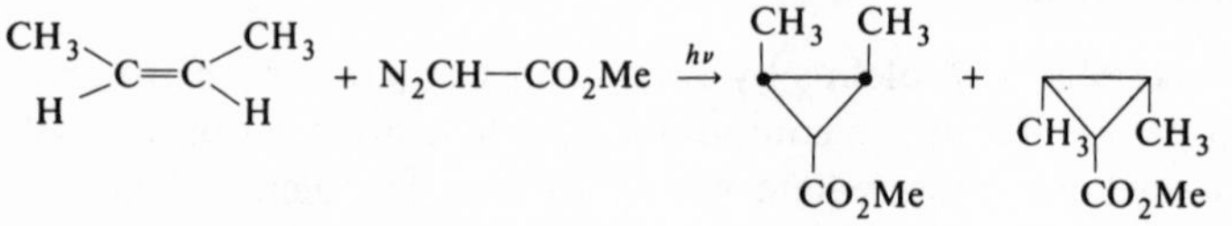

$$\begin{array}{c} CH_3 \\ \diagdown \\ H \end{array} C=C \begin{array}{c} CH_3 \\ \diagup \\ H \end{array} + N_2CH-CO_2Me \xrightarrow{h\nu} \qquad + \qquad \qquad (3)$$

28%       11%

When two isomers can be formed, the less crowded arrangement of substituents is preferred (13, 14). The ratio of the two isomers, however, depends on the carbene precursors. Discrimination in favor of the less hindered product was more pronounced with carboethoxycarbene produced by copper or cupric sulfate catalysis than with carboethoxycarbene generated by photolysis [Eqs. (4) and (5)] (14).

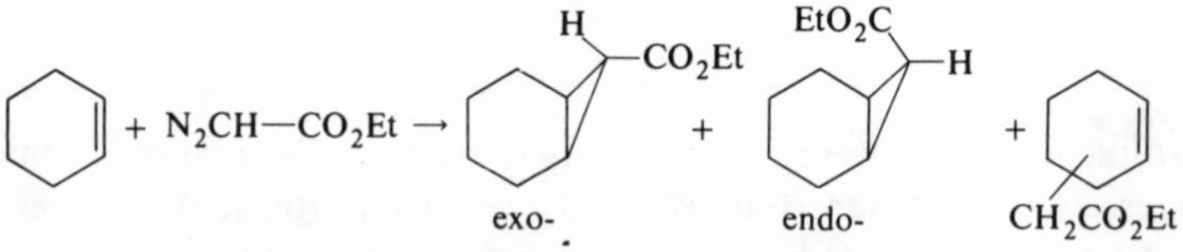

$$\qquad + N_2CH-CO_2Et \rightarrow \qquad + \qquad + \qquad (4)$$

| | exo- | endo- | CH_2CO_2Et |
|---|---|---|---|
| $h\nu$ | 31% | 16% | 21% |
| Cu | 69% | 4% | 0% |

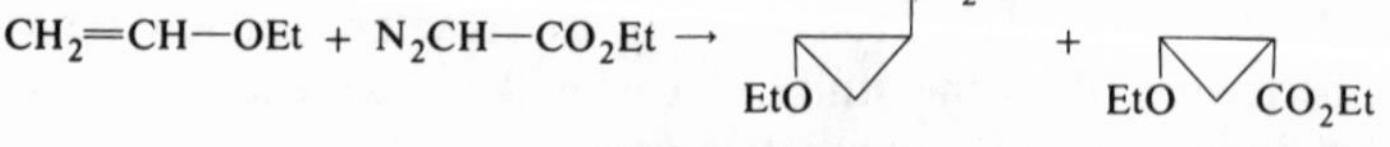

$$CH_2=CH-OEt + N_2CH-CO_2Et \rightarrow \qquad + \qquad (5)$$

| | | |
|---|---|---|
| $h\nu$ | 31% | 16% |
| CuSO_4 | 63% | 11% |

The influence of the catalyst has been explained in terms of a copper complex of the carbene (*14*). The complexation is thought to increase the bulk of the intermediate, but to leave the vacant orbital relatively free. In spite of the appreciable steric effects, competition experiments revealed only slight discrimination between different olefins (*15*) (relative rates: 1-hexene 1.0; cyclohexene 1.1; 2-methyl-2-butene 1.8; 2,3-dimethyl-2-butene 1.8).

Olefins to which carboethoxycarbene has been successfully added include cyclooctene (*16*), 1,1-diphenylethylene (*17*), and acenaphthylene (*18*). The presence of alkoxy groups or acyloxy groups in the olefin does not interfere with the addition of carboethoxycarbene [vinyl ethers (*19*, *20*), dihydrofurans and -pyrans (*21*), ketene acetal (*22*), vinyl acetate (*23*), allyl acetate (*24*)]. Smooth addition of carboethoxycarbene to unsaturated silanes and germanes has been reported (*24a*). If allyl alcohol (*25*) or allyl chloride (*26*) are employed, reactions of carboethoxycarbene with the O—H and C—Cl bonds occur which decrease the yields of cyclopropane derivatives. In most cases the stereochemistry of the products has not been elucidated.

Monoaddition of carboethoxycarbene to 1,3- and 1,4-dienes is achieved with ease. Predominant attack on the methyl substituted double bond of isoprene has been reported (*27*). The product, III, was converted to the diadduct IV in a second step.

$$\text{(isoprene)} + N_2CHCO_2Et \xrightarrow{\text{CuSO}_4} \text{(III)} \rightarrow \text{(IV)} \qquad (6)$$

(III)  (IV)

Cyclopentadiene reacted to give a monoadduct (probably *exo*-, 40% yield) and a diadduct (20% yield) in the copper-catalyzed decomposition of ethyl or *n*-butyl diazoacetate (*27a*).

1-Phenyl-1,3-butadiene appears to accept carboethoxycarbene at the terminal double bond (*28*). Various 1,3-pentadiene-1-carboxylic acids were found to react at the 3,4- rather than the 1,2-double bond (*29*). Cyclooctatetraene has been converted to a derivative of bicyclo[6.1.0]-nonatriene (V) [Eq. (7)] (*16*, *30*). Addition of carboethoxycarbene to the double bond of sabinene (VI) has been reported to involve isomerization of the cyclopropane structure [Eq. (8)] (*31*).

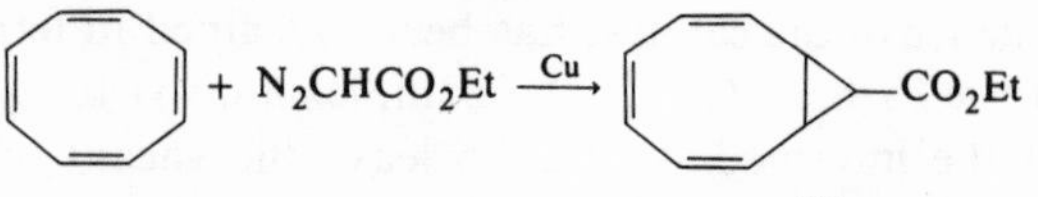

$$\text{(diagram)} + N_2CHCO_2Et \xrightarrow{Cu} \text{(diagram)} \text{—}CO_2Et \qquad (7)$$

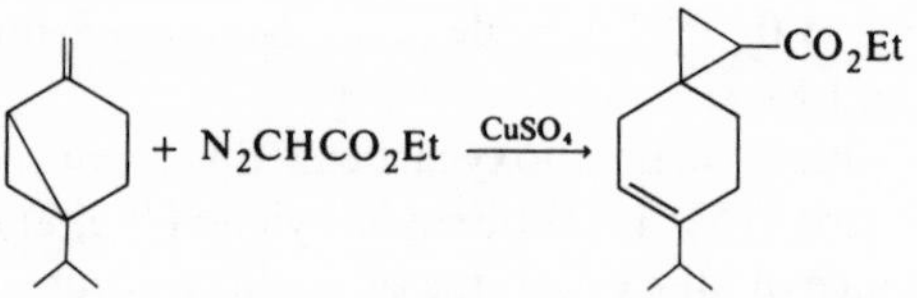

(V)

$$\text{(diagram)} + N_2CHCO_2Et \xrightarrow{CuSO_4} \text{(diagram)} \text{—}CO_2Et \qquad (8)$$

(VI)

The bicyclo[5.1.0]octadiene VII (2 stereoisomers) has been obtained by addition of carboethoxycarbene to cycloheptatriene (*31a*). Diels-Alder reactions established the 1,3-diene system of VII.

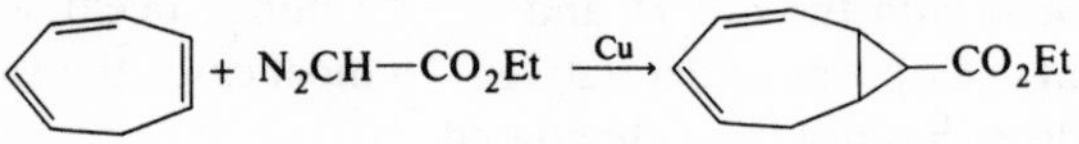

$$\text{(diagram)} + N_2CH\text{—}CO_2Et \xrightarrow{Cu} \text{(diagram)} \text{—}CO_2Et$$

(VII)

Carboethoxycarbene added to norbornadiene with formation of two stereoisomers the structure of which was assigned on the basis of nuclear magnetic resonance (N.M.R.) spectroscopy (*31b*).

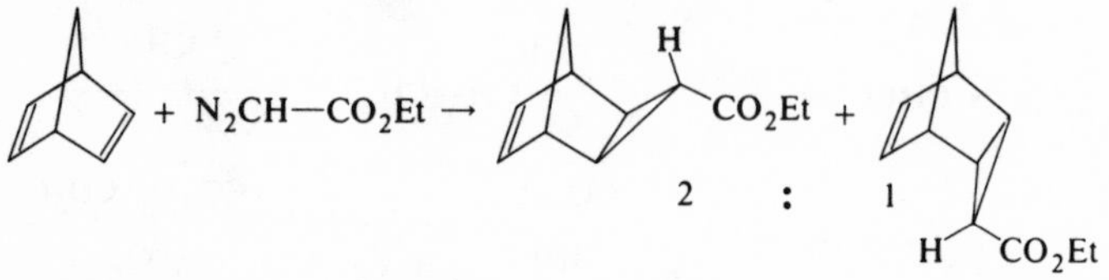

$$\text{(diagram)} + N_2CH\text{—}CO_2Et \rightarrow \text{(diagram)} CO_2Et + \text{(diagram)}$$

2 : 1

1′-Carboethoxy-2α,3α-cyclopropanoandrostane derivatives, 3α,4α- and 5β,6β-cyclopropanopregnene derivatives have been prepared from the corresponding steroidal olefins (*31c*). These additions of carbo-ethoxycarbene appear to be highly stereoselective.

## C. Addition to Acetylenes

The formation of substituted cyclopropenes from various acetylenes and ethyl diazoacetate was first reported by Dyakonov (*32*), and has also been studied by Breslow and his co-workers (*33–35*). Pyrolysis of ethyl diazoacetate without catalyst, or in the presence of copper powder, afforded 1,2-diaryl (or alkyl-)-3-carboethoxycyclopropenes (VIII). Cupric sulfate catalysis, however, produced isomers of VIII, which Dyakonov (36, 37) initially considered as 2,3-diaryl-1-carboethoxycyclopropenes (IX). The correct furan structure (X) was elucidated by Breslow (35). This assignment was confirmed by Dyakonov (38, 39), who also showed that the amount of cupric sulfate employed determines the structure of the product. With $10^{-3}$ moles of catalyst the cyclopropene VIII is formed exclusively, whereas the furan X is the only product with $10^{-2}$ moles (and more) of cupric sulfate. Mixtures of VIII and X were obtained in the presence of $4 \times 10^{-3}$ moles of catalyst (39).

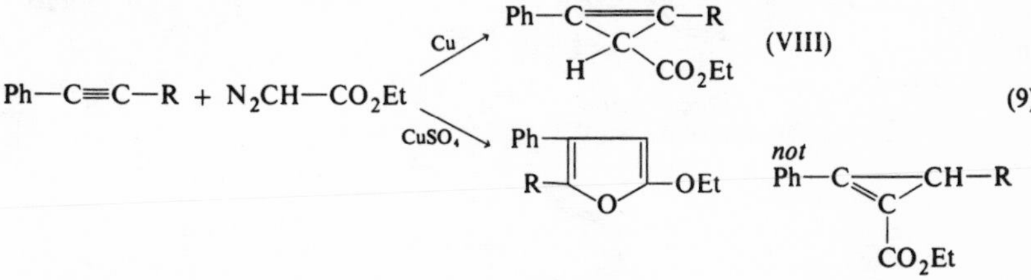

$$\text{(9)}$$

The furan X is the result of 1,3-dipolar addition of carboethoxycarbene to the acetylene (cf. Section II, I). Carbomethoxycarbene has been produced by photolysis of methyl diazoacetate and added to 2-butyne (40). Catalytic hydrogenation of the 1,2-dimethyl-2-carbomethoxy-cyclopropene (XI) formed has been useful to establish the structure of the cis-2-butene carbomethoxycarbene adducts [Eq. (3)].

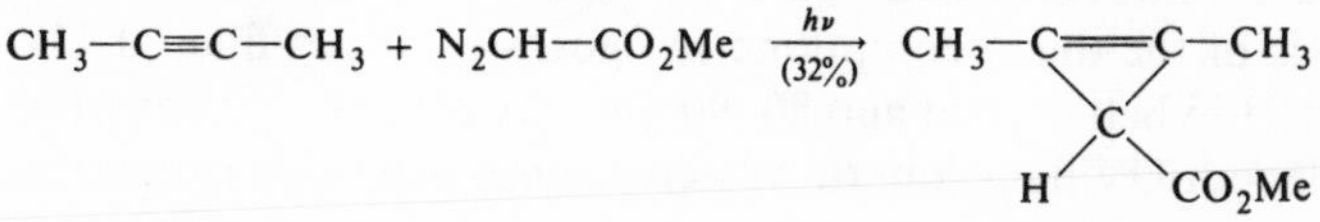

$$\text{(10)}$$

## D. Reaction with Aromatic and Heterocyclic Compounds

The decomposition of ethyl diazoacetate in the presence of benzene is one of the oldest carbene reactions known. After a first report by Buchner and Curtius in 1885 (41), the norcaradiene structure (XII) was assigned to the product in 1896 (42). Investigation of this compound was impeded by its facile isomerization (under the conditions of formation and saponification) to various cycloheptatrienecarboxylic acids, designated $\alpha$–$\delta$. Several attempts to attribute structures XIII–XVI to these isomers (43–45) led to conflicting results, but the norcaradiene structure XII of the "primary product" was retained until recently, as it was required to account for the existence of five isomers. Doering *et al.* (46) were able to show that the so-called "$\delta$"-Buchner acid was actually a mixture. The four remaining isomers were assigned structures XIII–XVI as shown below on the basis of N.M.R. spectroscopy and diene addition to dimethyl acetylenedicarboxylate.

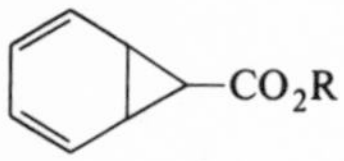

(XII) 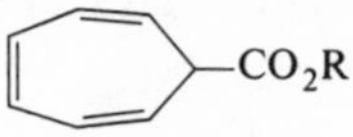         (XIII)         (XIV)         (XV)
        "norcaradiene-         "$\alpha$"-acid         "$\beta$"-acid
        carboxylic acid"

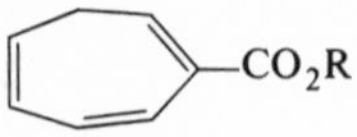

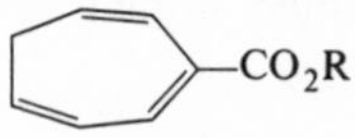

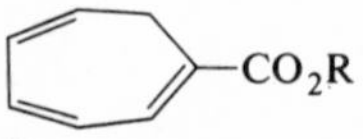

(XVI)
"$\gamma$"-acid

The N.M.R. pattern of the four methyl esters XIII–XVI is uniquely complicated in the vinyl C—H region and excludes a norcaradiene structure for any of the Buchner acids.

Pyrolysis of ethyl diazoacetate in the presence of benzene (130°–135°) leads to product mixtures which contain at most 20–30% of XIII (47, 48). Photolysis of the diazo compound by means of Pyrex-filtered UV light affords XIII in better yield and 80–90% purity (48, 49). Admission of short wavelength UV light (quartz vessels) causes extensive isomerization of XIII.

The attack of carbomethoxycarbene (produced by photolysis of methyl diazoacetate) on substituted benzenes appears to be sensitive to steric hindrance rather than to polar effects. Approximate isomer ratios have been determined by diene addition to dimethyl acetylenedicarboxylate and subsequent thermal cleavage to give (substituted) dimethyl phthalates (50). Some typical examples are recorded in Eq. (11). (The cycloheptatriene structure of the products is assumed by analogy and has not been proved.)

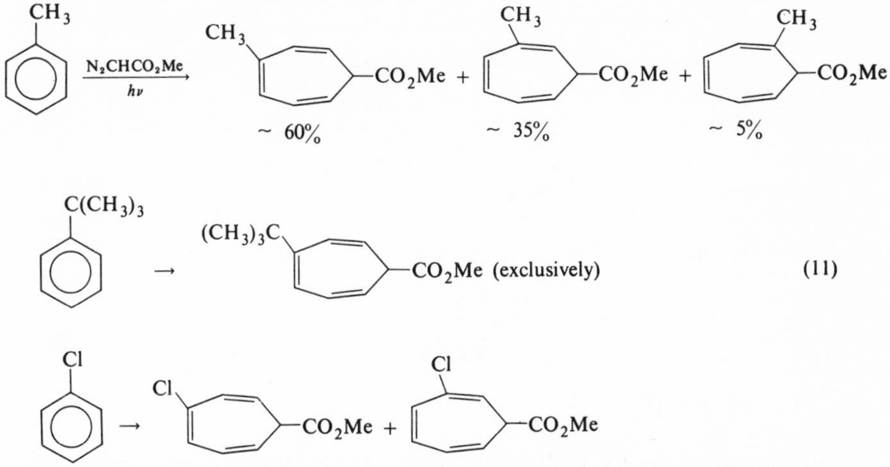

With increasing alkyl substitution of the benzene nucleus [xylene (51), mesitylene (52), durene (53), and prehnitene (54)], insertion of the carboalkoxycarbene into the carbon-hydrogen bonds of the methyl groups gradually increases at the expense of ring expansion. With phenolic ethers, ring expansion is accompanied by cleavage of the O-alkyl bond (cf. Section II, F) which leads to alkyl aryloxyacetates (55–57). Ethyl phenoxyacetate was the only product obtained from phenol and ethyl diazoacetate (58); previous reports of cycloheptatriene formation have not been confirmed (59).

In contrast to the results in the benzene series, the adduct of carboethoxycarbene to naphthalene (60) has been shown to contain a cyclopropane ring (61). N.M.R. and degradative evidence favor the exo-configuration (XVII). Resolution of the acid into optical antipodes has been achieved (62). In addition to XVII, two isomers of a diadduct were formed, as would be expected if exo-addition applies also to the second step of the reaction. The major isomer has been assigned the *trans*-structure XVIII on the basis of resolution into enantiomers (61).

The phenomenon of steric hindrance is again observed with methylnaphthalenes. Carboethoxycarbene attacks 2,3-dimethylnaphthalene preferentially in the unsubstituted ring (58% versus 37%) (63). The results obtained with 2,6-dimethylnaphthalene (64) are given in Eq. (13). The benzocycloheptatriene XX is probably an artifact arising from XIXb, not from XIXa. The partial rate factors for the two reaction

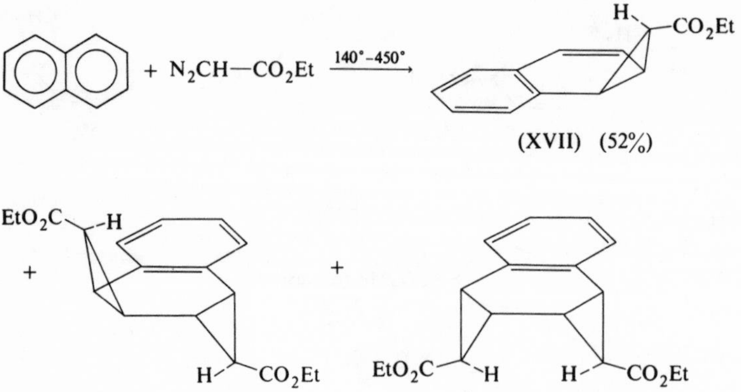

$$\text{(XVII)} \quad (52\%)$$

$$\text{(XVIII)} \quad (10\%) \qquad\qquad (4\%) \tag{12}$$

sites of 2,6-dimethylnaphthalene indicated in Eq. (13) are based on competition experiments with naphthalene (*64*).

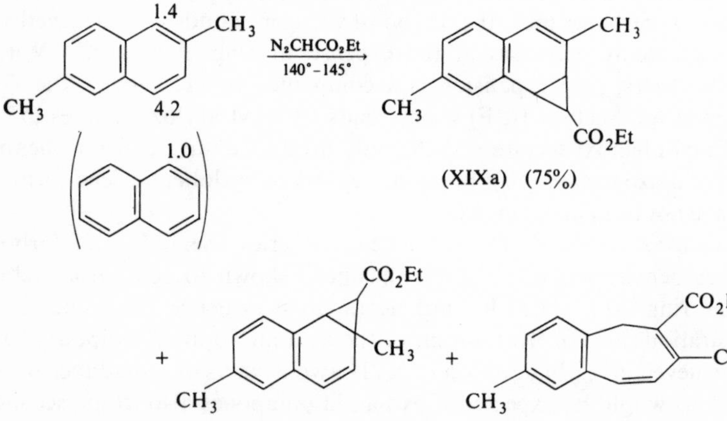

$$\text{(XIXa)} \quad (75\%)$$

$$\text{(XIXb)} \quad (15\%) \qquad\qquad \text{(XX)} \quad (9\%) \tag{13}$$

Carboalkoxycarbene adducts obtained from anthracene (*65*), and phenanthrene (*66*) have been assumed to contain cyclopropane rings, but no rigorous proof of structure has been given.

Ring expansion of the benzene nucleus of indans by carboalkoxy-carbenes has been frequently applied in the synthesis of azulenes. In most cases crude product mixtures have been saponified, decarboxylated, and dehydrogenated. The first synthesis by this route (*67*) was followed by numerous publications which may be found in reviews of azulene chemistry (*68, 69*).

The heterocyclic compounds, furan (*70*), benzofuran (*71*), thiophene (*70, 72*), and benzothiophene (*71, 73*), have been reported to accept carboalkoxycarbenes with the formation of cyclopropane rings [Eq. (14)]. According to a recent report (*73a*), benzothiophene accepts carboethoxycarbene at the benzene rather than the thiophene nucleus. The adduct has been converted to the thienotropylium cation. In contrast, pyrrole (*74*) and indole (*75*) give esters of pyrrylacetic acids and indolylacetic acids, respectively. Pyrrole, *N*-methylpyrrole, and 2,4-dimethylpyrrole are attacked in the α- (2- or 5-) positions [Eq. (15)], but β-attack has been observed with 2,3,5-trimethylpyrrole (*74*) [Eq. (16)]. Derivatives of 3-indolylacetic acid results from indole (*75*) [Eq. (17)].

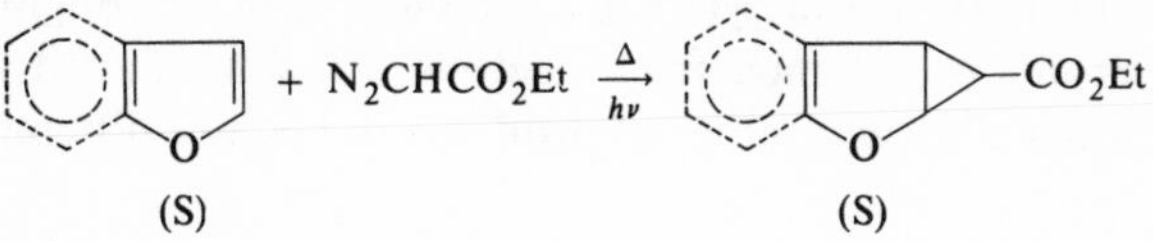

$$+ \ N_2CHCO_2Et \ \xrightarrow[h\nu]{\Delta} \quad \qquad -CO_2Et \qquad (14)$$

(S) (S)

$$+ \ N_2CHCO_2Et \ \rightarrow \qquad \qquad CH_2CO_2Et \qquad (15)$$

R=H, CH$_3$

$$+ \ N_2CHCO_2Et \ \rightarrow \qquad \qquad \qquad (16)$$

$$+ \ N_2CHCO_2Et \ \rightarrow \qquad \qquad -CH_2CO_2Et$$

$$+ \qquad \qquad -CH_2CO_2Et \ (24) \qquad (17)$$

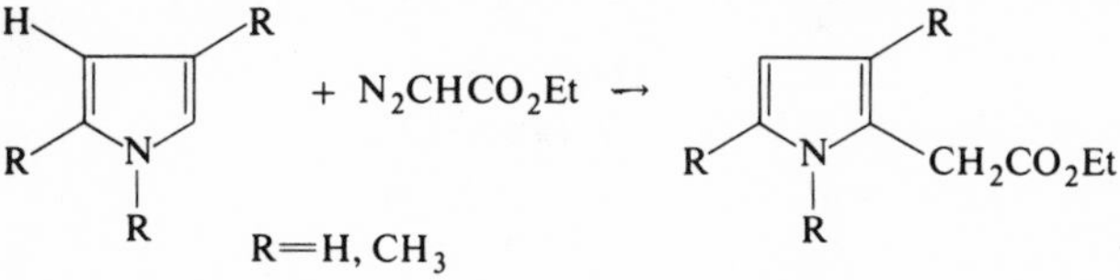

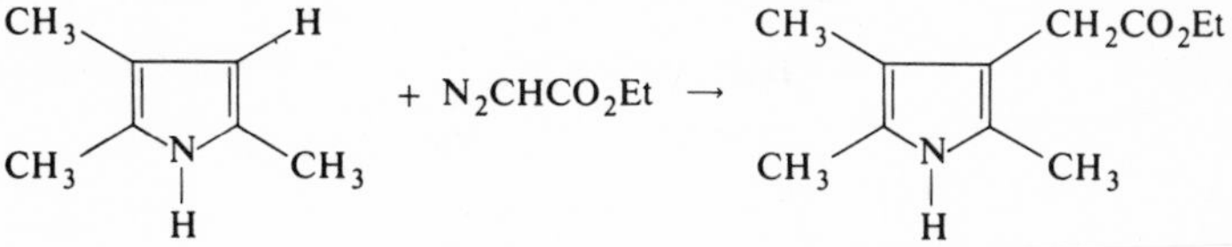

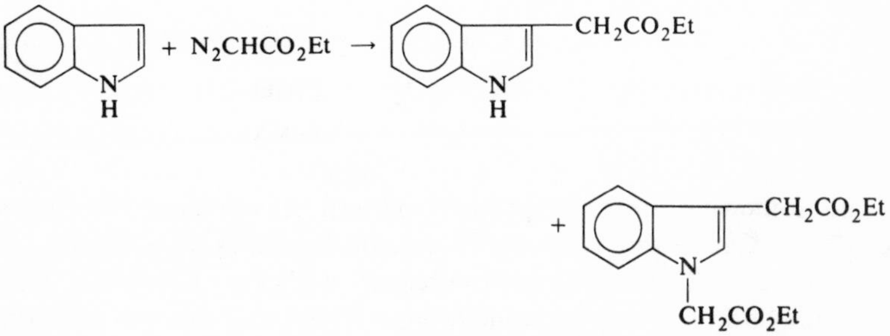

α-Pyridone, on heating with ethyl diazoacetate, undergoes predominantly O-alkylation and, in smaller amount, N-alkylation (76). These alkylations are possibly reactions of the diazo compound rather than the carbene.

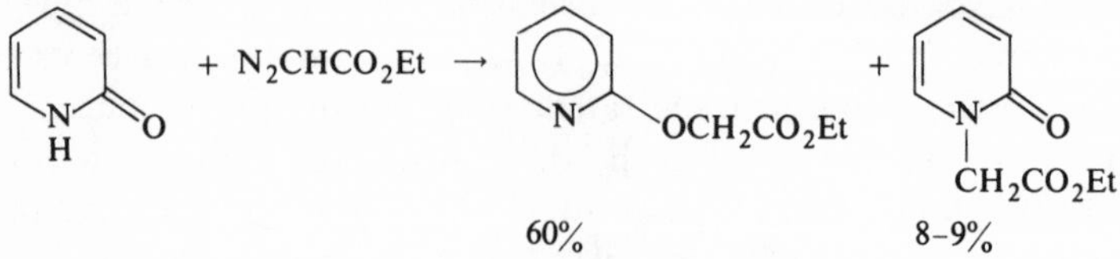

$$+ N_2CHCO_2Et \rightarrow$$

(18)

60%                    8–9%

## E. Reactions with Carbonyl Compounds

The action of carboethoxycarbene, produced from ethyl diazoacetate by copper catalysis, on acetone and cyclohexanone has been thoroughly studied (77). The products obtained from acetone are summarized in Eq. (19). Cyclohexanone affords analogous products in slightly different amounts.

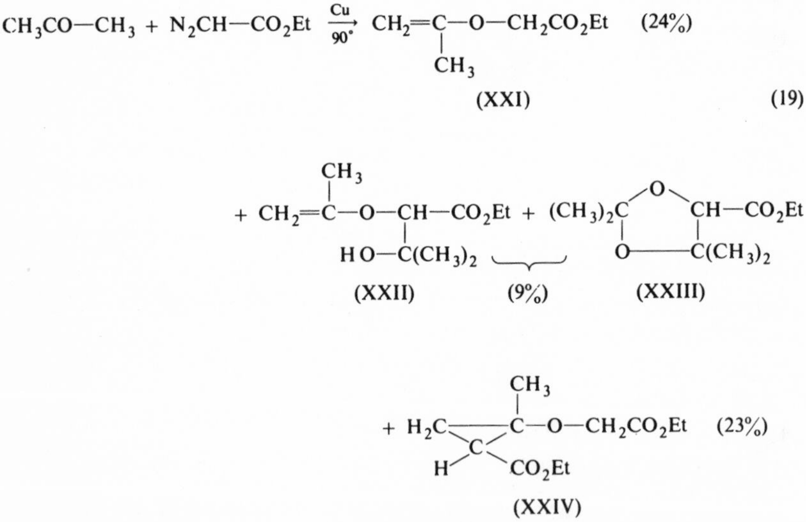

$$CH_3CO-CH_3 + N_2CH-CO_2Et \xrightarrow[90^\circ]{Cu} CH_2=\overset{|}{\underset{CH_3}{C}}-O-CH_2CO_2Et \quad (24\%)$$

(XXI)                                    (19)

$$+ \underset{HO-C(CH_3)_2}{CH_2=\overset{CH_3}{\overset{|}{C}}-O-CH-CO_2Et} + (CH_3)_2C\underset{O}{\overset{O}{<}}\underset{C(CH_3)_2}{CH-CO_2Et}$$

(XXII)          (9%)          (XXIII)

$$+ H_2C\underset{H}{\overset{CH_3}{<}}\overset{|}{\underset{C}{C}}-O-CH_2CO_2Et \quad (23\%)$$

(XXIV)

The somewhat puzzling product pattern is explained as follows [Eq. (20)]: Carboethoxycarbene is thought to attack initially the carbonyl oxygen. The resulting "zwitterion" (77) (or 1,3-dipole) (77a) (XXV) may add to excess acetone to give XXIII (1,3-dipolar addition).

By shift of a proton, (XXV) affords the enol ether (XXI), from which (XXIV) is derived by further addition of carboethoxycarbene.

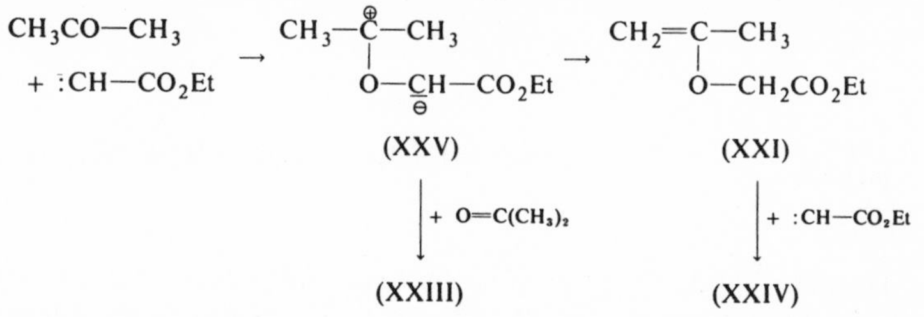

$$CH_3CO—CH_3 \quad \xrightarrow{} \quad CH_3-\overset{\oplus}{C}-CH_3 \quad \xrightarrow{} \quad CH_2{=}C—CH_3$$
$$+ \; :CH—CO_2Et \qquad \qquad O—\underset{\ominus}{C}H—CO_2Et \qquad \qquad O—CH_2CO_2Et$$

(XXV) (XXI) (20)

$$\Big\downarrow + \; O{=}C(CH_3)_2 \qquad\qquad \Big\downarrow + \; :CH—CO_2Et$$

(XXIII) (XXIV)

Formation of an enol ether has also been observed on heating ben-zosuberone with ethyl diazoacetate (50% yield) (78). The copper-cata-lyzed decomposition of ethyl diazoacetate in the presence of benzal-dehyde afforded the dioxolane XXVI (mixture of 2 stereoisomers) in 91% yield (77a).

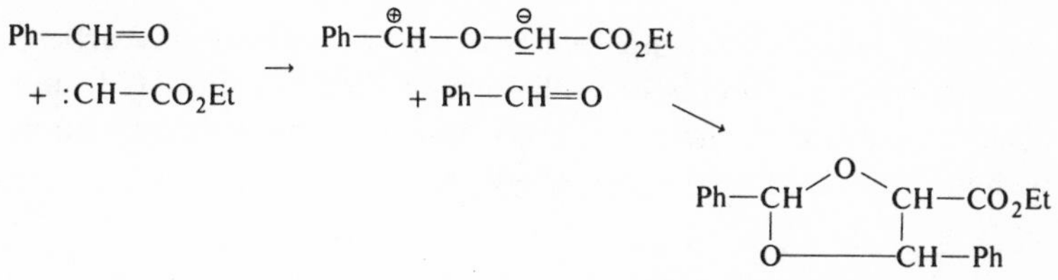

$$Ph—CH{=}O \quad \xrightarrow{} \quad Ph—\overset{\oplus}{C}H—O—\overset{\ominus}{C}H—CO_2Et$$
$$+ \; :CH—CO_2Et \qquad \qquad + \; Ph—CH{=}O$$

$$Ph—CH\overset{O}{\diagdown}CH—CO_2Et$$
$$O———CH—Ph$$

(XXVI) (20a)

The copper-catalyzed reaction of ethyl diazoacetate with thioketones produced $\alpha,\beta$-unsaturated esters, sulfur, and nitrogen (78a). The final products are thought to arise from intermediate thiiranes which are known to decompose with formation of olefins under similar conditions.

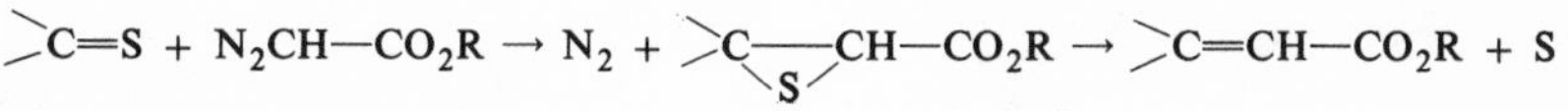

$$\diagup\!\!\diagup C{=}S + N_2CH—CO_2R \rightarrow N_2 + \diagup\!\!\diagup C\underset{\diagdown S \diagup}{———}CH—CO_2R \rightarrow \diagup\!\!\diagup C{=}CH—CO_2R + S$$

## F. Reactions with Ethers

Dialkyl ethers (79, 80) and alkyl aryl ethers (55-57, 79, 81) may undergo cleavage at the O-alkyl bond when treated with carboethoxy-carbene. This reaction competes with insertion into carbon-hydrogen bonds and addition to aromatic nuclei. With n-butyl ether the formation of 1-butene has been observed (79); therefore, the ether cleavage may be explained in terms of an ylide mechanism [Eq. (21)].

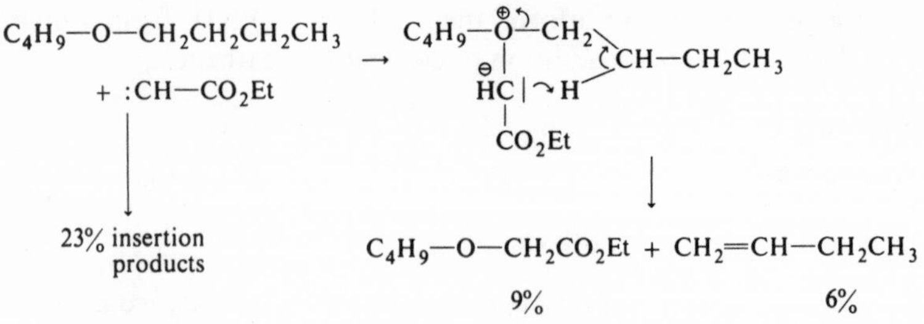

$$C_4H_9-O-CH_2CH_2CH_2CH_3 \quad \rightarrow \quad C_4H_9-\overset{\oplus}{\underset{\ominus}{O}}-CH_2\diagdown$$

$$+ :CH-CO_2Et \qquad\qquad \overset{\ominus}{HC}|\curvearrowright H \diagdown \overset{C}{C}H-CH_2CH_3$$

$$\underset{CO_2Et}{|} \tag{21}$$

23% insertion products

$$C_4H_9-O-CH_2CO_2Et + CH_2=CH-CH_2CH_3$$

9%                              6%

On the other hand, cleavage of *O*-methyl bonds occurs with a large number of substituted anisoles (*55–57, 79, 81*), and also with *n*-heptyl methyl ether (*79*). In the latter case, elimination of the *n*-heptyl group, which can follow Eq. (21), is not even favored over elimination of the methyl group, the fate of which is unknown.

$$C_7H_{15}-O-CH_3 + :CH-CO_2Et \rightarrow CH_3O-CH_2CO_2Et + C_7H_{15}O-CH_2CO_2Et$$

$$30\% \qquad\qquad 45\% \tag{22}$$

There are some examples of apparent insertion of carboethoxycarbene into the carbon-oxygen bonds of cyclic acetals (*78, 81*) [Eqs. (23) and (24)]. The mechanism of these reactions deserves further investigation as no such insertion is known with methylene.

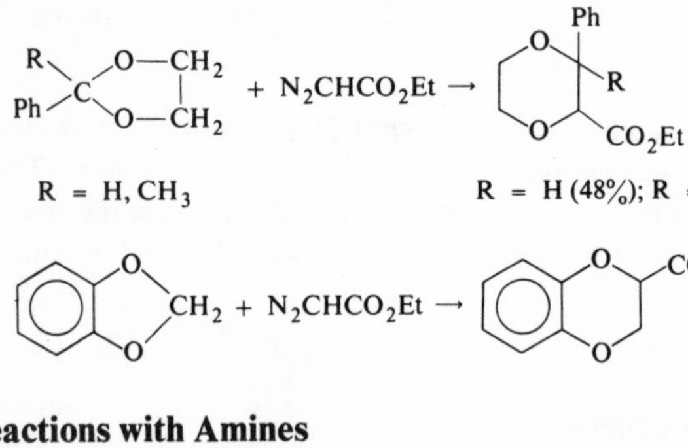

$$\underset{Ph}{\overset{R}{\diagdown}}C\underset{O-CH_2}{\overset{O-CH_2}{\diagup}} + N_2CHCO_2Et \rightarrow$$

R = H, CH$_3$              R = H (48%); R = CH$_3$(6.5%)

$$\tag{23}$$

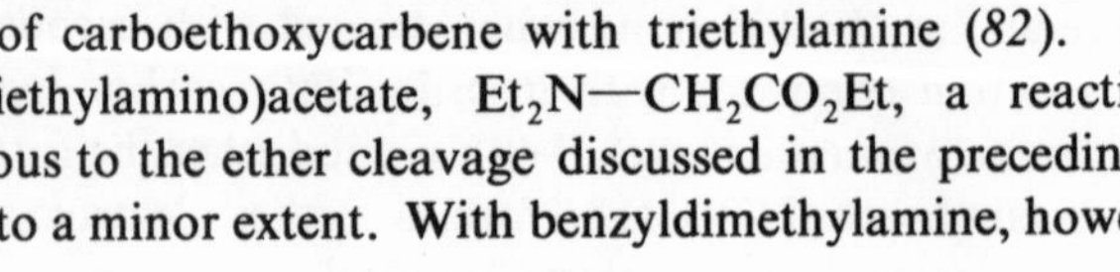

$$\tag{24}$$

## G. Reactions with Amines

Insertion into the carbon-hydrogen bonds is the predominant reaction of carboethoxycarbene with triethylamine (*82*). Formation of ethyl(diethylamino)acetate, $Et_2N-CH_2CO_2Et$, a reaction which is analogous to the ether cleavage discussed in the preceding paragraphs, occurs to a minor extent. With benzyldimethylamine, however, insertion of carboethoxycarbene into the carbon-nitrogen bond competes with insertion into carbon-hydrogen bonds. This behavior of benzylamines may be due to particularly facile ylide rearrangement of the benzyl group [Eq. (25)] (82).

$$PhCH_2\text{---}N(CH_3)_2 + :CH\text{---}CO_2Et \rightarrow PhCH_2\text{---}\overset{\oplus}{N}(CH_3)_2$$
$$\underset{}{\overset{}{\ominus}}\overset{|}{CH}\text{---}CO_2Et \qquad (25)$$
$$\rightarrow Ph\text{---}CH_2\text{---}\underset{\underset{CO_2Et}{|}}{CH}\text{---}N(CH_3)_2$$

## H. Reactions with Halides

Carboethoxycarbene is capable of insertion into carbon-halogen bonds. Ethyl bromide afforded only a small amount of ethyl-$\alpha$-bromobutyrate (83), but excellent yields have been reported with allyl bromide (26, 84, 85), allyl iodide (86), and 2,3-dibromopropene (87). Addition of carboethoxycarbene to the double bond competes effectively with insertion into the carbon-chlorine bond of allyl chloride (26) and 2,3-dichloropropene (88), whereas no cyclopropanes have been obtained from allyl bromides and iodides.

The insertion reaction of carboethoxycarbene with allylic halides obviously involves an intermediate displaying allylic resonance. Mixtures of the $\alpha$-halo esters XXVII and XXVIII were obtained from both 1-chloro-2-butene (crotyl chloride) and 3-chloro-1-butene (methallyl chloride) (85) [Eq. (26)].

$$CH_3CH\text{=}CH\text{---}CH_2\underset{\underset{Cl}{|}}{CH}\text{---}CO_2Et \qquad \overset{CH_3}{\overset{|}{CH_2}}\text{=}CH\text{---}CH\text{---}\underset{\underset{Cl}{|}}{CH}\text{---}CO_2Et$$

$$(XXVII) \qquad\qquad\qquad (XXVIII)$$

$$N_2CH\text{---}CO_2Et$$
$$+ \ CH_3CH\text{=}CH\text{---}CH_2Cl \ \rightarrow \quad 35\% \qquad\qquad 25\%$$
$$\qquad\qquad\qquad\qquad\qquad\qquad\qquad\qquad\qquad\qquad (26)$$
$$+ \ CH_2\text{=}CH\text{---}\underset{\underset{CH_3}{|}}{CH}\text{---}Cl \quad \rightarrow \quad 40\% \qquad\qquad 10\%$$

1,1-Dichloropropene and 1,3-dichloropropene were reported to give the same insertion product, **XXIX** (*85*):

$$CH_3-CH=CCl_2$$
$$+ N_2CH-CO_2Et \rightarrow ClCH=CH-CH_2CH-CO_2Et \quad (27)$$
$$ClCH_2CH=CHCl \qquad\qquad\qquad\qquad\qquad | $$
$$\qquad\qquad\qquad\qquad\qquad\qquad\qquad Cl$$
$$(\textbf{XXIX})$$

Polyhalomethanes appear to undergo normal insertion reactions with carboethoxycarbene (*89*)—in contrast to methylene which initiates a radical chain process (cf. Chapter 2, Section II,G).

$$CHCl_3 + N_2CH-CO_2Me \xrightarrow{h\nu} Cl_2CH-\underset{\underset{Cl}{|}}{C}H-CO_2Me \qquad (28)$$

$$CCl_4 + N_2CH-CO_2Me \xrightarrow{h\nu} Cl_3C-\underset{\underset{Cl}{|}}{C}H-CO_2Me \rightarrow Cl_2C=\underset{\underset{Cl}{|}}{C}-CO_2Me$$
$$\qquad\qquad\qquad\qquad\qquad\qquad\qquad\qquad\qquad\qquad\qquad (29)$$

Elimination of hydrogen halides, presumably following the insertion reaction as indicated in Eq. (29), has been observed in other instances. It may proceed with migration of aryl groups as in the case of triphenyl-methyl and benzhydryl halides (*90, 91*):

$$Ph_3C-Br + N_2CH-CO_2Et \xrightarrow{CuSO_4} Ph_2C=\underset{\underset{Ph}{|}}{C}-CO_2Et \quad (61\%) \qquad (30)$$

$$Ph_2CH-Br + N_2CH-CO_2Et \rightarrow Ph-\underset{\underset{Br}{|}}{C}H-\underset{\underset{Ph}{|}}{C}H-CO_2Et \quad (31\%) \qquad (31)$$

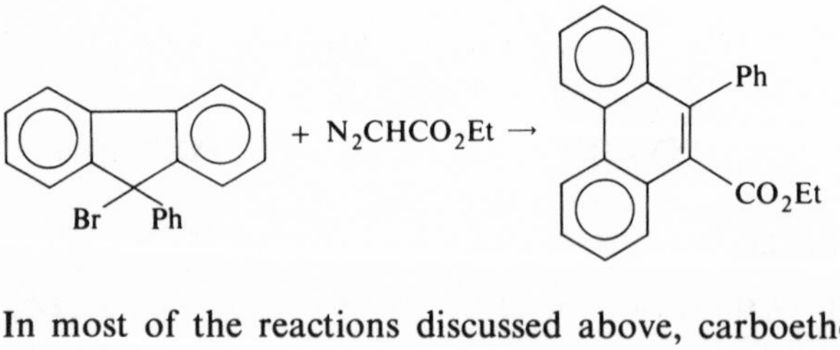

+ $N_2CHCO_2Et \rightarrow$ (18%) (32)

In most of the reactions discussed above, carboethoxycarbene also abstracts halogen, or hydrogen halide, to give ethyl haloacetates. The abstraction may be considered as a sequence of radical reactions, but a concerted mechanism, Eq. (33), has also been proposed (*83*).

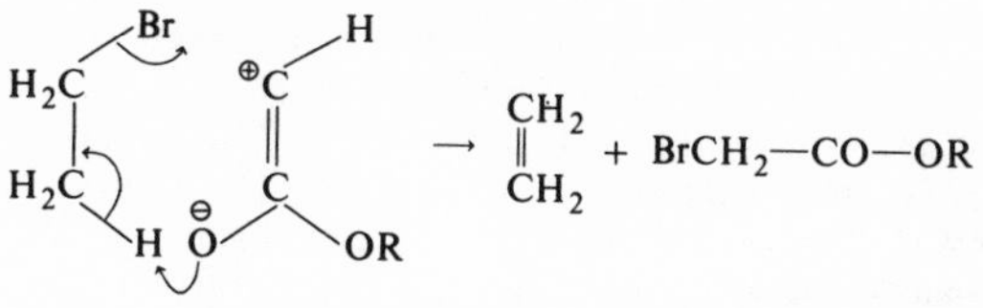

$$\text{(structure)} \longrightarrow \begin{array}{c} CH_2 \\ \parallel \\ CH_2 \end{array} + BrCH_2\text{—}CO\text{—}OR \tag{33}$$

Equation (33) cannot be generally applicable, however, as ethyl haloacetates are also formed from halides not containing suitable hydrogen, such as chloroform (*89*) or triphenylmethylbromide (*90*).

## I. 1,3-Dipolar Additions

The divalent carbon atom is the reactive site in most carboalkoxy-carbene reactions. A few additions to multiple bonds, however, proceed with participation of both the carbene carbon and the carbonyl oxygen. These reactions are referred to as "1,3-dipolar additions" (*92*) since they may be explained in terms of a polar resonance structure (**XXXb**) of the carboalkoxycarbene. The formation of furans from acetylenes has been mentioned in Section C, and the oxazole **XXXI** has been obtained from benzonitrile and ethyl diazoacetate (*92*). (for related reactions of keto-carbenes, cf. Chapter 7, Section II,B,6).

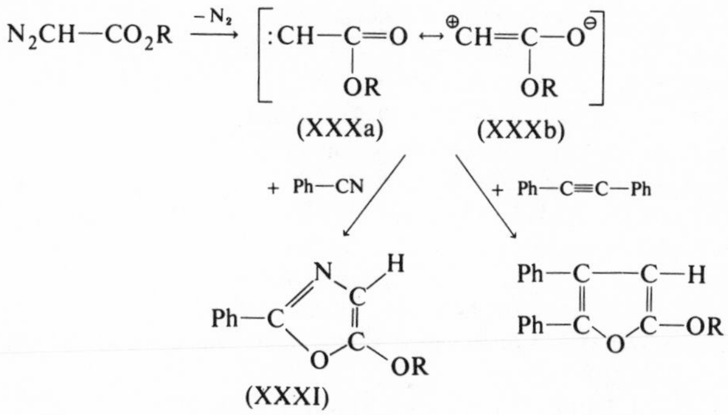

$$N_2CH\text{—}CO_2R \xrightarrow{-N_2} \left[ \begin{array}{cc} :CH\text{—}C{=}O & \overset{\oplus}{\longleftrightarrow} \, ^{\oplus}CH{=}C\text{—}O^{\ominus} \\ \quad | & \quad | \\ \quad OR & \quad OR \end{array} \right]$$

$$\text{(XXXa)} \qquad \text{(XXXb)} \tag{34}$$

+ Ph—CN / \ + Ph—C≡C—Ph

(**XXXI**)

### REFERENCES

1. I. A. Dyakonov, M. I. Komendatov, Fu Guj-sija, and L. G. Koricev, *Zhur. Obshchei Khim.* **32**, 928 (1962).
2. E. Wolf, *Z. physik. Chem.* **B17**, 46 (1932).
3. A. Loose, *J. prakt. Chem.* [2] **79**, 507 (1909).
4. K. Lorey, *J. prakt. Chem.* [2] **124**, 185 (1930).
5. W. v. E. Doering and L. H. Knox, *J. Am. Chem. Soc.* **78**, 4947 (1956).

6. W. v. E. Doering and L. H. Knox, *J. Am. Chem. Soc.* **83**, 1989 (1961).
7. I. A. Dyakonov, *Zhur. Obshchei Khim.* **19**, 1734 (1949).
8. E. Buchner and J. Geronimus, *Ber. deut. chem. Ges.* **36**, 3782 (1903).
9. F. Ebel, R. Brunner, and P. Mangelli, *Helv. Chim. Acta* **12**, 19 (1929).
10. A. Burger and W. L. Yost, *J. Am. Chem. Soc.* **70**, 2198 (1948).
11. D. G. Markees and A. Burger, *J. Am. Chem. Soc.* **70**, 3329 (1948).
12. H. L. de Waal and G. W. Perold, *Chem. Ber.* **85**, 574 (1952).
13. W. v. E. Doering and T. Mole, *Tetrahedron* **10**, 65 (1960).
14. P. S. Skell and R. M. Etter, *Proc. Chem. Soc.* **1961**, 443.
15. P. S. Skell and R. M. Etter, *Chem. & Ind. (London)* **1958**, 624.
16. S. Akiyoshi and T. Matsuda, *J. Am. Chem. Soc.* **77**, 2476 (1955).
17. H. M. Walborsky and F. M. Hornyak, *J. Am. Chem. Soc.* **77**, 6026 (1955).
18. R. Pettit, *Chem. & Ind. (London)* **1956**, 1306.
19. I. A. Dyakonov, *Zhur. Obshchei Khim.* **19**, 1891 (1949).
20. I. A. Dyakonov and N. A. Lugovtsova, *Zhur. Obshchei Khim.* **21**, 839 (1951).
21. R. Paul and S. Tchelitcheff, *Compt. rend.* **244**, 2806 (1957).
22. M. F. Dull and P. G. Abend, *J. Am. Chem. Soc.* **81**, 2588 (1959).
23. I. A. Dyakonov, *Zhur. Obshchei Khim.* **20**, 2289 (1950).
24. I. A. Dyakonov and O. V. Guseva, *Zhur. Obshchei Khim.* **22**, 1355 (1952).
24a. I. E. Dolgij, A. P. Mescerjakov, and G. K. Gajvoronskaja, *Izv. Akad. Nauk S.S.S.R., Otdel. Khim. Nauk* **1963**, 572.
25. I. A. Dyakonov and N. D. Pirogova, *Zhur. Obshchei Khim.* **21**, 1979 (1951).
26. I. A. Dyakonov and N. B. Vinogradova, *Zhur. Obshchei Khim.* **22**, 1349 (1952).
27. I. A. Dyakonov and V. F. Myznikova, *Sbornik Statei Obshchei Khim., Akad. Nauk S.S.S.R.* **1**, 489 (1953); *Chem. Abstr.* **49**, 883 (1955).
27a. B. Föhlisch, *Chem. Ber.* **97**, 88 (1964); cf. also P. Besinet, R. Fraisse, R. Jaquier, and P. Viallefont, *Bull. soc. chim. France* **1960**, 1377.
28. C. von der Heide, *Ber. deut. chem. Ges.* **37**, 2101 (1904).
29. S. H. Harper and H. W. B. Reed, *J. Chem. Soc.* **1955**, 779.
30. D. D. Phillips, *J. Am. Chem. Soc.* **77**, 5179 (1955).
31. M. I. Gorjajev and G. A. Tolstikov, *Zhur. Obshchei Khim.* **32**, 310 (1962).
31a. F. Korte, K. H. Büchel, and F. F. Wiese, *Ann.* **664**, 114 (1963).
31b. R. R. Sauers and P. E. Sonnet, *Chem. & Ind. (London)* **1963**, 786.
31c. L. H. Knox, U. S. Patents 3,079,406 and 3,080,386 (1963).
32. I. A. Dyakonov and M. I. Komendatov, *Vestnik Leningrad Univ.* **11**, No. 22, *Ser. Fiz. i Khim.* No. 4, 166 (1956); *Chem. Abstr.* **52**, 2762 (1958).
33. R. Breslow and M. Battiste, *Chem. & Ind. (London)* **1958**, 1143.
34. R. Breslow, R. Winter, and M. Battiste, *J. Org. Chem.* **24**, 415 (1959).
35. R. Breslow and D. Chipman, *Chem. & Ind. (London)* **1960**, 1105.
36. I. A. Dyakonov and M. I. Komendatov, *Zhur. Obshchei Khim.* **29**, 1749 (1959).
37. I. A. Dyakonov, M. I. Komendatov, J. Gokhmanova, and R. Kostikov, *Zhur. Obshchei Khim.* **29**, 3848 (1959).
38. I. A. Dyakonov and M. I. Komendatov, *Zhur. Obshchei Khim.* **31**, 3881 (1961).
39. I. A. Dyakonov, M. I. Komendatov, and S. P. Korsunov, *Zhur. Obshchei Khim.* **32**, 923 (1962).
40. W. v. E. Doering and T. Mole, *Tetrahedron* **10**, 65 (1960).
41. E. Buchner and Th. Curtius, *Ber. deut. chem. Ges.* **18**, 2377 (1885).

42. E. Buchner, *Ber. deut. chem. Ges.* **29**, 106 (1896).
43. E. Buchner, *Ber. deut. chem. Ges.* **31**, 2241 (1898).
44. A. W. K. De Jong, *Rec. trav. chim.* **56**, 198 (1937).
45. Ch. Grundmann and G. Ottmann, *Ann.* **582**, 163 (1953).
46. W. v. E. Doering, G. Laber, R. Vonderwahl, N. F. Chamberlain, and R. B. Williams, *J. Am. Chem. Soc.* **78**, 5448 (1956).
47. W. Braren and E. Buchner, *Ber. deut. chem. Ges.* **34**, 982 (1901).
48. G. O. Schenck and H. Ziegler, *Naturwissenschaften* **38**, 356 (1951); *Ann.* **584**, 221 (1953).
49. F. J. L. Sixma and E. Detilleux, *Rec. trav. chim.* **72**, 173 (1953).
50. K. Alder, R. Munders, W. Krane, and P. Wirtz, *Ann.* **627**, 59 (1959).
51. E. Buchner and P. Schulze, *Ann.* **377**, 259 (1910).
52. E. Buchner and K. Schottenhammer, *Ber. deut. chem. Ges.* **53**, 865 (1920).
53. L. I. Smith and P. O. Tawney, *J. Am. Chem. Soc.* **56**, 2167 (1934).
54. L. I. Smith and C. L. Agre, *J. Am. Chem. Soc.* **60**, 648 (1938).
55. J. R. Bartels-Keith, A. W. Johnson, and W. I. Taylor, *J. Chem. Soc.* **1951**, 2352.
56. J. R. Bartels-Keith, A. W. Johnson, and A. Langemann, *J. Chem. Soc.* **1952**, 4461.
57. R. B. Johns, A. W. Johnson, and J. Murray, *J. Chem. Soc.* **1954**, 198.
58. E. Baltazzi, *Compt. rend.* **241**, 321 (1955).
59. N. E. Searle, US Patent 2,532,575 (1950); *Chem. Abstr.* **45**, 3873 (1951).
60. E. Buchner and S. Hediger, *Ber. deut. chem. Ges.* **36**, 3502 (1903).
61. R. Huisgen and G. Juppe, *Chem. Ber.* **94**, 2332 (1961).
62. A. A. Fredga, *Arkiv Kemi* **12**, 547 (1958).
63. G. Juppe and R. Huisgen, *Ann.* **646**, 1 (1961).
64. R. Huisgen and G. Juppe, *Tetrahedron* **15**, 7 (1961).
65. G. M. Badger, J. W. Cook, and A. R. M. Gibb, *J. Chem. Soc.* **1951**, 3456.
66. N. L. Drake and T. R. Sweeney, *J. Org. Chem.* **11**, 67 (1946).
67. A. S. Pfau and P. A. Plattner, *Helv. Chim. Acta* **22**, 202 (1939).
68. H. Pommer, *Angew. Chem.* **62**, 281 (1950).
69. K. Hafner, *Angew. Chem.* **70**, 419 (1958).
70. G. O. Schenck and R. Steinmetz, *Angew. Chem.* **70**, 504 (1958); *Ann.* **668**, 19 (1963).
71. G. M. Badger, B. J. Christie, H. J. Rodda, and J. M. Pyrke, *J. Chem. Soc.* **1958**, 1179.
72. W. Steinkopff and H. Augestad-Jensen, *Ann.* **428**, 154 (1922); R. Pettit, *Tetrahedron Letters No.* **23**, 11 (1960).
73. G. M. Badger, H. J. Rodda, and J. M. Sassee, *J. Chem. Soc.* **1958**, 4777.
73a. D. Sullivan and R. Pettit, *Tetrahedron Letters* **1963**, 401.
74. C. D. Nenitzescu and E. Solomonica, *Ber. deut. chem. Ges.* **64**, 1924 (1931).
75. R. W. Jackson and R. H. Manske, *Can. J. Res.* **B13**, 170 (1935).
76. J. Maas, G. B. R. de Graaf, and H. J. den Hertog, *Rec. trav. chim.* **74**, 175 (1955).
77. M. S. Kharasch, T. Rudy, W. Nudenberg, and G. Büchi, *J. Org. Chem.* **18**, 1030 (1953).
77a. R. Huisgen and R. Bermes, *Angew. Chem.* **75**, 630 (1963).
78. C. D. Gutsche and M. Hillman, *J. Am. Chem. Soc.* **76**, 2236 (1954).
78a. A. Schönberg and E. Frese, *Chem. Ber.* **96**, 2420 (1963).
79. G. B. R. de Graaf, J. H. van Dijk-Rothuis, and G. van de Kolk, *Rec. trav. chim.* **74**, 143 (1955).
80. G. B. R. de Graaf and G. van de Kolk, *Rec. trav. chim.* **77**, 224 (1958).

81. A. W. Johnson, A. Langemann, and J. Murray, *J. Chem. Soc.* **1953**, 2136.
82. V. Franzen and H. Kuntze, *Ann.* **627**, 15 (1959).
83. V. Franzen, *Ann.* **627**, 22 (1959).
84. I. A. Dyakonov and N. B. Vinogradova, *Zhur. Obshchei Khim.* **21**, 851 (1951).
85. D. D. Phillips, *J. Am. Chem. Soc.* **76**, 5385 (1954).
86. I. A. Dyakonov and N. B. Vinogradova, *Zhur. Obshchei Khim.* **23**, 66 (1953).
87. I. A. Dyakonov and T. V. Domareva, *Zhur. Obshchei Khim.* **25**, 934 (1955).
88. I. A. Dyakonov and T. V. Domareva, *Zhur. Obshchei Khim.* **25**, 1486 (1955).
89. W. H. Urry and J. W. Wilt, *J. Am. Chem. Soc.* **76**, 2594 (1954).
90. I. A. Dyakonov and N. B. Vinogradova, *Zhur. Obshchei Khim.* **23**, 244 (1953).
91. I. A. Dyakonov and T. V. Domareva, *Zhur. Obshchei Khim.* **29**, 3098 (1959).
92. R. Huisgen, H. König, G. Binsch, and H. J. Sturm, *Angew. Chem.* **83**, 368 (1961).

# CHAPTER 7

# Ketocarbenes

REARRANGEMENT OF THE CARBON SKELETON is at most a side reaction in alkylcarbene chemistry (cf. Chapter 3). In contrast, the alkyls and aryls bonded to the carbonyl group of ketocarbenes migrate readily to the divalent carbon. While this phenomenon is not yet fully understood, it is also observed with other electron-deficient species, such as nitrenes. Frequently a single rearranged product is obtained from diazoketones, and a carbene intermediate is assumed only by analogy. Concerted mechanisms may adequately explain these products, and have indeed been proposed. In other cases the product pattern indicates a carbene intermediate with more or less certainty. It must be admitted that in large parts of this chapter the use of carbene terminology is justified by little more than the absence of contrary evidence.

## I. FORMATION OF KETOCARBENES

Diazoketones are decomposed by light, heat, and various catalysts. The nature of the products frequently depends on the decomposition procedure (cf. Section II). The relationship between structure and quantum yield in photolysis has been studied with a variety of diazo-ketones (1) (Table I). The quantum yields decrease with increasing polarization of the diazo group, i.e., with increasing contribution of resonance structure Ib [which may be estimated from the infrared (IR) spectra (2)].

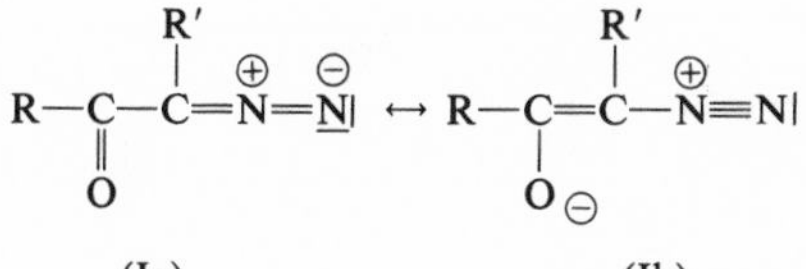

$$R-\underset{\underset{O}{\|}}{C}-\overset{\overset{R'}{|}}{C}=\overset{\oplus}{N}=\overset{\ominus}{\underline{N}|} \quad \leftrightarrow \quad R-\underset{\underset{\ominus}{O}}{\overset{\overset{R'}{|}}{C}}=\overset{\oplus}{C}-\overset{\oplus}{N}\equiv N|$$

$$\text{(Ia)} \qquad\qquad\qquad \text{(Ib)}$$

115

TABLE I

QUANTUM YIELDS OF DIAZOKETONE PHOTOLYSIS

(Irradiation in Methanol at the UV Absorption Maximum)

| Diazoketone | Quantum yield | Diazoketone | Quantum yield |
|---|---|---|---|
| $C_2H_5CO\!-\!CHN_2$ | 0.66 | $C_6H_5CO\!-\!CN_2\!-\!CO_2Me$ | 0.35 |
| 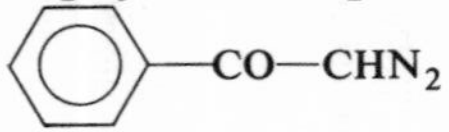 $CH_3$—〇—$CO\!-\!CHN_2$ | 0.46 | $(C_6H_5CO)_2CN_2$ | 0.31 |
| 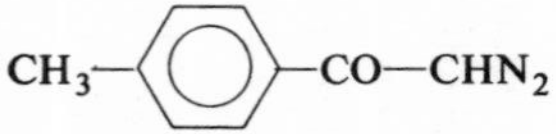 $Cl$—〇—$CO\!-\!CHN_2$ | 0.42 | 2-Diazo-1-indanone | 0.14 |
| 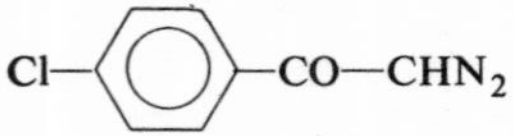 $C_6H_5$—〇—$CO\!-\!CHN_2$ | 0.41 | 2-Diazo-1-tetralone | 0.21 |
| 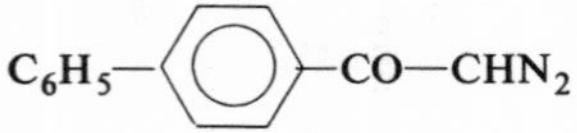 $C_6H_5CO$—〇—$CO\!-\!CHN_2$ | 0.27 | Diazocamphor | 0.24 |
| 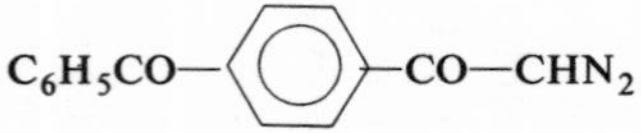 $CH_3SO_2$—〇—$CO\!-\!CHN_2$ | 0.28 | $N_2CHCO(CH_2)_4COCHN_2$ | 0.34 |
| 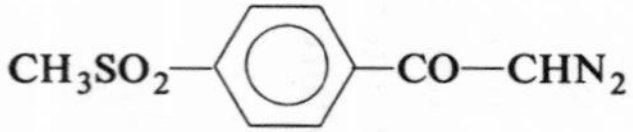 $O_2N$—〇—$CO\!-\!CHN_2$ | 0.29 | $N_2CH\!-\!CO\!-\!CO\!-\!CHN_2$ | 0.31 |
| 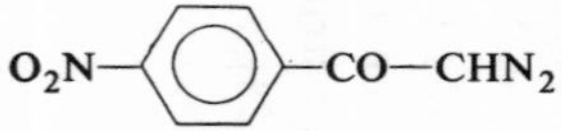  | 0.18 |  $N_2CH\!-\!CO$—〇—$CO\!-\!CHN_2$ | 0.15 |

Attempts to correlate the quantum yields ($\phi$) with the Hammett equation (*1a*) resulted in a satisfactory plot of log $\phi \cdot \epsilon$ versus $\sigma$, although its significance is somewhat uncertain. A recent study of solvent effects (*1b*) showed a notable lowering of $\phi$ in polar and hydroxylic media. The following values obtained in hexane may be compared to those of Table I: diazoacetophenone 0.55, *p*-CH$_3$ 0.62, *p*-Cl 0.62, *p*-NO$_2$ 0.31.

The reaction of acetylenes with nitrous oxide at high pressures and temperatures (*3*) probably proceeds by way of diazoketones and keto-carbenes:

$$R-C{\equiv}C-R + N_2O \rightarrow R-C{=\!=\!=}C-R \rightleftharpoons R-CO-CN_2-R$$

$$\xrightarrow{-N_2} R-CO-\underset{\cdot\cdot}{C}-R \rightarrow R_2C{=}C{=}O \tag{1}$$

The oxidation of acetylenes by peracids affords products which are also obtained by decomposition of related diazoketones (*4, 5*). Intervention of a ketocarbene therefore appears likely.

$$R-C{\equiv}C-CH_2R' \xrightarrow{CH_3CO_3H} R-CO-\underset{\cdot\cdot}{C}-CH_2R' \underset{+H_2O}{\overset{\nearrow R-CO-CH=CH-R'}{\searrow HO_2C-\underset{R}{\overset{|}{C}H}-CH_2R'}} \tag{2}$$

The $\alpha$-elimination of hydrogen halides from $\alpha$-haloketones is particularly interesting as a possible route to ketocarbenes. When treated with alkali, most $\alpha$-haloketones undergo the Favorskii rearrangement which is in many aspects similar to the rearrangement of diazoketones via keto-carbenes. Present evidence indicates, however, that the Favorskii reaction involves neither $\alpha$-elimination nor carbene intermediates (cf. Section II,A,1,*d*).

Reaction of the phosphorus ylide (II) with phenacyl bromide leads to III, IV, and V. It has been assumed that dibenzoylethylene (IV) and tribenzoylcyclopropane (V) arise by way of benzoylcarbene (*6*).

$$\overset{\oplus}{Ph_3P}-\overset{\ominus}{\underset{\cdot\cdot}{C}H}-CO-Ph + Ph-CO-CH_2Br \rightarrow \overset{\oplus}{Ph_3P}-CH_2CO-Ph \quad Br^{\ominus} \tag{3}$$

(II)                                                 (III) (95%)

$$+ Ph-CO-CH{=}CH-CO-Ph + Ph-CO-CH{\underset{\overset{\diagdown}{\underset{H}{C}}\diagup}{\phantom{xxxx}}}CH-CO-Ph$$

(IV) (50%)                               H     CO-Ph

(V) (7%)

The benzoylcarbene hypothesis appears improbable in view of recent work in phosphorus ylide chemistry (7). The following mechanism is in accord with pertinent facts in the literature (7–9):

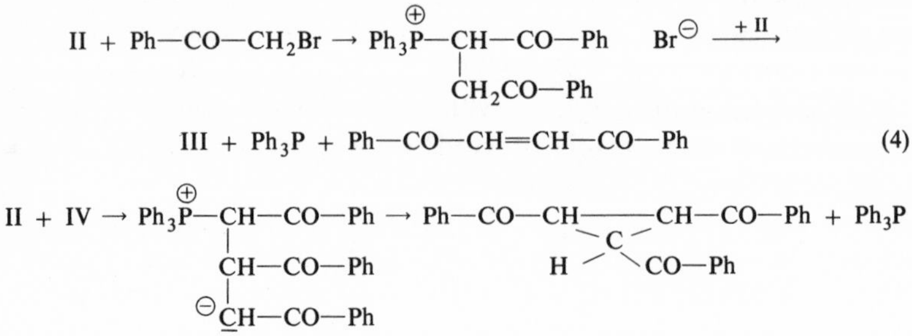

$$II + Ph—CO—CH_2Br \rightarrow \overset{\oplus}{Ph_3P}—\underset{\underset{CH_2CO—Ph}{|}}{CH}—CO—Ph \quad Br^{\ominus} \xrightarrow{+II}$$

$$III + Ph_3P + Ph—CO—CH{=}CH—CO—Ph \tag{4}$$

$$II + IV \rightarrow \overset{\oplus}{Ph_3P}—\underset{\underset{\underset{\ominus CH—CO—Ph}{|}}{CH—CO—Ph}}{\overset{|}{CH}}—CO—Ph \rightarrow Ph—CO—CH{\underset{H}{\overset{}{—}}}\underset{}{\overset{C}{{}}}{\underset{CO—Ph}{}}CH—CO—Ph + Ph_3P$$

## II. REACTIONS OF KETOCARBENES

## A. Intramolecular Reactions

### 1. Wolff Rearrangement

Because of its usefulness in converting acids to derivatives of the homologous acids (Arndt-Eistert synthesis), several reviews of the Wolff rearrangement have been published (10–14). Much special information may be obtained from these reviews which has not been incorporated in the present chapter.

When decomposing dicarbonyl diazo compounds in aqueous solution, L. Wolff (15) isolated products formed by rearrangement of the carbon skeleton. Later he realized that his reaction was analogous to the Curtius degradation of carbonyl azides. The products were rationalized by assuming a ketene intermediate (16).

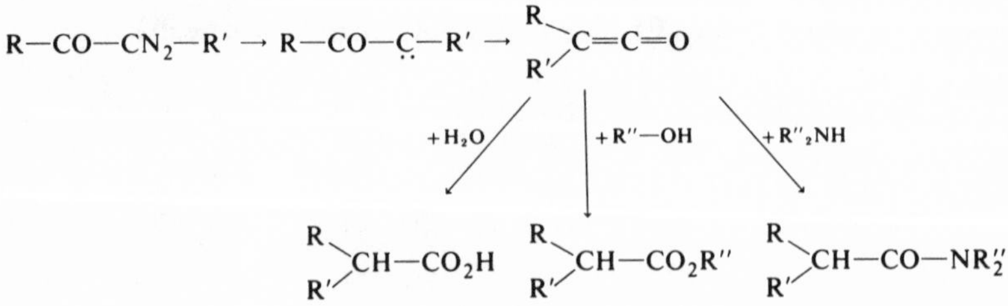

$$R—CO—CN_2—R' \rightarrow R—CO—\overset{..}{C}—R' \rightarrow \underset{R'}{\overset{R}{}}{C}{=}C{=}O$$

$$\underset{+H_2O}{\swarrow} \quad \underset{+R''—OH}{\downarrow} \quad \underset{+R''_2NH}{\searrow} \tag{5}$$

$$\underset{R'}{\overset{R}{}}CH—CO_2H \qquad \underset{R'}{\overset{R}{}}CH—CO_2R'' \qquad \underset{R'}{\overset{R}{}}CH—CO—NR''_2$$

This view was strongly supported by the preparation of diphenyl-ketene (*17*), and of other stable ketenes (*18, 19*), from diazoketones. Applications of the Wolff rearrangement were limited, however, until the efficient synthesis of diazoketones from acid chlorides and diazoalkanes was discovered (*20, 21*). Ready access to the starting materials prompted a first systematic study of the Wolff rearrangement (*22*), followed by numerous publications. The most relevant results are summarized in the subsequent paragraphs.

*a. Experimental Procedures. Pyrolysis:* Replacement of the diazo group without rearrangement may occur in protic solvents at moderate temperatures. Diazoacetone and diazoacetophenone were converted to the related ketols, $R-CO-CH_2OH$, by boiling water (*16*). Azibenzil (VI), in methanol at 50°, afforded 70% of methyl diphenylacetate (product of Wolff rearrangement) and 30% of benzoin methyl ether (*23*).

$$Ph-CO-CN_2-Ph + CH_3OH \xrightarrow{50°} Ph_2CH-CO_2CH_3 + Ph-CO-\underset{\underset{OCH_3}{|}}{CH}-Ph \qquad (6)$$

$$(VI)$$

Elevated temperatures favor the Wolff rearrangement. Diazoketones have been converted to acid anilides in refluxing aniline (*16, 22*), and to benzyl esters in refluxing benzyl alcohol (*24*). The latter method is recommended for diazoketones containing carbon-hydrogen bonds $\alpha$ to the diazo group, $R-CO-CN_2-CHR'_2$, in order to minimize the formation of unsaturated ketones (cf. Section 2).

*Photolysis:* UV irradiation of diazoketones in suitable solvents (dioxane–water, tetrahydrofuran–water, alcohols) affords rearranged products in good yields (*25, 26*). Photolysis was often successful when other methods failed, e.g., with VII (*27*) and VIII (*28*).

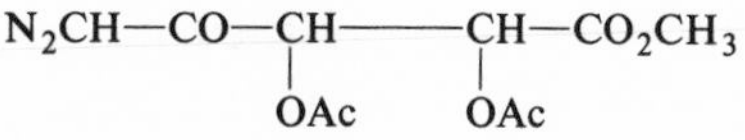

$$N_2CH-CO-\underset{\underset{OAc}{|}}{CH}\text{------}\underset{\underset{OAc}{|}}{CH}-CO_2CH_3$$

$$(VII)$$

$$N_2CH-CO-\overset{\phantom{x}}{\underset{\phantom{x}}{\bigcirc}}-SO_2-\overset{\phantom{x}}{\underset{\phantom{x}}{\bigcirc}}-COCHN_2$$

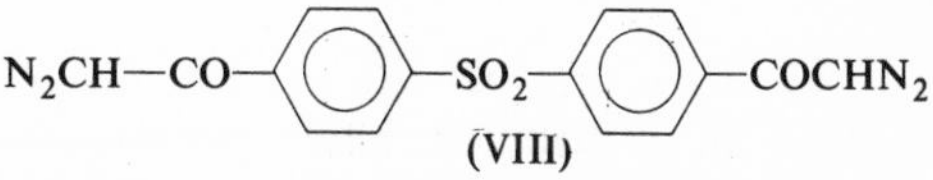

$$(VIII)$$

Light brought about the "normal" rearrangement of triphenyl-diazoacetone (IX) and related compounds, whereas "abnormal" products (X) resulted from pyrolysis (*29*).

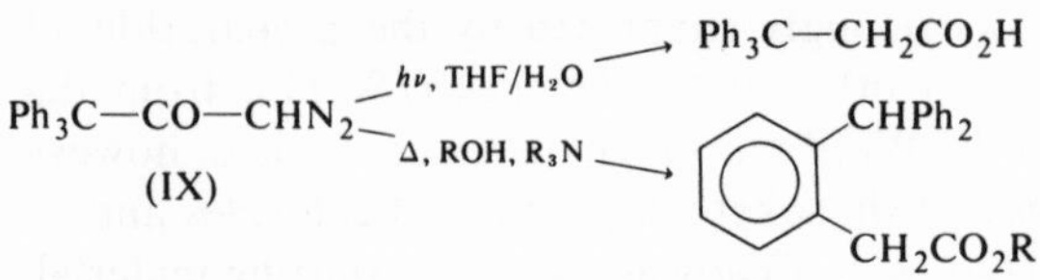

$$\text{Ph}_3\text{C—CO—CHN}_2 \xrightarrow[\Delta,\ \text{ROH},\ \text{R}_3\text{N}]{h\nu,\ \text{THF/H}_2\text{O}} \begin{array}{l} \text{Ph}_3\text{C—CH}_2\text{CO}_2\text{H} \\ \\ \end{array} \tag{7}$$

(IX)                                        (X)

with Ph$_3$C—CH$_2$CO$_2$H, and ring structure bearing CHPh$_2$ and CH$_2$CO$_2$R substituents (X).

Photolysis is the only suitable method for the synthesis of strained bicyclic systems from diazoketones. Thus diazocamphor (30–32) and diazonorcamphor (33) afforded bicyclo[2.1.1]hexane derivatives (XI) by ring contraction. Similarly, benzocyclobutene derivatives (XII) have been prepared from diazoindanones (34–36).

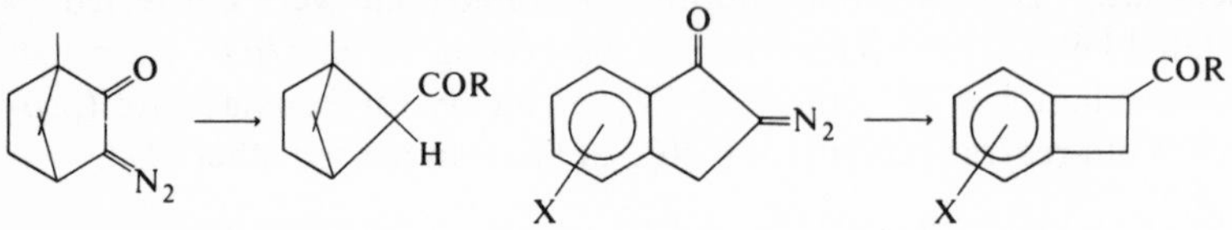

$$\tag{8}$$

(XI)                                                    (XII)

(R = OH, OR, NR$_2$)

*Catalysis:* The accelerating effect of silver salts on the decomposition of diazoketones had already been noticed by Wolff (16). By means of silver catalysts, "pyrolyses" of diazoketones may be conducted at moderate temperatures. The following compositions were found particularly useful:

Dioxane–water–Ag$^{\oplus}$–ammonia, for converting diazoketones to the amides of the homologous acids (22) (the yields of amides are frequently better than those of the free acids).

Dioxane–water–Ag$^{\oplus}$–thiosulfate, for converting diazoketones to the homologous acids.

Alcohol–silver oxide (22), alcohol–silver benzoate–triethylamine (37), and alcohol–cuprous iodide–acetonitril (38), for converting diazoketones to esters of the homologous acids.

The active form of the catalyst—whether silver ion in complex coordination, or colloidal silver produced by reduction—is not known. Silver powder is without effect. Copper powder and most copper salts catalyze the decomposition of diazoketones but lead to intermolecular reactions (cf. Section II, B) rather than to the Wolff rearrangement. Cuprous iodide is an exception to this rule (38), and a few cases of rearrangement by cupric oxide have been reported (39, 40).

*b. Scope and Limitations.* The presence of further functional groups within the diazoketone molecule may lead to side reactions and restrict the application of the Wolff rearrangement. Simultaneous elimination of hydrogen halide has been observed with $\alpha$-halodiazoketones (*41*), e.g.,

$$Cl_3C—CCl_2—CO—CHN_2 \rightarrow Cl_3C—CCl{=}CH—CO_2H \qquad (9)$$

Halogen in a more remote position does not interfere (*42*). 3,3,3-Trifluoro- and 3,3,3-trichloro-1-diazo-2-propanone have been rearranged with 40 and 74% yields, respectively, of the esters $CX_3CH_2CO_2Et$ (*43*). Fluorinated diazoketones of the structure $CF_3(CF_2)_x(CH_2)_nCOCHN_2$ fail to undergo the Wolff reaction unless $n \geq 2$ (*44*).

Multiple bonds not conjugated to the carbonyl group have little effect on the diazoketone rearrangement (*45*). The conversion, in several steps, of dehydroepiandrosterone (XIII) to D-norprogesterone (XIV) (*46*) is a recent example.

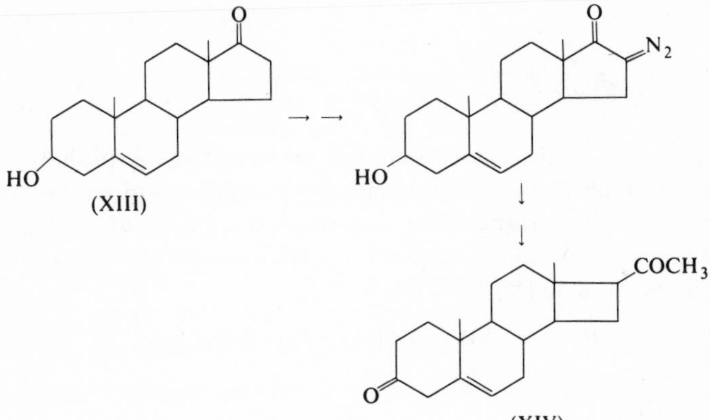

(XIII)                                                           (10)

(XIV)

D-Norsteroids have also been synthesized from 16-diazoandrostan-3$\beta$-ol-17-one (*46, 46a*) and 16-diazoestrone methyl ether (*46b*). An $A$-noroleanone derivative was prepared by means of the Wolff rearrangement (*46c*).

With $\alpha, \beta$-unsaturated compounds, the attempted synthesis of diazoketones from acid chlorides proceeds with simultaneous addition of diazomethane to the polar double bond (*45*). Treatment of these products according to the usual procedure may lead to unexpected results, as illustrated by the sequence in Eq. (11), starting from triacetylshikimic acid chloride (XV) (*47*).

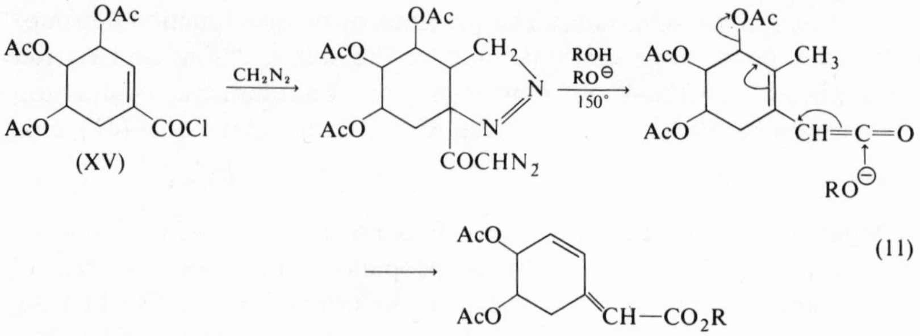

(11)

4-Phenyl-1-diazo-3-buten-2-one (XVI), which in contrast to previous claims (45) is not accessible from cinnamoyl chloride, was prepared from the related oxime and chloroamine. On photolysis, XVI afforded the normal Wolff product (XVII) (48).

$$Ph-CH=CH-CO-CH=NOH \xrightarrow[HO^{\ominus}]{NH_2Cl} Ph-CH=CH-CO-CHN_2$$
$$\text{(XVI)} \tag{12}$$

$$\xrightarrow[H_2O]{h\nu} Ph-CH=CH-CH_2-CO_2H$$
$$\text{(XVII)}$$

The Arndt-Eistert synthesis has been applied to convert $N$-phthalyl-$\alpha$-amino acids to $N$-phthalyl-$\beta$-amino acids (49). Addition of $\alpha$-amino esters during the Wolff rearrangement resulted in the formation of peptides (50). Similarly, the $\gamma$-glutamyl peptide XIX was obtained from $N$-trifluoroacetylaspartic acid (XVIII) (51):

$$RO_2C-CH-CH_2-CO-CHN_2 + H_2N-CH-CH_2CH_2-CO_2R$$
$$\quad\quad | \quad\quad\quad\quad\quad\quad\quad\quad\quad\quad\quad | $$
$$\quad NH-COCF_3 \quad\quad\quad\quad\quad\quad CO_2R$$
$$\text{(XVIII)} \tag{13}$$

$$\xrightarrow[Ag_2O]{} RO_2C-CH-CH_2CH_2-CO-NH-CH-CH_2CH_2-CO_2R$$
$$\quad\quad\quad\quad | \quad\quad\quad\quad\quad\quad\quad\quad\quad\quad\quad\quad | $$
$$\quad\quad NH-COCF_3 \quad\quad\quad\quad\quad\quad CO_2R$$
$$\text{(XIX)}$$

The ring contraction of cyclic diazoketones has already been mentioned. This reaction has been extended without difficulty to small rings ($n$ = 4,5) (30–36, 46) and to medium-sized rings ($n$ = 8–10) (52). The synthesis of the [8]paracyclophane ring system by a ring contraction via the photolysis of an diazoketone has been described (52a). Unsaturated cyclic diazoketones, so-called "quinonediazides" or "diazooxides" (e.g., XX), have received much attention. The formation of azo dyes (e.g.,

XXII) from these compounds, on photolysis under suitable conditions, is utilized in photo printing processes. XXII results from XX by coupling of unchanged XX with the product of Wolff rearrangement, XXI (53, 54).

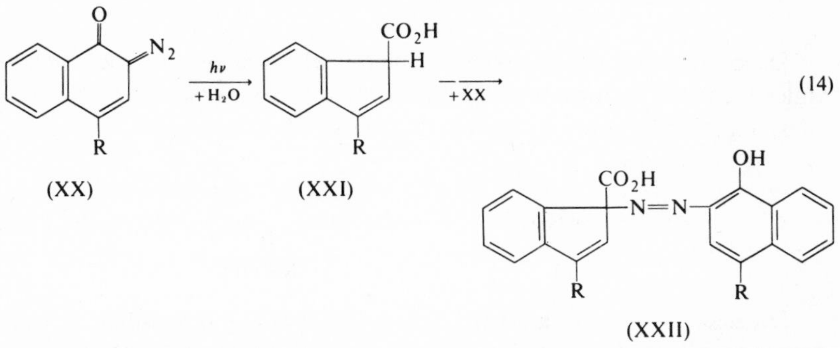

(14)

The reaction, Eq. (14), has been applied in the synthesis of numerous polycyclic and heterocyclic compounds (55–59). Control of the pH is essential to avoid excessive azo coupling. On the other hand, replacement of the diazo group by hydroxyl, without ring contraction, may occur in acidic solution (60, 61). The rearrangement of 3-diazo-2-pyridone (XXIII) is unique as it proceeds with migration of a nitrogen function. Such reactions have not been observed with acyclic diazo amides.

The photolysis of quinonediazides derived from (substituted) indanes offers access to partially hydrogenated derivatives of pentalene, e.g., XXIV (57, 62).

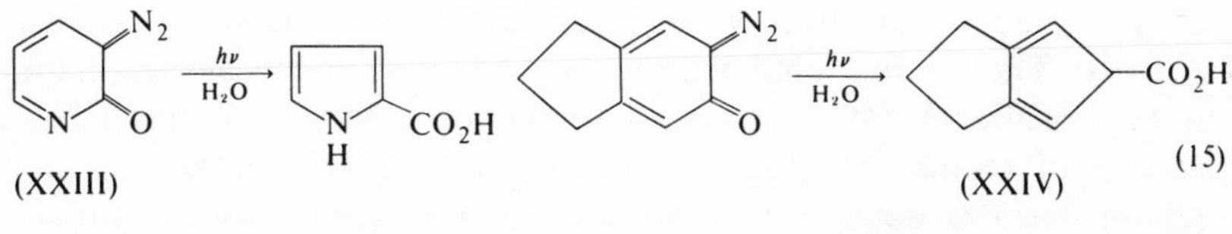

(15)

c. Mechanism of the Wolff Rearrangement. Ketenes are now generally regarded as the primary products of the Wolff rearrangement, although occasionally mechanisms have been proposed which involve an attack of nucleophiles (water, alcohols, amines) before rearrangement (11). Unstable ketenes have been trapped by addition to azomethines, with formation of $\beta$-lactams (63), or by addition to azo compounds (64).

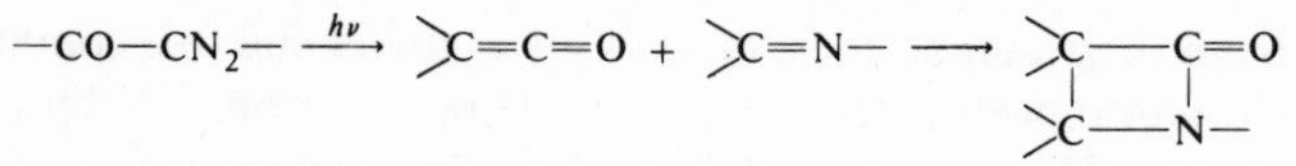

$$-CO-CN_2- \xrightarrow{h\nu} \Big>C{=}C{=}O \;+\; \Big>C{=}N- \;\longrightarrow\; \begin{matrix} \Big>C{-\!-}C{=}O \\ | \qquad | \\ \Big>C{-\!-}N- \end{matrix} \qquad (16)$$

$$-CO-CN_2- \xrightarrow{h\nu} \Big>C{=}C{=}O \;+\; -N{=}N- \;\longrightarrow\; \begin{matrix} \Big>C{-\!-}C{=}O \\ | \qquad | \\ -N{-\!-}N- \end{matrix} \qquad (17)$$

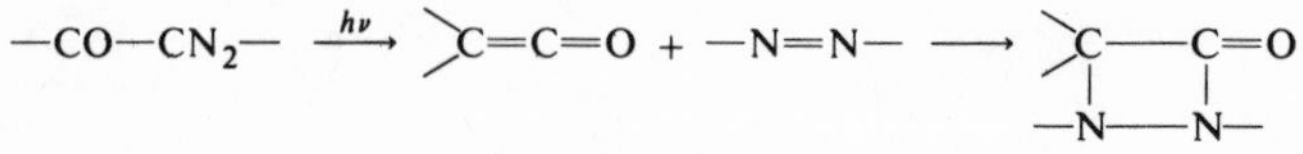

Decomposition of diazoketones in the absence of suitable nucleophiles leads to the formation of unsaturated lactones (so-called butenolides), e.g., XXVI from 3,3-dimethyl-1-diazo-2-butanone (XXV) (65):

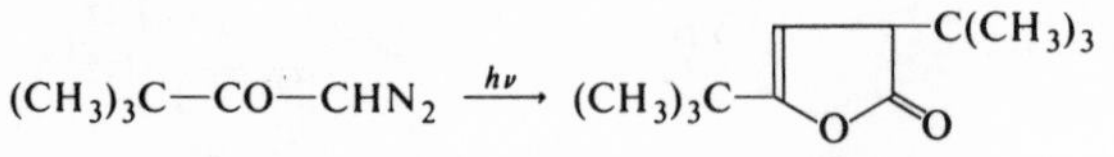

$$(CH_3)_3C-CO-CHN_2 \xrightarrow{h\nu} (CH_3)_3C{-}\!\!\underset{O}{\overset{\displaystyle\frown}{\bigcirc}}\!\!\overset{C(CH_3)_3}{\underset{O}{\phantom{X}}} \qquad (18)$$

(XXV)                      (XXVI)

Diazoacetophenone afforded the corresponding butenolide XXVII only in small yield, the major product was a "dimer" (XXVIII) derived from XXVII by oxidation (66):

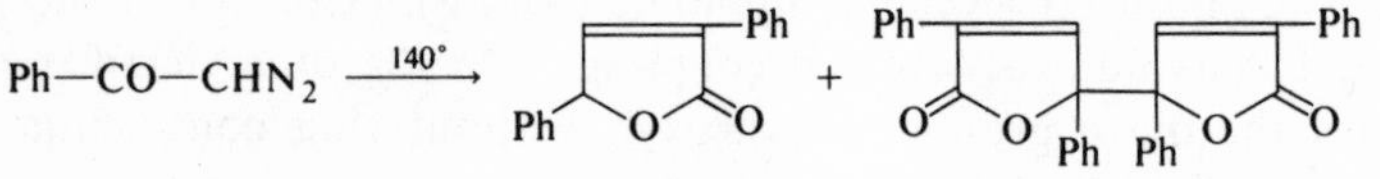

$$Ph-CO-CHN_2 \xrightarrow{140°} \quad + \quad \qquad (19)$$

(XXVII) (4%)              (XXVIII) (24%)

The butenolides contain a rearranged and an unrearranged fragment of the original diazoketone; they might arise from a ketocarbene and a ketene by 1,3-dipolar addition (cf. Section II, B,6) (67). The actual path of formation, however, is probably attack of the ketene on unchanged diazoketone. These reactants were shown to give butenolides with ease, even at room temperature (68).

Quinonediazides afford ketene acetals on decomposition in inert solvents. The product obtained by pyrolysis of both 1,2- and 2,1-naphthoquinonediazide (69) was assigned structure XXIX (70), and a large number of related compounds were prepared (71). If ketenes and quinonediazides were brought together at low temperatures, adducts still containing nitrogen were produced which on heating lost nitrogen with formation of ketene acetals (72).

Although the Wolff reaction may lead to a variety of final products, all of them can be derived from the intermediate ketene. The following discussion is concerned, therefore, with the rearrangement step producing the ketene. Information concerning the nature of the migrating

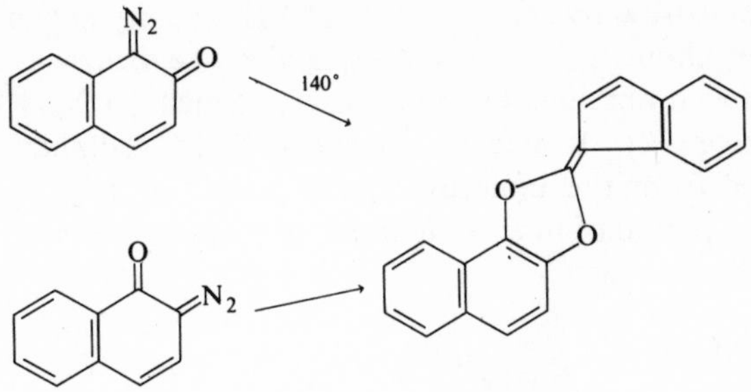

(20)

(XXIX)

group has been gathered from studies on optically active diazoketones, with the asymmetric center adjacent to the carbonyl group (73–77). Rearrangement was found to proceed with predominant or complete retention of configuration. The degree of retention depended somewhat on the experimental procedure. Some typical results are recorded in Table II (77).

TABLE II
STERIC COURSE OF THE WOLFF REARRANGEMENT

$$Ph—CH_2—\overset{*}{C}H—CO—CHN_2 \rightarrow Ph—CH_2—\overset{*}{C}H—CH_2CO_2H$$
$$\underset{CH_3}{|} \qquad\qquad\qquad \underset{CH_3}{|}$$

| Experimental procedure | Retention (%) |
|---|---|
| Dioxane–water–Ag$^+$–thiosulfate | 72 |
| Methanol–silver oxide | 78 |
| Methanol–silver benzoate–triethylamine | 90 |
| Methanol–UV light | 81 |

Retention of configuration has been confirmed with the geometrical isomers of 2-phenylcyclohexanecarboxylic acid (XXX and XXXI) (78) which were converted to the homologous acids by Arndt-Eistert synthesis. Degradation of these acids by the Barbier-Wieland procedure afforded pure XXX and XXXI, respectively.

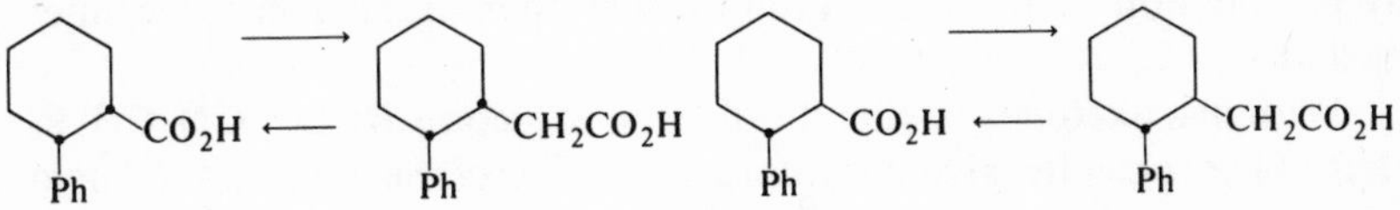

(XXX)  (XXXI)  (21)

In the optically active diazoketone **XXXII**, activity depends on hindered rotation about the axis connecting the two benzene rings. The homologous acid obtained by Wolff rearrangement of **XXXII** was also optically active (79). It may be concluded that the diphenyl system is not separated from the molecule in the course of rearrangement—at least not for a period of time comparable to that required for rotation.

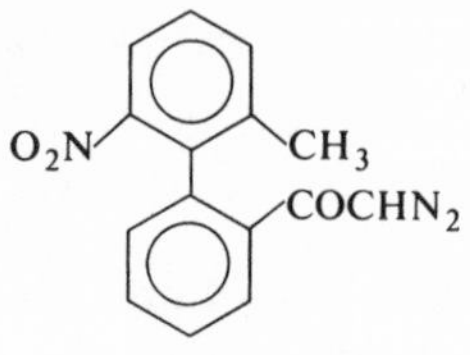

(XXXII)

If applied to benzoic acid-1-$C^{13}$ the Arndt-Eistert synthesis led to quantitative incorporation of the $C^{13}$-label in the carboxyl group of the resulting phenylacetic acid (80). A similar study has been made with $C^{14}$-labeled azibenzil to demonstrate the absence of an acetylene oxide, or other symmetrical intermediate, in the rearrangement (81).

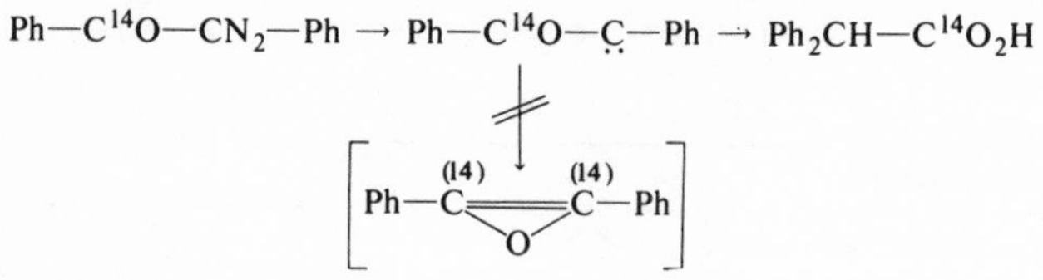

$$Ph-C^{14}O-CN_2-Ph \rightarrow Ph-C^{14}O-\underset{\cdot\cdot}{C}-Ph \rightarrow Ph_2CH-C^{14}O_2H$$

(22)

Little evidence is available concerning the intermediacy of keto-carbenes in the Wolff rearrangement. Loss of nitrogen from the diazoketone and migration of the alkyl or aryl group may well be considered as concerted processes. The trapping of ketocarbenes by 1,3-dipolar addition to multiple bonds is restricted to special cases (82) (cf. Section II,B,6). Unrearranged products, ketols and ketol ethers, are often obtained from diazoketones by reaction with water and alcohols (cf. Section II,B,5). The ketol derivatives, however, are most probably formed by protonation of the diazo group rather than from a carbene intermediate.

With diazoketones having the general structure $RCO-CN_2CH_2R'$, shift of hydrogen [to give unsaturated ketones (cf. Section II,A,2)] competes with rearrangement. The two products were obtained in nearly the same quantities whether the decomposition was effected by light or by catalysts. The constant product ratio is a good argument in favor of a common ketocarbene intermediate (83).

   d. *Mechanism of the Favorskii Reaction* (84–86). The rearrangement of α-haloketones discovered by Favorskii (87) [Eq. (23)], bears, at first sight, a close resemblance to the Wolff rearrangement. Evidence against a ketocarbene mechanism of the Favorskii reaction is therefore briefly summarized.

$$R-CO-\overset{|}{\underset{|}{C}}-Cl + R'O^{\ominus} \rightarrow R'O-CO-\overset{|}{\underset{|}{C}}-R + Cl^{\ominus} \tag{23}$$

   Rearrangement of α-haloketones having no α-hydrogen is easily achieved. Obviously, α-elimination to give a ketocarbene requires such hydrogen. 2-Chlorocyclohexanone-2-$C^{14}$ afforded cyclopentanecarboxylic acid which contained equal amounts of the $C^{14}$-label in the 1- and 2-positions (88). This observation requires a symmetrical intermediate such as the cyclopropanone XXXIII which most probably arises by intramolecular displacement of chloride ion. α-Elimination of hydrogen chloride, followed by Wolff rearrangement, should lead to cyclopentane-carboxylic acid-1-$C^{14}$ exclusively.

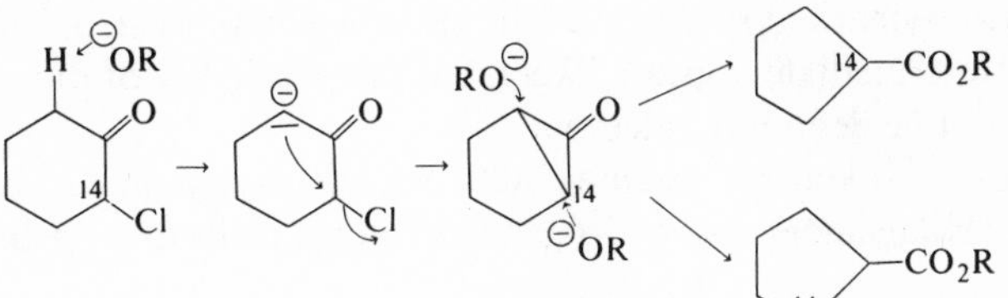

$$\tag{24}$$

   The Favorskii reaction of some haloketones which do not contain hydrogen in either of the α-positions has been explained by a mechanism which resembles that of the benzilic acid rearrangement (89):

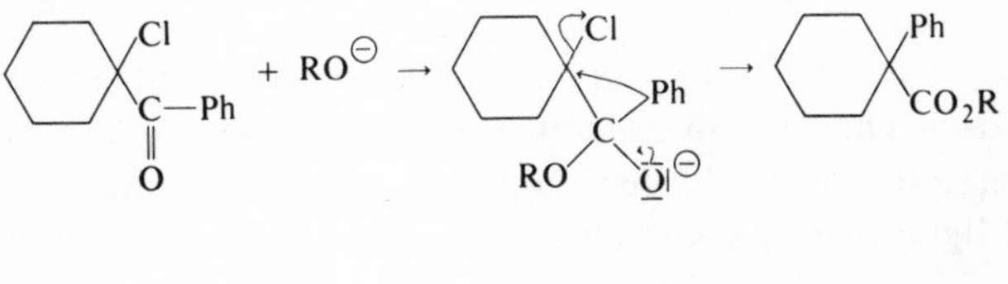

$$\tag{25}$$

### 2. Hydrogen and Alkyl Shift

Ketocarbenes containing carbon-hydrogen bonds adjacent to the divalent carbon may undergo shift of hydrogen with formation of $\alpha,\beta$-unsaturated ketones:

$$-\overset{\overset{\displaystyle H}{|}}{\underset{|}{C}}-\ddot{C}-CO-R \rightarrow \ >C=\overset{\overset{\displaystyle H}{|}}{C}-CO-R \qquad (26)$$

Decomposition of benzoyldiazoethane (**XXXIV**) in the presence of aniline afforded $\beta$-anilinopropiophenone (**XXXV**) instead of the expected rearranged product (90). Phenyl vinyl ketone, produced by hydrogen shift, may well be an intermediate in this reaction:

$$Ph-CO-CN_2-CH_3 \rightarrow Ph-CO-CH=CH_2 \xrightarrow{+PhNH_2} Ph-COCH_2CH_2NH-Ph$$

$$\text{(XXXIV)} \hspace{5cm} \text{(XXXV)} \qquad (27)$$

The hydrogen shift was thoroughly studied by Franzen (83) with a variety of suitable diazoketones. According to his observations, shift of hydrogen predominates at low temperatures whereas the Wolff rearrangement is favored by elevated temperatures. At a given temperature the product ratio is fairly independent of the mode of decomposition, whether by light or silver oxide catalyst.

Unsaturated ketones are also formed by peracid oxidation of disubstituted acetylenes (5). Since Wolff rearrangement also occurs, a ketocarbene intermediate appears likely, but the possibility of direct $\alpha$-oxidation cannot be definitely ruled out.

1,3-Bisdiazoketones, such as **XXXVI**, display some combination of Wolff rearrangement and hydrogen shift which leads to $\alpha, \beta$-unsaturated acids (91):

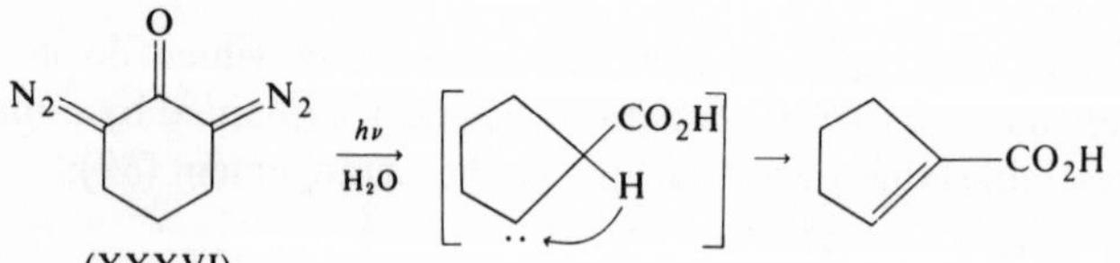

In rare cases, methyl groups may take the place of hydrogen in reaction (26). Thus the diazoketone **XXXVII** does not contain suitable hydrogen, and the Wolff rearrangement appears to be sterically hindered. Migration of a methyl group was shown to predominate (92).

$$(CH_3)_3C—CN_2CO—C(CH_3)_3 \xrightarrow{h\nu} (CH_3)_2C=\overset{\overset{\displaystyle CH_3}{|}}{C}—CO—C(CH_3)_3$$

(XXXVII)                    (80–90%)                    (29)

$$+ \ CH_2=\overset{\overset{\displaystyle CH_3}{|}}{\underset{\underset{\displaystyle CH_3}{|}}{C}}—CH—CO—C(CH_3)_3 \ + \ [(CH_3)_3C]_2C=C=O$$

(1–5%)                    (0–3%)

The bicyclic diazoketone **XXXVIII** undergoes a unique methyl shift with formation of a cyclopropane ring rather than a double bond (*93*):

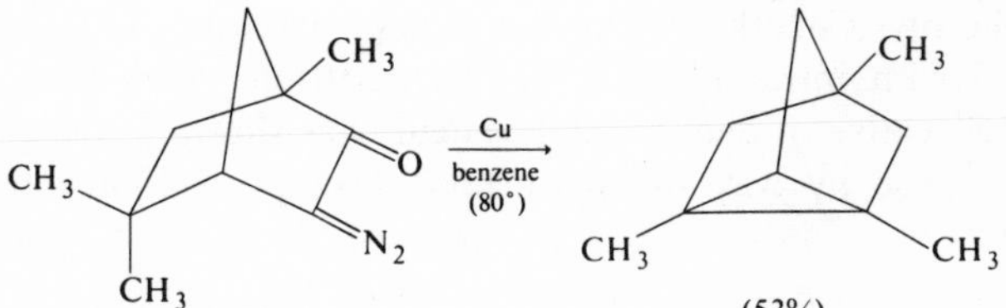

(30)

(53%)

(XXXVIII)

### 3. Intramolecular Insertion

Pyrolysis of diazocamphor leads to intramolecular insertion of the divalent carbon into neighboring carbon-hydrogen bonds [Eq. (31)]. The Wolff rearrangement predominates in the photolysis of diazocamphor, reaction (31) occurring to only a minor extent. The tricyclic structure **XXXIX** of the product was established by Bredt and Holz (*94*).

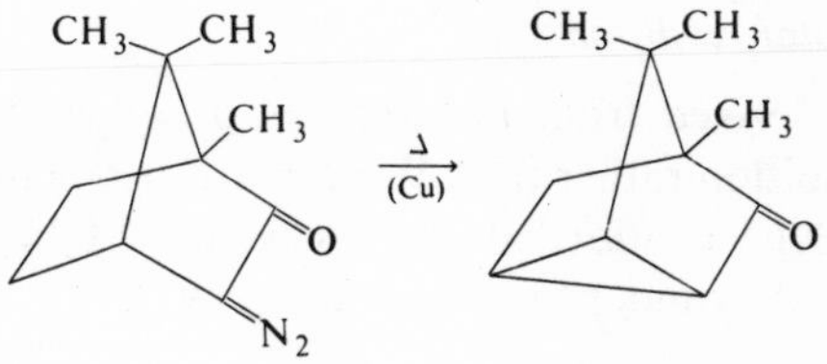

(31)

(XXXIX)

Intramolecular insertion has also been reported with *o-tert*-butyl-diazoacetophenone (**XL**) (*95*). In a nonpolar solvent, benzene, C—H insertion occurred with formation of **XLI**, whereas a small amount of apparent C—C insertion was observed in dimethyl sulfoxide.  A dipolar transition state has been proposed for the latter reaction.

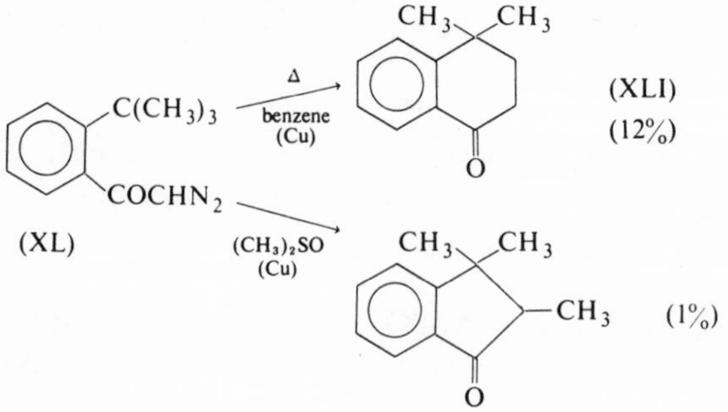

$$
\begin{array}{c}
\text{(XL)} \xrightarrow[\text{benzene}]{\Delta\ (Cu)} \text{(XLI)} \quad (12\%) \\[2mm]
\xrightarrow[\text{(CH}_3)_2\text{SO}]{(Cu)} \quad (1\%)
\end{array}
\tag{32}
$$

The photolysis of ethyl trichloroacetyldiazoacetate (XLII) was found to proceed with intramolecular C—Cl insertion.  The final product, XLIV, a derivative of dichloromaleic acid, was shown by means of $C^{14}$-labeling to arise by way of an unstable cyclopropanone intermediate (XLIII) (96).

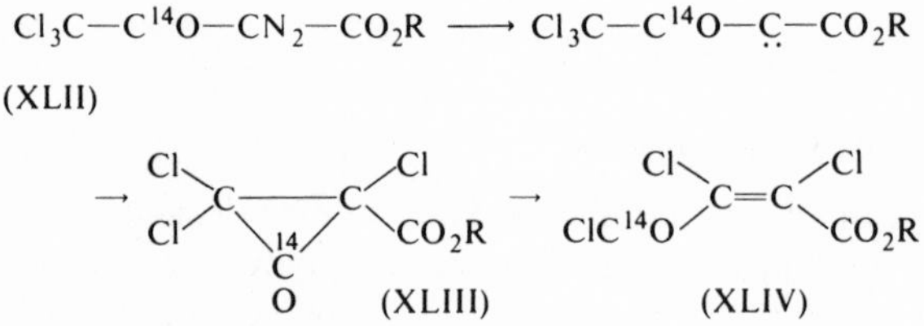

$$
Cl_3C-C^{14}O-CN_2-CO_2R \longrightarrow Cl_3C-C^{14}O-\underset{\cdot\cdot}{C}-CO_2R
$$

(XLII)

$$
\longrightarrow \underset{Cl}{\overset{Cl}{\diagdown}}C-\underset{\underset{O}{\overset{14}{C}}}{C}\overset{Cl}{\underset{CO_2R}{\diagup}} \longrightarrow \underset{ClC^{14}O}{\overset{Cl}{\diagdown}}C=C\overset{Cl}{\underset{CO_2R}{\diagup}}
\tag{33}
$$

(XLIII)                         (XLIV)

In contrast to XLII, ethyl trichloroacryloyldiazoacetate has been photolyzed to give products of the Wolff rearrangement (96a).

### 4. Intramolecular Addition

Ketocarbenes derived from unsaturated diazoketones may undergo intramolecular addition rather than Wolff rearrangement.  Thus 1-diazo-6-hepten-2-one (XLV) afforded the bicyclo[4.1.0]heptanone XLVI, which was identified by independent synthesis (97).

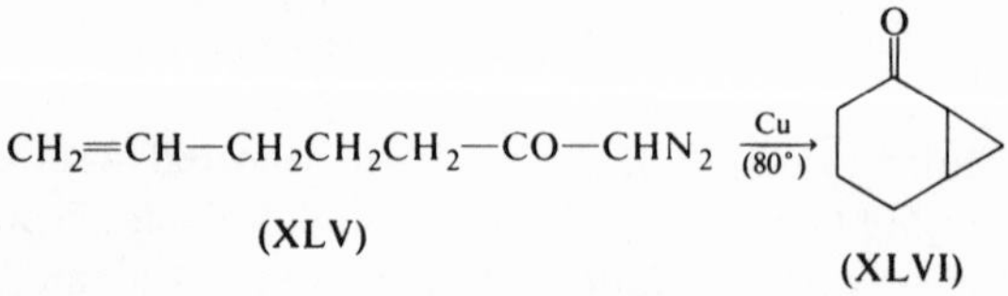

$$
CH_2=CH-CH_2CH_2CH_2-CO-CHN_2 \xrightarrow[(80°)]{Cu}
\tag{34}
$$

(XLV)                                        (XLVI)

The diazoketone XLVII, accessible from cycloheptatriene-7-carboxylic acid, has been converted to the tricyclic ketone XLVIII (98). The particularly fast internal Cope rearrangement of XLVIII produces a unique N.M.R. spectrum which reveals only three sets of equivalent protons.

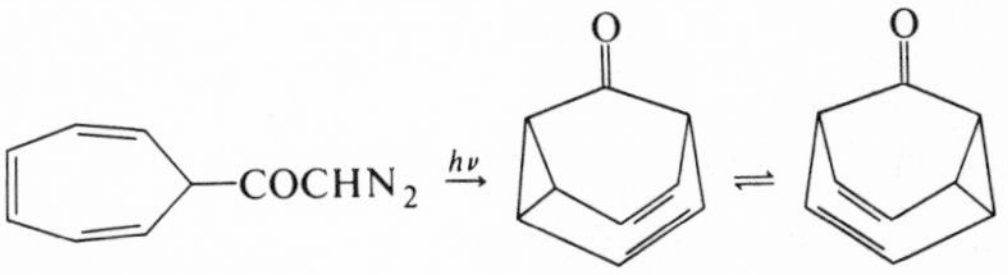

$$\text{(XLVII)} \xrightarrow{h\nu} \text{(XLVIII)} \rightleftharpoons \qquad\qquad (35)$$

## B. Intermolecular Reactions

Many diazoketones which undergo Wolff rearrangement on photolysis or pyrolysis may be utilized for intermolecular reactions if decomposed in the presence of copper powder or cupric (cuprous) halides. Aside from this catalytic effect, frequently ascribed to "deactivation" of the intermediate involved, there are some ketocarbenes which react exclusively in an intramolecular fashion. Among these, the carbene derived from ethyl trifluoroacetyldiazoacetate (IL) (99, 100), $CF_3CO$ —C—$CO_2Et$, and some carbenes derived from quinonediazides (82, 101–103), are eminent.

### 1. Formation of Dimers

Diazoketones have been converted to diacylethylenes by treatment with cupric oxide in inert solvents such as benzene, toluene, or ligroin (104, 105). The diacylethylenes are formally [53] dimers of the ketocarbenes, but probably arise by attack of the ketocarbene (in coordination with the catalyst) on excess diazoketone.

$$2\,R\text{—}CO\text{—}CHN_2 \xrightarrow{CuO} R\text{—}CO\text{—}CH\text{=}CH\text{—}CO\text{—}R \qquad (36)$$

Diazoketoesters of the general structure $N_2CH\text{—}CO(CH_2)_nCO_2R$ afforded "dimers" in satisfactory yield if $n \geq 2$ (106, 107). Similarly, yields were low with o-carboethoxy-diazoacetophenone, but increased considerably with the m- and p-isomers (108). Mixtures of diazoketones produced the symmetrical and unsymmetrical "dimers." If an easily accessible diazoketone was used in excess, only two "dimers" were obtained and separation was improved (*109*).   Unsymmetrical "dimers" derived from diazoketones and diazoesters were also prepared (*110*).

$$R—COCHN_2 + CH_3COCHN_2 \rightarrow R—COCH=CHCO—CH_3$$

$$\text{(excess)} \qquad\qquad\qquad + CH_3COCH=CHCO—CH_3$$

$$(37)$$

$$+ RO_2C—CHN_2 \rightarrow R—COCH=CH—CO_2R$$

$$+ RO_2C—CH=CH—CO_2R$$

### 2. Reaction with Carbon-Hydrogen Bonds

Trifluoroacetyl-carboethoxycarbene is exceptional among the keto-carbenes in its ability to insert into carbon-hydrogen bonds of saturated hydrocarbons, e.g., cyclohexane [Eq. (38)] (*99*). Insertion into the allylic methylene groups competes with the addition to the double bond of cyclohexene [Eq. (40)] (*100*). Reaction with carbon-hydrogen bonds of benzene (*99*), toluene, xylene, chlorobenzene, and bromobenzene (*100*) was also observed. In the latter cases, substitution occurred in the *o*- and *p*-positions, without attack on the aromatic nucleus (with ring expansion) and the side chain.

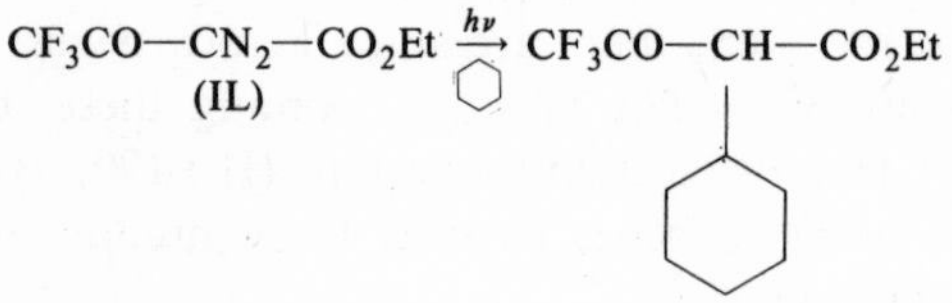

$$CF_3CO—CN_2—CO_2Et \xrightarrow{h\nu} CF_3CO—CH—CO_2Et \quad (26\%) \qquad (38)$$
$$\text{(IL)}$$

Irradiation of IL in alcohols produced ethyl trifluoroacetoacetate, with simultaneous dehydrogenation of the alcohol to an aldehyde or ketone (*99*).

### 3. Addition to Olefins

Acetylcarbene, generated by copper-catalyzed decomposition of diazoacetone, added easily to olefins such as styrene, cyclohexene, cyclopentene (*111*). The presence of acetoxy groups (vinyl acetates) did not interfere with this reaction. Addition was also observed with dihydropyran and benzofuran, whereas pyrroles, indoles, and thiophenes underwent substitution (see following paragraph).

$$R—CO—CHN_2' + {>}C=C{<} \xrightarrow{Cu} {>}C{\underset{{>}C{<}}{\phantom{-}}}CH—CO—R \qquad (39)$$

Benzoylcarbene (*112*) and *p*-phenylbenzoylcarbene (*113*) were found to react with olefins even in the uncatalyzed pyrolysis of the related diazoketones, but the yields were considerably improved by the presence of copper powder.

Photolysis of ethyl trifluoroacetyldiazoacetate (IL) in the presence of cyclohexene afforded two stereoisomers of the norcarane L, in addition to the insertion product LI (*100*).

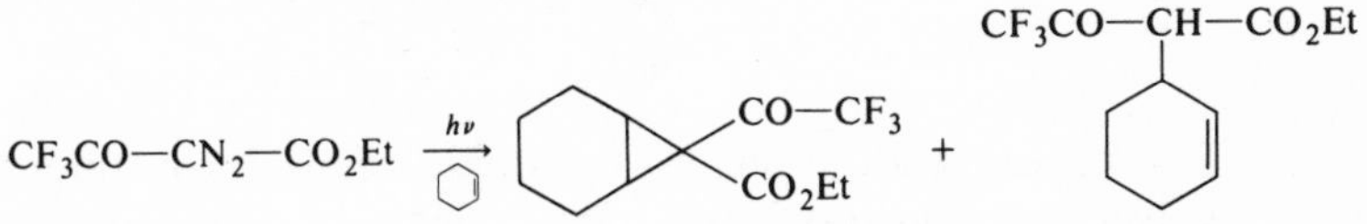

$CF_3CO—CN_2—CO_2Et$
hν
CO—$CF_3$
$CO_2Et$
+
$CF_3CO—CH—CO_2Et$

(IL) (L) (LI) (40)

## 4. *Reactions with Aromatic and Heterocyclic Compounds*

The substitution of benzene derivatives by trifluoroacetylcarboethoxycarbene, derived from IL, has been mentioned in Section II,B,2. Acetylcarbene from the copper-catalyzed pyrolysis of diazoacetone attacks anisole in low yield, but does not react with benzene (*111*). On the other hand, ring expansion as well as substitution by benzoylcarbene and acetylcarbene have been observed in the indan series (*114*).

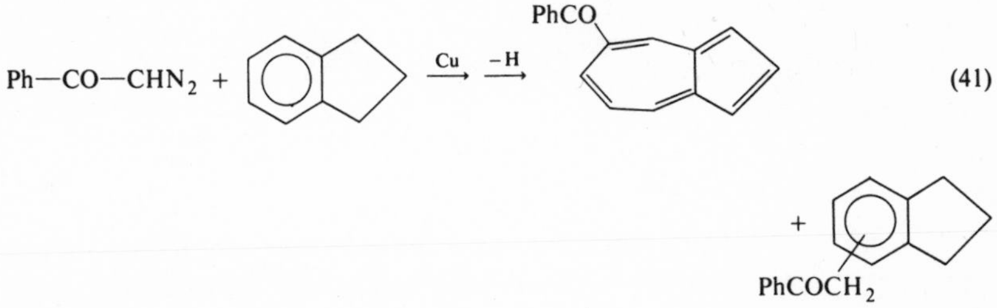

Ph—CO—$CHN_2$ +
Cu
-H
PhCO
+
$PhCOCH_2$

(41)

Acetylcarbene attacks *N*-methylpyrrole (*115*) and thiophene (*111*) in the 2-position whereas indole affords a 3-acetonyl derivative (*111*). Similar results have been obtained with diazoketones of the general structure $N_2CH—CO(CH_2)_nCO_2R$ ($n$ = 0–2) in the presence of copper (*116*). In the absence of a catalyst the reaction proceeds with Wolff rearrangement and acylation of the pyrrole by the resulting ketene (*117*).

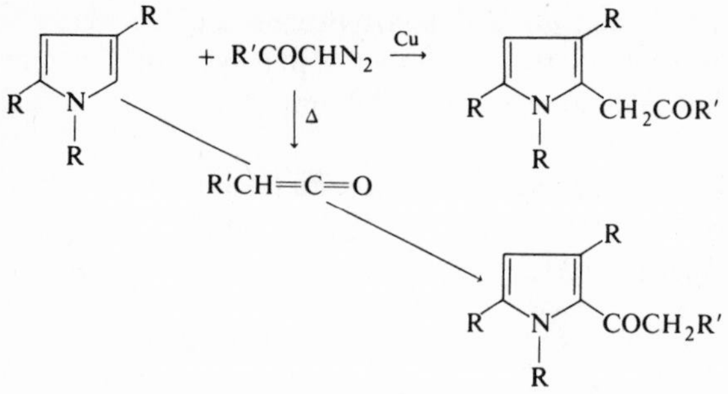

$$(42)$$

The attack of ketocarbenes, produced by copper catalysis, on furan derivatives involves ring cleavage to give unsaturated diketones or keto-aldehydes ($118$):

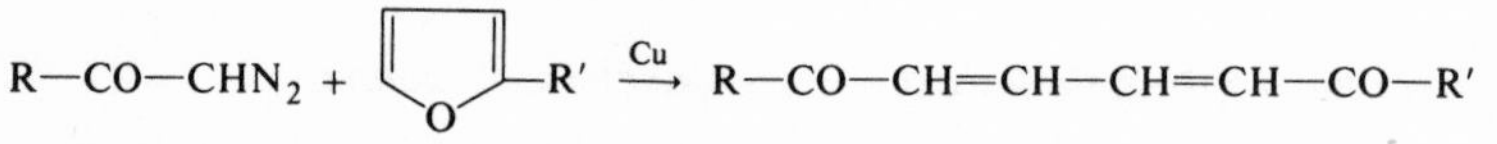

$$R—CO—CHN_2 + \underset{O}{\boxed{\phantom{O}}}-R' \xrightarrow{Cu} R—CO—CH=CH—CH=CH—CO—R' \quad (43)$$

In contrast to the ketocarbenes derived from $o$-quinonediazides, the intermediates derived from $p$-quinonediazides are incapable of rearrangement. Irradiation of $p$-quinonediazides in benzene, benzene derivatives, and pyridine afforded $p$-hydroxydiphenyls and $p$-hydroxyphenylpyridine, respectively ($101$). Products of high molecular weight, probably having a polyphenyl ether composition, were also formed.

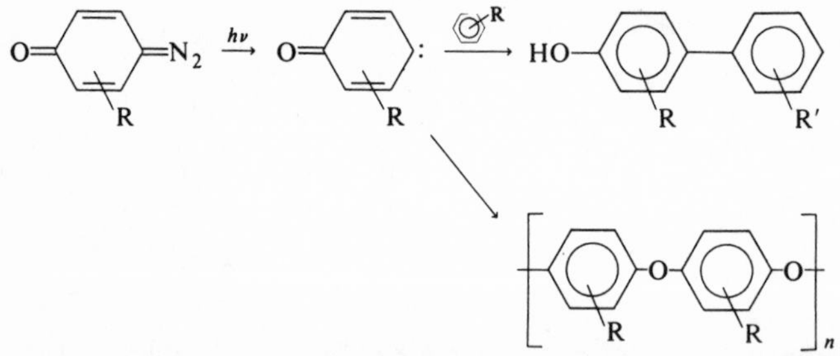

$$(44)$$

$p$-Quinoneazine appears to give rise to a similar intermediate. On refluxing in benzene solution, $p$-hydroxydiphenyl was obtained whereas photolysis led to a high melting (polymeric?) substance ($103$).

The pyrolysis of 2,6-dibromo-1,4-benzoquinonediazide (LII) has been thoroughly studied with respect to the reaction mechanism ($102$). In chlorobenzene the two diphenyl derivatives, LIII and LIV, were formed, but fair yields were obtained only after addition of approximately 1% of water or alcohols. Otherwise polymers resulted, containing both bromine and chlorine. Considerable amounts of bromine were liberated. These observations have been explained in terms of a diradical structure of the intermediate carbene [ Eq. (45)].

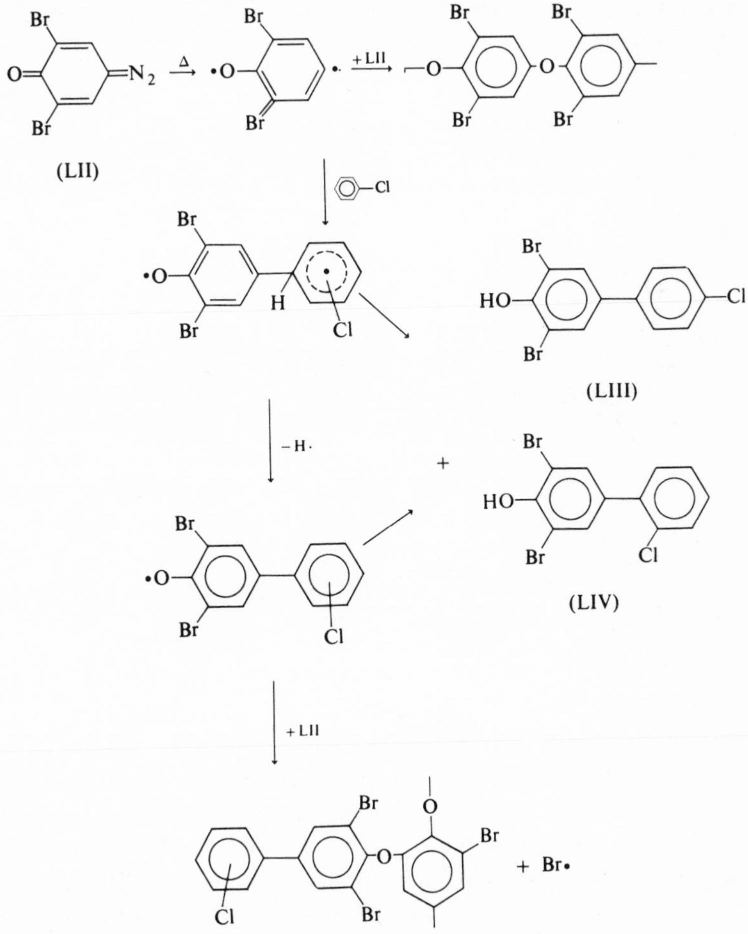

(LII)

(LIII)                          (45)

(LIV)

$+ \mathrm{Br}\cdot$

Slightly different results were obtained with 2,6-dimethyl-1,4-benzoquinonediazide (LV) (102a). In chlorinated solvents (e.g., methylene chloride) LV eliminated chlorine from the solvent to give the corresponding diazonium chloride (LVI). The thermal decomposition of LV in chlorobenzene gave LVI, 3,5-dimethyl-4-hydroxydiphenyl (LVIa), and 3,5-dimethyl-4'-chloro-4-hydroxydiphenyl (LVIb). The formation of LVIa fits with the formation of LVI.

LVIa was also obtained by refluxing or irradiating LV in benzene solution. Polymers were formed only in cyclic ethers (tetrahydrofuran, dioxane); the analytical data indicate a one-to-one copolymer with the solvent (*102a, b*).

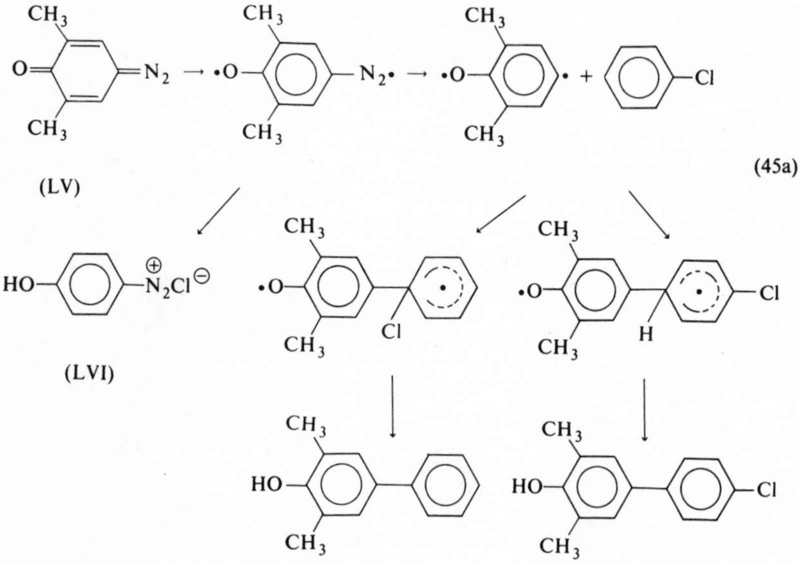

$$(45a)$$

## 5. Reactions with Hydroxy Compounds and Amines

The Wolff rearrangement of diazoketones in the presence of water, alcohols, carboxylic acids, etc., may be virtually eliminated by cupric oxide (*40*), copper powder (*119*), and cupric chloride (*120*). The products of these catalyzed reactions are ketols, and their alkyl and acyl derivatives, respectively.

$$R-CO-CN_2-R' + HO-R'' \rightarrow R-CO-CH-R' \qquad (46)$$
$$\underset{OR''}{|}$$

After fortuitous observations in the steroid series (40), an extended investigation was published by Yates (119). Protonation of the diazo group, leading to a carbonium ion, may account for some of these reactions. The following mechanism [Eq. (47)] (122) appears to be well established for the conversion of o-methoxy- and o-acetoxydiazoacetophenone (LVII) to α-coumaranone (LVIII) (121):

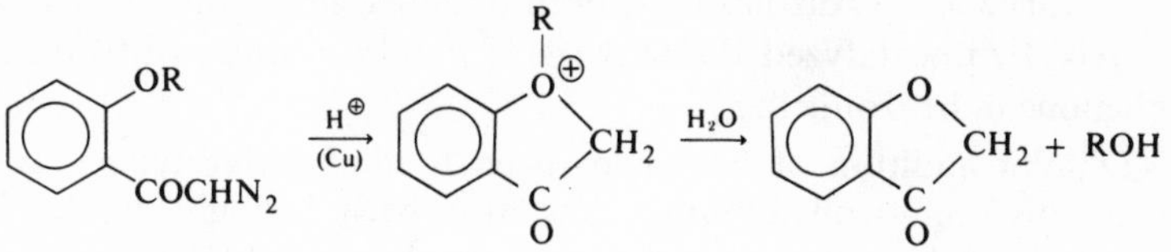

(LVII)                    (LVIII)

(R = $CH_3, -COCH_3$)

The copper-catalyzed reaction of diazoacetophenone with phenol involves nuclear attack as well as formation of a ketol ether; the former reaction may be indicative of a (complexed) carbene intermediate (119).

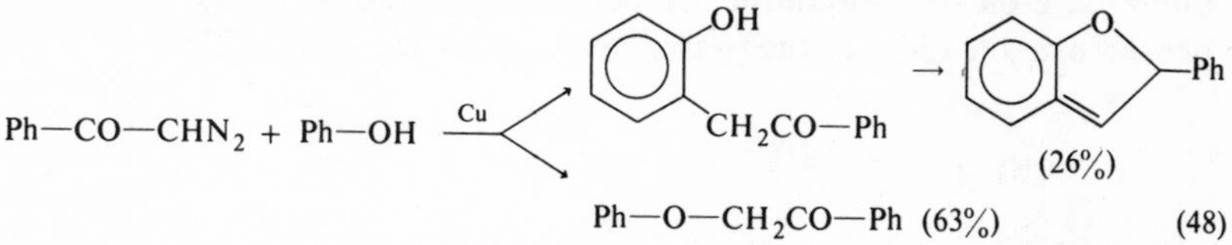

$Ph-CO-CHN_2 + Ph-OH \xrightarrow{Cu}$

$Ph-O-CH_2CO-Ph$ (63%)      (48)

A similar mechanistic ambiguity is found concerning the formation of α-amino ketones from diazoketones and amines in the presence of copper powder (119).

$$Ph-CO-CHN_2 + Ph-NH_2 \xrightarrow[\substack{EtOH \\ 65°-70°}]{Cu} Ph-CO-CH_2-NH-Ph \quad (33\%) \quad (49)$$

### 6. 1,3-Dipolar Additions

The addition of ketocarbenes to multiple bonds may proceed with participation of both carbon and oxygen ("1,3-dipolar addition") (82). Copper catalysis appears to favor this type of addition, too. Only 0.4% of 2,5-diphenyloxazole (LIX) were collected from the uncatalyzed pyrolysis of diazoacetophenone in benzonitrile, whereas copper powder and various copper salts afforded LIX in 12–17% yield.

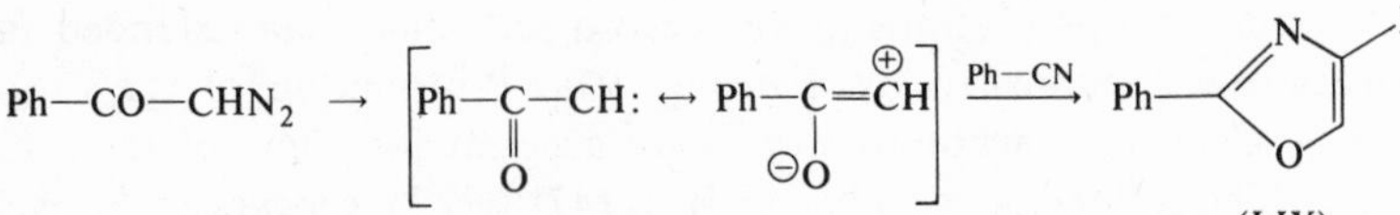

$$Ph-CO-CHN_2 \rightarrow \left[ Ph-\underset{\underset{O}{\|}}{C}-CH: \leftrightarrow Ph-\underset{\underset{\ominus O}{|}}{C}=\overset{\oplus}{CH} \right] \xrightarrow{Ph-CN} Ph-\underset{\underset{(LIX)}{}}{\diamond}^{Ph} \qquad (50)$$

Electron-attracting *p*-substituents facilitate the 1,3-dipolar addition of benzoylcarbenes. Oxazoles have been obtained in 35 and 46% yield, respectively, by uncatalyzed thermolysis of *p*-chloro- and *p*-nitrodiazo-acetophenone in benzonitrile.

1,3-Dipolar addition of benzoylcarbene to diphenylacetylene, with formation of 2,3,5-triphenylfuran, has also been brought about by copper-catalyzed decomposition of diazoacetophenone (*122a*).

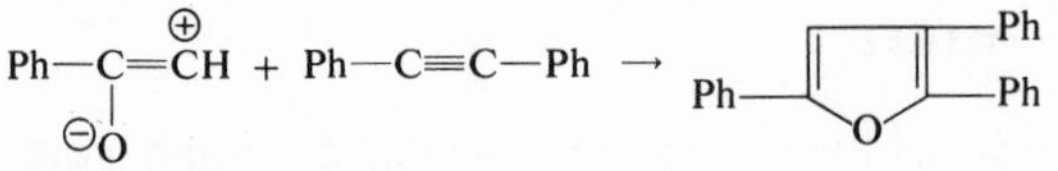

$$Ph-\underset{\underset{\ominus O}{|}}{C}=\overset{\oplus}{CH} + Ph-C\equiv C-Ph \rightarrow Ph-\diamond^{Ph}_{Ph} \qquad (50a)$$

Ring contraction leading to strained rings appears to impede the Wolff rearrangement of cyclic ketocarbenes. Decomposition of 4,7-dimethyl-2-diazo-1-indanone in benzonitrile afforded 11% of a condensed oxazole (34% in the presence of copper catalyst) (*122a*).

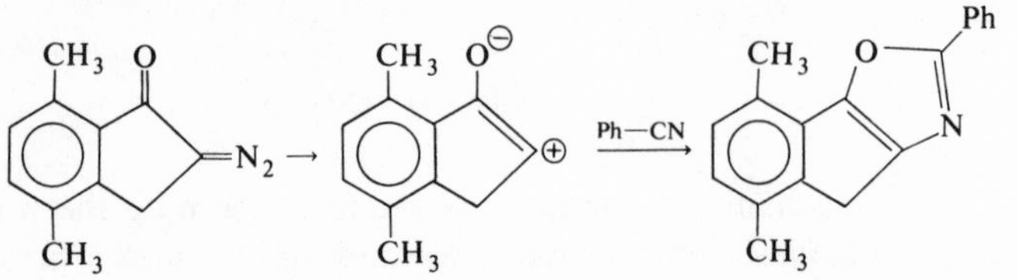

$$(50b)$$

Ketocarbenes not undergoing Wolff rearrangement are particularly suited for 1,3-dipolar addition. Thus the carbene derived from tetra-chloro-*o*-quinonediazide (LX) added smoothly to a variety of double and triple bonds (*82*). Acetylenes were added to give substituted benzo-furans; nitriles afforded benzoxazoles [cf. Eqs. (50) and (50a)]. Dioxoles could be prepared from cyclohexanone and acetone [cf. Eq. (52)] if competitive azo coupling was suppressed by low temperature photolysis of LX. The ketocarbene attacked the C=N bond of isocyanates and the C=S bond of isothiocyanates (*122a*). Carbon disulfide was the most efficient "dipolarophile" (80% yield of adduct). The reaction with olefins was not stereospecific, in contrast to other 1,3-dipolar additions. Both diethyl fumarate and maleate afforded the *trans*-adduct LXI.

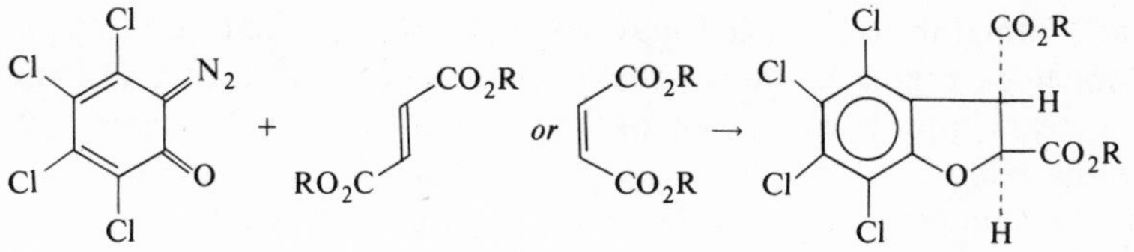

$$\text{(LX)} + \text{or} \rightarrow \text{(LXI)} \qquad (51)$$

Trifluoroacetyl-carboethoxycarbene, noted already in Sections II,B, 1 and 2 for its intermolecular reactions, attacks not only nitriles but also ketones according to the 1,3-dipolar addition scheme (*100*).

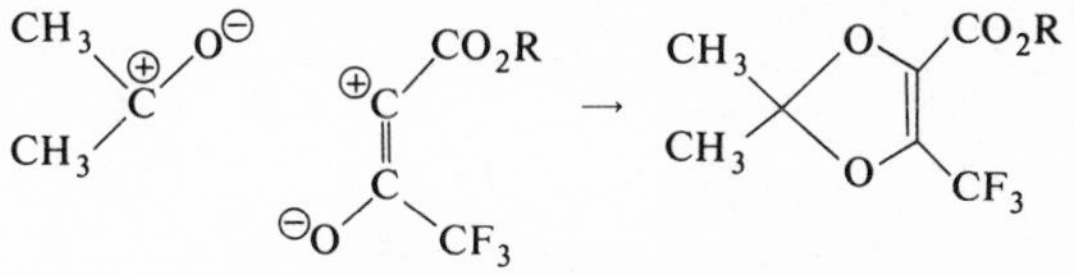

$$(52)$$

## III. THIOKETOCARBENES

Replacement of the diazoketone oxygen by sulfur leads to 1,2,3-thiadiazoles (LXII). The heterocyclic structure of these compounds is evident from the absence of the characteristic diazo absorption in the IR spectra. 1,2,3-Thiadiazoles are readily decomposed by UV irradiation to give derivatives of 1,3-dithiacyclopentene (LXIII) (*123*) which have been termed "dithiafulvenes." In some cases 1,4-dithia-2,5-cyclohexadienes (LXIV) were also obtained (*123*). The dithiafulvenes (LXIII) contain a rearranged fragment of the precursor LXII which indicates some tendency of the hypothetical thioketocarbene intermediate LXV to undergo Wolff rearrangement.

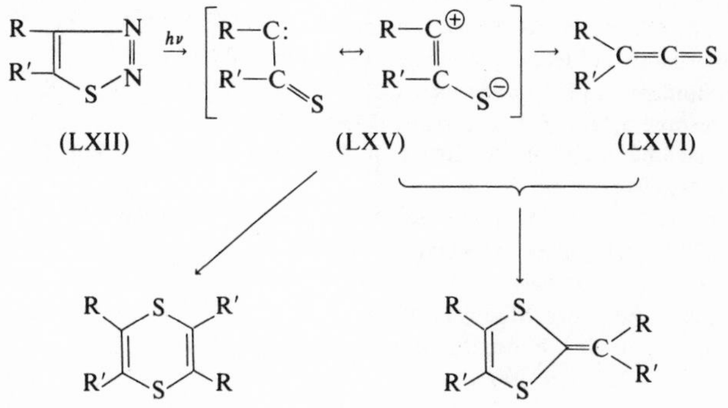

$$(53)$$

(LXII)      (LXV)      (LXVI)

(LXIV)      (LXIII)

The "dithiafulvenes" LXIII may result from 1,3-dipolar addition of the thioketocarbene LXV to the thioketene LXVI. Attack of LXVI on LXII appears improbable in view of the inertness of LXII. Attempts to utilize the related intermediate LXVII from 1,2,3-benzothiadiazole in 1,3-dipolar additions revealed, however, a surprising selectivity (*124*). Alkenes, alkynes, and nitriles were inert toward LXVII whereas carbon-sulfur double bonds accepted LXVII readily.

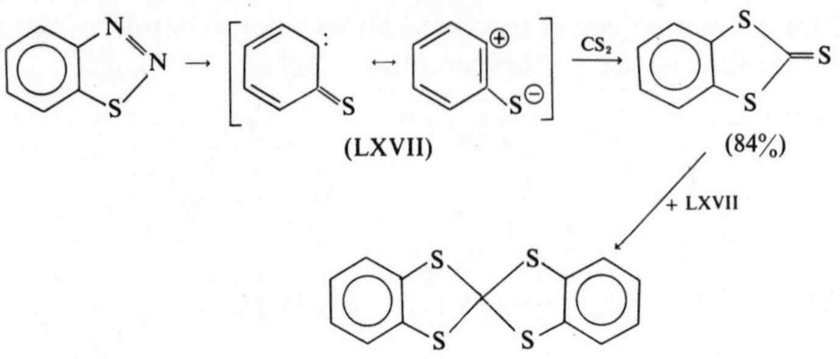

(LXVII)                                    (84%)                    (54)

+ LXVII

(69%)

## REFERENCES

1. W. Kirmse and L. Horner, *Ann.* **625**, 34 (1959).
1a. H. Ziffer and N. E. Sharpless, *J. Org. Chem.* **27**, 1944 (1962).
1b. U. Mazzucato, G. Cauzzo, and A. Foffani, *Tetrahedron Letters* **1963**, 1525.
2. P. Yates, B. L. Shapiro, N. Yoda, and J. Fugger, *J. Am. Chem. Soc.* **79**, 5756 (1957).
3. G. D. Buckley and W. J. Levy, *J. Chem. Soc.* **1951**, 3016.
4. V. Franzen, *Chem. Ber.* **87**, 1219 (1954).
5. V. Franzen, *Chem. Ber.* **87**, 1478 (1954).
6. M. Siematycki and H. Strzelecka, *Compt. rend.* **250**, 3489 (1960).
7. H. J. Bestmann and H. Schulz, *Angew. Chem.* **73**, 620 (1961).
8. R. Mechoulam and F. Sondheimer, *J. Am. Chem. Soc.* **80**, 4386 (1958).
9. J. P. Freeman, *Chem. & Ind. (London)* **1959**, 1254.
10. W. E. Bachmann and W. S. Struve, *in* "Organic Reactions" Vol. I, p. 38. Wiley, New York, 1942.
11. B. Eistert, *in* "Neuere Methoden der präparativen organischen Chemie" (W. Foerst, ed.), 3rd ed, Verlag Chemie, Weinheim, 1949.
12. R. Huisgen, *Angew. Chem.* **67**, 439 (1955).
13. V. Franzen, *Chem. Ztg.* **81**, 359 (1957).
14. F. Weygand and H. J. Bestmann, *Angew. Chem.* **72**, 535 (1960).
15. L. Wolff, *Ann.* **325**, 129 (1902).
16. L. Wolff, *Ann.* **394**, 23 (1912).
17. G. Schroeter, *Ber. deut. chem. Ges.* **42**, 2336 (1909).

18. H. Staudinger and H. Hirzel, *Ber. deut. chem. Ges.* **49**, 2522 (1916).
19. H. Gilman and Ch. E. Adams, *Rec. trav. chim.* **48**, 464 (1929).
20. F. Arndt, B. Eistert, and W. Partale, *Angew. Chem.* **40**, 1099 (1927); *Ber. deut. chem. Ges.* **60**, 1364 (1927); F. Arndt and J. Amende, *Ber. deut. chem. Ges.* **61**, 1122 (1928); F. Arndt, B. Eistert and J. Amende, *Ber. deut. chem. Ges.* **61**, 1949 (1928).
21. W. Bradley and R. Robinson, *J. Chem. Soc.* **1928**, 1310.
22. F. Arndt and B. Eistert, *Ber. deut. chem. Ges.* **68**, 200 (1935).
23. G. Schroeter, *Ber. deut. chem. Ges.* **42**, 3356 (1909).
24. A. L. Wilds and A. L. Meader, Jr., *J. Org. Chem.* **13**, 763 (1948).
25. L. Horner, E. Spietschka, and A. Gross, *Ann.* **573**, 17 (1951).
26. L. Horner and E. Spietschka, *Ĉhem. Ber.* **85**, 225 (1952).
27. A. J. Ultée and J. B. J. Soons, *Rec. trav. chim.* **71**, 565 (1952); Photolysis: H. J. Bestmann and R. Schmiechen, unpublished, cf. (*14*).
28. E. Spietschka, Dissertation, University of Frankfurt, 1953.
29. A. L. Wilds, J. v. d. Berghe, C. L. Winestock, R. L. v. Trebra, and N. F. Woolsey, *J. Am. Chem. Soc.* **84**, 1503 (1962).
30. L. Horner and E. Spietschka, *Chem. Ber.* **88**, 934 (1955).
31. K. B. Wiberg, B. R. Lowry, and T. H. Colby, *J. Am. Chem. Soc.* **83**, 3998 (1961).
32. J. Meinwald, A. Lewis, and P. G. Gassman, *J. Am. Chem. Soc.* **82**, 2649 (1960); **84**, 977 (1962).
33. J. Meinwald and P. G. Gassman, *J. Am. Chem. Soc.* **82**, 2857 (1960).
34. L. Horner, W. Kirmse, and K. Muth, *Chem. Ber.* **91**, 430 (1958).
35. L. Horner, K. Muth, and H. G. Schmelzer, *Chem. Ber.* **92**, 2953 (1959).
36. M. P. Cava, R. L. Litle, and D. R. Napier, *J. Am. Chem. Soc.* **80**, 2257 (1958).
37. M. S. Newman and Ph. F. Beal, *J. Am. Chem. Soc.* **72**, 5163 (1950).
38. P. Yates and J. Fugger, *Chem. & Ind. (London)* **1957**, 1511.
39. H. Erlenmeyer and M. Aeberli, *Helv. Chim. Acta* **31**, 28 (1948).
40. R. Casanova and T. Reichstein, *Helv. Chim. Acta* **33**, 417 (1950).
41. A. Roedig and H. Lunk, *Chem. Ber.* **87**, 971 (1954).
42. F. J. Buckle, F. L. M. Pattison, and B. C. Saunders, *J. Chem. Soc.* **1949**, 1471, 2774.
43. F. Brown and W. K. R. Musgrave, *J. Chem. Soc.* **1953**, 2087.
44. J. D. Parker, E. R. Larsen, H. v. Haller, and J. R. Lacher, *J. Org. Chem.* **23**, 1166 (1958).
45. J. H. Wotiz and S. N. Buco, *J. Org. Chem.* **20**, 210 (1955).
46a. J. L. Mateos, O. Chao, and H. Flores, *Tetrahedron* **19**, 1051 (1963).
46b. M. P. Cava and E. Moroz, *J. Am. Chem. Soc.* **84**, 115 (1962).
46c. S. Huneck, *Tetrahedron Letters* **1963**, 375.
46. J. Meinwald, G. G. Curtis, and P. G. Gassman, *J. Am. Chem. Soc.* **84**, 116 (1962); G. Muller, Ch. Huynh, and J. Mathieu, *Bull. Soc. chim. France* **1962**, 296; A. Hassner, A. W. Coulter, and W. S. Seese, *Tetrahedron Letters* **1962**, 759.
47. R. Grewe and A. Bokranz, *Chem. Ber.* **88**, 49 (1955).
48. W. Kirmse, Habilitationsschrift, University of Mainz, 1959.
49. K. Balenović and N. Stimac, *Croatica Chem. Acta* **29**, 153 (1957) and previous work, cf. (14).
50. D. Fles and M. Markovac-Prpić, *Croatica Chem. Acta* **28**, 73 (1956); **29**, 79 (1957).
51. F. Weygand, P. Klinke, and I. Eigen, *Chem. Ber.* **90**, 1896 (1957).
52. A. T. Blomquist and F. W. Schlaefer, *J. Am. Chem. Soc.* **83**, 4547 (1961).

52a. N. L. Allinger, L. A. Freiberg, R. B. Hermann, and M. A. Miller, *J. Am. Chem. Soc.* **85**, 1171 (1963).
53. O. Süs, *Ann.* **556**, 65, 85 (1944).
54. J. de Jonge and R. Dijkstra, *Rec. trav. chim.* **67**, 328 (1948).
55. O. Süs, *Ann.* **579**, 133 (1953).
56. O. Süs, M. Glos, K. Möller, and H. D. Eberhardt, *Ann.* **583**, 150 (1953).
57. O. Süs and K. Möller, *Ann.* **593**, 91 (1955).
58. K. Möller and O. Süs, *Ann.* **612**, 153 (1958).
59. O. Süs, H. Steppan, and R. Dietrich, *Ann.* **617**, 20 (1958).
60. J. de Jonge and R. Dijkstra, *Rec. trav. chim.* **68**, 426 (1949).
61. J. de Jonge, R. J. H. Alink, and R. Dijkstra, *Rec. trav. chim.* **69**, 1448 (1950).
62. L. Horner, H. G. Schmelzer, H. U. v. d. Eltz, and K. Habig, *Ann.* **661**, 44 (1963).
63. W. Kirmse and L. Horner, *Chem. Ber.* **89**, 2759 (1956).
64. L. Horner and E. Spietschka, *Chem. Ber.* **89**, 2765 (1956).
65. K. B. Wiberg and Th. W. Hutton, *J. Am. Chem. Soc.* **76**, 5367 (1954).
66. P. Yates and T. J. Clark, *Tetrahedron Letters* **1961**, 435.
67. R. Huisgen, H. König, G. Binsch, and H. J. Sturm, *Angew. Chem.* **73**, 368 (1961).
68. W. Ried and H. Mengler, *Angew. Chem.* **73**, 218 (1961).
69. E. Bamberger, M. Baum, and L. Schlein, *J. prakt. Chem.* [2] **105**, 266 (1922).
70. P. Yates and E. W. Robb, *J. Am. Chem. Soc.* **79**, 5760 (1957).
71. W. Ried and R. Dietrich, *Naturwissenschaften* **46**, 474 (1959); *Ann.* **639**, 32 (1961).
72. W. Ried and R. Dietrich, *Naturwissenschaften* **47**, 445 (1960); *Ann.* **666**, 113, 135 (1963).
73. N. A. Preobrashenski, A. M. Poljakowa, and W. A. Preobrashenski, *Ber. deut. chem. Ges.* **68**, 850 (1935).
74. J. F. Lane, J. Willenz, A. Weissberger, and E. S. Wallis, *J. Org. Chem.* **5**, 276 (1940).
75. J. F. Lane and E. S. Wallis, *J. Am. Chem. Soc.* **63**, 1674 (1941).
76. K. J. Sax and W. Bergmann, *J. Am. Chem. Soc.* **77**, 1910 (1955).
77. K. B. Wiberg and Th. W. Hutton, *J. Am. Chem. Soc.* **78**, 1640 (1956).
78. C. D. Gutsche, *J. Am. Chem. Soc.* **70**, 4150 (1948).
79. J. F. Lane and E. S. Wallis, *J. Org. Chem.* **6**, 443 (1941).
80. C. Huggett, R. T. Arnold, and T. I. Taylor, *J. Am. Chem. Soc.* **64**, 3043 (1942).
81. V. Franzen, *Ann.* **614**, 31 (1958).
82. R. Huisgen, G. Binsch, H. König, and H. J. Sturm, *Angew. Chem.* **73**, 368 (1961).
83. V. Franzen, *Ann.* **602**, 199 (1957).
84. R. Jaquier, *Bull. soc. chim. France* **1950**, D 35.
85. R. B. Loftfield, *J. Am. Chem. Soc.* **73**, 4707 (1951).
86. H. Henecka *in* "Houben-Weyl Methoden der organischen Chemie," 4th ed., Vol. VIII/3, p. 458. Georg Thieme, Stuttgart, 1952.
87. A. Favorskii, *J. prakt. Chem.* [2] **51**, 533 (1895).
88. R. B. Loftfield, *J. Am. Chem. Soc.* **72**, 632 (1950).
89. C. L. Stevens and E. Farkas, *J. Am. Chem. Soc.* **74**, 5352 (1952).
90. G. Baddeley, G. Holt, and J. Kenner, *Nature* **163**, 766 (1949).
91. W. Kirmse, L. Horner, and K. Muth, unpublished; cf. *Angew. Chem.* **71**, 539 (1959).
92. M. S. Newman and A. Arkell, *J. Org. Chem.* **24**, 385 (1959).
93. P. Yates and S. Danishefsky, *J. Am. Chem. Soc.* **84**, 879 (1962).
94. J. Bredt and W. Holz, *J. prakt. Chem.* [2] **95**, 133 (1917).

95.  P. T. Lansbury and J. G. Colson, *Chem. & Ind. (London)* **1962**, 821.
96.  F. Weygand and K. Koch, *Angew. Chem.* **73**, 531 (1961).
96a. A. Roedig, E. Fahr, and H. Aman, *Chem. Ber.* **97**, 77 (1964).
97.  G. Stork and J. Ficini, *J. Am. Chem. Soc.* **83**, 4678 (1961).
98.  W. v. E. Doering and B. Ferrier, unpublished; cf. W. v. E. Doering and W. R. Roth, *Angew. Chem.* **75**, 27 (1963).
99.  F. Weygand, W. Schwenke, and H. J. Bestmann, *Angew. Chem.* **70**, 506 (1958).
100. F. Weygand, H. Dworschak, K. Koch, and St. Konstas, *Angew. Chem.* **73**, 409 (1961).
101. O. Süs, K. Möller, and H. Heiss, *Ann.* **598**, 123 (1956).
102. M. J. S. Dewar and A. N. James, *J. Chem. Soc.* **1958**, 917, 4265.
102a. T. Kunitake and C. C. Price, *J. Am. Chem. Soc.* **85**, 761 (1963).
102b. J. K. Stille, P. Cassidy, and L. Plummer, *J. Am. Chem. Soc.* **85**, 1318 (1963).
103. C. H. Wang, *Proc. Chem. Soc.* **1961**, 309.
104. Ch. Grundmann, *Ann.* **536**, 29 (1938).
105. I. Ernest and J. Staněk, *Chem. listy* **52**, 302 (1958); *Collection Czech. Chem. Communs.* **24**, 530 (1959).
106. I. Ernest, *Chem. listy* **48**, 847 (1954); *Collection Czech. Chem. Communs.* **19**, 1179 (1954).
107. V. Hněvsová, V. Smělý, and I. Ernest, *Chem. listy* **50**, 573 (1956); *Collection Czech. Chem. Communs.* **21**, 1459 (1956).
108. I. Ernest and Z. Linhartová, *Chem. listy* **52**, 350 (1958); *Collection Czech. Chem. Communs.* **24**, 2072 (1959).
109. I. Ernest and Z. Linhartová, *Chem. listy* **52**, 348 (1958); *Collection Czech. Chem. Communs.* **24**, 1022 (1959).
110. I. Ernest and J. Jelínková, *Collection Czech. Chem. Communs.* **24**, 3341 (1959).
111. J. Novák, J. Ratuský, V. Šneberk, and F. Šorm, *Chem. listy* **51**, 479 (1957); *Collection Czech. Chem. Communs.* **22**, 1836 (1957).
112. H. Strzelecka and M. Simalty-Siematycki, *Compt. rend.* **252**, 3821 (1961).
113. R. J. Mohrbacker and N. H. Cromwell, *J. Am. Chem. Soc.* **79**, 401 (1957).
114. W. Treibs and M. Quarg, *Ann.* **598**, 38 (1956).
115. F. Šorm, *Collection Czech. Chem. Communs.* **12**, 245 (1947).
116. J. Ratuský and F. Šorm, *Chem. listy* **51**, 1091 (1957); *Collection Czech. Chem. Communs.* **23**, 467 (1958).
117. C. D. Nenitzescu and E. Solomonica, *Ber. deut. chem. Ges.* **64**, 1924 (1931).
118. J. Novák and F. Šorm, *Chem. listy* **51**, 1693 (1957); *Collection Czech. Chem. Communs.* **23**, 1126 (1958).
119. P. Yates, *J. Am. Chem. Soc.* **74**, 5376 (1952).
120. J. L. E. Erickson, J. M. Dechary, and M. R. Kesling, *J. Am. Chem. Soc.* **73**, 5301 (1951).
121. P. Pfeiffer and E. Endres, *Chem. Ber.* **84**, 247 (1951).
122. A. K. Bose and P. Yates, *J. Am. Chem. Soc.* **74**, 4703 (1952).
122a. G. Binsch, Dissertation, University of Munich, 1963; cf. R. Huisgen, *Angew. Chem.* **75**, 634 (1963).
123. W. Kirmse and L. Horner, *Ann.* **614**, 4 (1958).
124. R. Huisgen and V. Weberndörfer, *Experientia* **17**, 566 (1961).

# CHAPTER 8

# Halocarbenes

## I. DIHALOCARBENES

### A. Formation of Dihalocarbenes

#### 1. Basic Hydrolysis of Haloforms

THE IDEA THAT dichlorocarbene is an intermediate in the basic hydrolysis of chloroform was first expressed by Geuther in 1862 (1). He suggested that chloroform is actually $CCl_2 \cdot HCl$ from which hydrogen chloride may be removed by alkali to give "carbon dichloride." The formation of carbon monoxide, in addition to formate ion, was taken as evidence for the intermediacy of dichlorocarbene by Geuther and a number of other authors [see (2) for references]. It was not until 1950, however, that the mechanism of the basic hydrolysis of chloroform was elucidated by J. Hine and his co-workers. Today the reactions of haloforms with base are the most thoroughly investigated examples of $\alpha$-elimination.

*a. Two-Step (Carbanion) Mechanism.* The rate of the basic hydrolysis of chloroform is first order with respect to both chloroform and hydroxide ion concentrations [in 66.7% aqueous dioxane (2), and in pure water (3)]. Nucleophilic attack of hydroxide ion on chloroform ($S_N2$ displacement) [Eq. (1)] may be ruled out by several lines of argument.

$$CHCl_3 + HO^{\ominus} \xrightarrow{\text{slow}} CHCl_2OH + Cl^{\ominus}$$

$$CHCl_2OH \xrightarrow[HO^{\ominus}, H_2O]{\text{fast}} CO, HCO_2^{\ominus} \tag{1}$$

In general the replacement of a hydrogen attached to the $\alpha$-carbon of an alkyl halide by halogen decreases $S_N2$ reactivity. Chloroform, however, is much (about one thousandfold) more reactive in basic hydrolysis than methylene chloride or carbon tetrachloride (2, 4). Every bromine-containing haloform studied (5) (CHBrClF, CHBrCl_2, CHBr_2Cl,

CHBr$_3$) is at least 600 times as reactive toward hydroxide ions in 66.7% aqueous dioxane as bromochloromethane or methylene bromide.

Toward weakly basic nucleophiles the predicted reactivity order is obeyed; haloforms have been found to be less reactive than the related methylene halides in all of the cases studied (4, 6). The reaction of chloroform, bromodichloromethane, dibromochloromethane, and bromoform with sodium thiophenoxide, or sodium p-thiocresolate (2, 5), is strongly accelerated, however, by the presence of hydroxide ions.

This observation is quite unexplainable in terms of Eq. (1). Apparently the strongly basic hydroxide ions are required to furnish an intermediate which is more susceptible to nucleophilic attack than the starting haloform. The base would be expected to abstract a proton from the haloform to produce a trihalocarbanion:

$$CHX_3 + HO^{\ominus} \underset{k_{-1}}{\overset{k_1}{\rightleftharpoons}} X_3C^{\ominus} + H_2O \tag{2}$$

The formation of trichloromethylcarbinols from ketones, chloroform, and base is evidence for the occurrence of the trichlorocarbanion (7-11):

$$Cl_3C^{\ominus} + \overset{R'}{\underset{R}{>}}C{=}O \rightarrow Cl_3C{-}\overset{\overset{R'}{|}}{\underset{\underset{R}{|}}{C}}{-}O^{\ominus} \xrightarrow{H_2O} Cl_3C{-}\overset{\overset{R'}{|}}{\underset{\underset{R}{|}}{C}}{-}OH \tag{3}$$

and also the reaction of chloroform with sodium hypobromite to give bromotrichloromethane (12) [CHBr$_3 \rightarrow$ CBr$_4$ (13)].

Quantitative information on reaction (2) was provided by investigation of the base-catalyzed hydrogen-deuterium exchange of haloforms. By use of a heterogeneous mixture of chloroform and alkaline heavy water, Sakamoto (14) has shown that the exchange reaction is rapid as compared to the basic hydrolysis. J. Hine et al. (15-19) have measured the rates of the hydroxide-catalyzed transformations of deuterated haloforms to the corresponding protonated compounds in homogeneous aqueous solution. With nonfluorine-containing haloforms, the rate constant for the basic hydrolysis was only 0.1-0.001% of that for deuterium exchange, i.e., the exchange reaction was pseudounimolecular. With haloforms such as CHCl$_2$F, CHBrClF, and CHBr$_2$F, that contain one fluorine atom, the rates of hydrolysis and deuterium exchange were

comparable, and the kinetic treatment was considerably more complicated. (For difluorinated compounds see below.)

Comparison of the resultant data gave the reactivity series $CDI_3$
$\sim CDBr_3 > CDBr_2Cl > CDBrCl_2 \sim CDCl_2I > CDFI_2 > CDBr_2F$
$> CDCl_3 > CDBrClF > CDCl_2F$ (17, 19), showing that the $\alpha$-halogen
substituents facilitate carbanion formation in the order I $\sim$ Br > Cl > F.
To account for the effect of the $\alpha$-halogens (which is almost the reverse
of that expected from the inductive effect) several factors might be considered (17). B-strain (repulsions between the three halogen atoms in the
tetrahedral haloform) does not seem to be important in view of the equal
reactivity of $CDBr_3$ and $CDI_3$. $d$-Orbital resonance, i.e., contribution
of structures with ten electrons in the outer shell of the halogen, may
explain why fluorine is least effective in facilitating deuterium exchange.
Doering et al. (20–22) have attributed the greater ease of carbanion
formation by sulfonium and phosphonium salts, in comparison to
ammonium salts, to $d$-orbital resonance. On the other hand, polarizability also increases in the order F < Cl < Br < I—the largest change
occurring between fluorine and chlorine—and it is difficult to assess the
relative importance of polarizability and $d$-orbital resonance.

The kinetic isotope effect in the abstraction of a proton from haloforms [Eq. (2)] is of interest with regard to the nature of the transition
state. It has been measured directly with the rapidly hydrolyzing haloforms $CHCl_2F$ ($k_H/k_D = 1.76$ at $0°$ and 1.52 at $20°$) (16) and $CHBrClF$
($k_H/k_D = 1.74$ at $0°$ and 1.69 at $15°$) (17). With chloroform the rate of
exchange of $CDCl_3$ in alkaline $H_2O$ has been compared to the rate of exchange of $CHCl_3$ in alkaline $D_2O$ (15). From these data the isotope
effect may be estimated if it is assumed that the reactivity of $DO^-$ in $D_2O$
relative to that of $HO^-$ in $H_2O$ is in the same range (1.36–1.42) as it is for
the reaction with nitroethane and 2-nitropropane (23). The resultant
estimate for chloroform is $k_H/k_D = 1.48$ at 20°C. (16). The small
isotope effects suggest a transition state with little stretching of the
carbon-hydrogen bond, i.e., the proton transfer either has not proceeded
very far, or is nearly complete. The latter explanation appears more
probable, taking into account the effect of the $\alpha$-halogens as discussed
in the preceding paragraph.

Having shown that trihalocarbanions are formed from most haloforms in a fast and reversible reaction, the rate-determining step of the
over-all hydrolysis remains to be located among the subsequent reactions
of the trihalocarbanions. Two possible mechanisms which fit the ob-

served kinetics should be considered:

$$Cl_3C^{\ominus} \xrightarrow{\text{slow}} \; :CCl_2 + Cl^{\ominus}$$

$$:CCl_2 \xrightarrow[HO^{\ominus},\,H_2O]{\text{fast}} CO \text{ and } HCO_2{}^{\ominus} \qquad (4)$$

$$(:CCl_2 + X^{\ominus} \rightarrow Cl_2XC^{\ominus})$$

$$Cl_3C^{\ominus} + H_2O \xrightarrow{\text{slow}} H_2\overset{\oplus}{O}\text{---}\overset{\ominus}{C}Cl_2 + Cl^{\ominus}$$

$$H_2\overset{\oplus}{O}\text{---}\overset{\ominus}{C}Cl_2 \xrightarrow[HO^{\ominus},\,H_2O]{\text{fast}} CO \text{ and } HCO_2{}^{\ominus} \qquad (5)$$

$$(Cl_3C^{\ominus} + X^{\ominus} \rightarrow Cl_2XC^{\ominus} + Cl\;)^{\ominus}$$

Mechanism (4) is a $S_N1$ reaction of the trihalocarbanion, proceeding via the dihalocarbene intermediate, whereas mechanism (5) involves a $S_N2$ displacement at the trihalocarbanion. In the dihalocarbene mechanism (4) the nucleophilic attack on carbon occurs *after* the rate-controlling step of the reaction, whereas in mechanism (5) the rate-controlling step is itself a nucleophilic attack. It is impossible to distinguish between (4) and (5) if water, present in large excess, is the only nucleophile available. The two mechanisms lead to different predictions, however, concerning the effect of additional nucleophilic anions. The case of chloride ion, added to the basic hydrolysis of chloroform, is particularly instructive. No kinetic effect at all will result from the operation of mechanism (5) as products and reactants of the displacement $Cl_3C^{\ominus} + Cl^{\ominus} \rightarrow Cl_3C^{\ominus} + Cl^{\ominus}$ are identical. With mechanism (4), however, the combination of $Cl^{\ominus}$ with $:CCl_2$ to give $Cl_3C^{\ominus}$ is a reversal of the rate-determining step. Therefore the over-all rate will be slowed by a "mass-law" effect.

The rate of the basic hydrolysis of chloroform in the presence of 0.08 and 0.16 $N$ sodium chloride was shown to be 92.9 and 86.6%, respectively, of that observed in the presence of an equal amount of sodium perchlorate, nitrate, or fluoride (3). A specific salt effect appears improbable as chloride ions slow the basic hydrolysis of chloroform as effectively in the presence of 1.5 $N$ sodium perchlorate as in its absence ("swamping salt" principle).

The rate of the basic hydrolysis of chloroform is diminished even more by the presence of bromide and iodide ions. Dichloroiodomethane has been isolated from the latter reaction. The halide ions are thought to compete with water for the dihalocarbene intermediate, reverting some of it to haloform:

$$:CCl_2 + H_2O \xrightarrow{k_w} H_2\overset{\oplus}{O}-\overset{\ominus}{\underset{.}{C}}Cl_2 \quad (\rightarrow CO + HCO_2^{\ominus})$$

$$:CCl_2 + X^{\ominus} \xrightarrow{k_x} X-\overset{\ominus}{\underset{.}{C}}Cl_2 \quad (\rightleftharpoons HCXCl_2)$$

Competition factors $k_x/k_w$ have been evaluated from the rate equation, and log $k_x/k_w$ was shown to be a linear function of the nucleophilic constants ($n$) of Swain and Scott (24).

Extension of these studies to bromodichlormethane (19) afforded competition constants which were within experimental error of those previously obtained for chloroform. This observation further supports the carbene mechanism (4) because chloroform and bromodichloromethane give rise to different trihalocarbanions but form the same carbene, $:CCl_2$. The competition constants derived from the hydrolysis of dibromochloromethane, probably pertaining to bromochlorocarbene, are much the same as those for dichlorocarbene (19). In contrast, the rate of the basic hydrolysis of dibromofluoromethane is not affected by the addition of halide ions (19). The fluorine-containing carbene, $:CBrF$, might have been expected to be more stable and to discriminate better between the solvent and the more nucleophilic halide ions. No satisfactory explanation of its failure to combine with halide ions has been given so far.

Accepting the carbene mechanism (4) as generally valid, the over-all rate constants for the basic hydrolysis of haloforms may be expressed in terms of the rate constants of the individual steps as follows:

$$CHX_3 + HO^{\ominus} \underset{k_{-1}}{\overset{k_1}{\rightleftharpoons}} X_3C^{\ominus} + H_2O$$

$$X_3C^{\ominus} \xrightarrow{k_2} :CX_2 + X^{\ominus}$$

$$:CX_2 \xrightarrow[HO^{\ominus}, H_2O]{fast} CO \text{ and } HCO_2^{\ominus}$$

$$k_h = \frac{k_1(k_2/k_{-1})}{1 + (k_2/k_{-1})} \qquad (6)$$

The values of $k_1$ are known or may be closely approximated from data obtained on deuterated haloforms by use of deuterium kinetic isotope effects. A correlation of the values of $k_2/k_{-1}$ has been attempted by means of Eq. (7), which refers to the generalized reaction (8) (25).

$$\log \frac{(k_2/k_{-1})_{CHXYZ}}{(k_2/k_{-1})_{CHCl_3}} = M_x + M_y + N_z + \log(n_z/3) + (c\text{-}d)\log \frac{(k_1)_{CHXYZ}}{(k_1)_{CHCl_3}} \qquad (7)$$

$$\text{CHXYZ} \xrightleftharpoons[+\text{H}_2\text{O}]{k_{-1}} \text{XYZC}^{\ominus} \xrightarrow{k_2} :\text{CXY} + \text{Z}^{\ominus} \qquad (8)$$

Equation (7) contains parameters for: (1) the relative abilities of the various halogens to stabilize dihalocarbenes $(M)$; (2) the relative ease with which halogens separate as anions from the intermediate trihalo-carbanions $(N)$; and (3) the relative carbanion character of the transition states for protonation and carbene formation $(c\text{-}d)$. Log $(n_z/3)$ is a statistical correction for the number of Z-atoms present in the haloform. The parameters derived from rate measurements on 12 haloforms $(26)$ are given in Table I.

TABLE I

$M$- AND $N$-PARAMETERS OF EQ. (7)

| | | | |
|---|---|---|---|
| $M_F$ = | 3.071 | $N_{Br}$ = | 1.090 |
| $M_{Cl}$ = | 0.000 (standard) | $N_I$ = | 0.327 |
| $M_{Br}$ = | −1.164 | $N_{Cl}$ = | 0.000 (standard) |
| $M_I$ = | −1.696 | $c\text{-}d$ = | 0.114 |

The $k_2/k_{-1}$ values calculated with the aid of these parameters approximate the experimental values with a maximum deviation of 12%. Because of the large number of parameters contained in Eq. (7), the excellent agreement cannot be taken as additional evidence supporting the carbene mechanism [Eqs. (4) and (6)]. But inasmuch as the reaction mechanism is established by independent evidence given above, Eq. (7) affords a consistent quantitative estimate of the factors operating in carbene formation.

According to the values of the $M$-parameters (Table I), halogens facilitate carbene formation in the order $F \gg Cl > Br > I$. Assuming a singlet state of the dihalocarbenes, this order may be attributed to the relative abilities of the halogens to supply electrons to the carbon atom by mesomeric effects

$$\underline{X}-\underline{\overset{..}{C}}-\underline{X} \leftrightarrow \overset{\oplus}{X}=\overset{\ominus}{\underset{..}{C}}-\underline{X} \leftrightarrow \underline{X}-\overset{\ominus}{\underset{..}{C}}=\overset{\oplus}{X}$$

The $N$-parameters indicate the order $Br > I > Cl$ for the abilities of the halogens to depart as halide ions from the trihalocarbanions. This reactivity series is not the most common one in nucleophilic displacements but has been occasionally observed $(6, 27, 28)$. The superiority of bromide as a leaving group has been substantiated by studying the hydrolysis of bromochloroiodomethane $(26)$.

$$\text{HCBrClI} + \text{HO}^{\ominus} \rightleftharpoons \text{BrClIC}^{\ominus} \underset{k_3}{\overset{k_2}{\rightleftharpoons}} \begin{array}{l} \nearrow :\text{CBrCl} + \text{I}^{\ominus} \\ \searrow :\text{CClI} + \text{Br} \end{array} \quad (9)$$

Kinetic measurements in the presence of added sodium iodide gave $k_3/(k_2 + k_3) = 0.72$, i.e., the production of chloroiodocarbene and bromide ion is the major path of the reaction.

*b. One-Step (Concerted) Mechanism.* As mentioned above, the replacement of a bromine or chlorine atom in haloforms by fluorine considerably *decreases* the rate constant of carbanion formation, $k_1$ [Eqs. (2) and (6)]. The over-all rate of basic hydrolysis, however, *increases* because fluorine facilitates carbene formation from the trihalocarbanion. Because of the increase in $k_2$, the ratio $k_2/k_{-1}$ of haloforms such as $CHBr_2F$, $CHBrClF$, and $CHCl_2F$ is in the order of 2–10.

One should expect carbanion formation to become rate controlling upon introduction of a second fluorine atom, with a corresponding *decrease* of the over-all rate of hydrolysis. The difluorinated compounds, chlorodifluoromethane (*18, 29, 30*), bromodifluoromethane (*18*), and difluoroiodomethane (*30*) were found, however, to hydrolyze much faster than they were expected (from extrapolation of data on other haloforms) to form carbanions. The basic hydrolysis of deuterobromodifluoromethane, $CDBrF_2$, was shown to proceed with negligible isotopic exchange (*18*). ($S_N2$ displacement at the haloform has been ruled out by the same evidence as that presented for the carbanion mechanism.)

The lack of isotopic exchange would be consistent with irreversible carbanion formation, i.e., formation of a carbanion which invariably loses a halide ion and never reverts to the starting material, $k_2/k_{-1}$ infinite. This assumption does not account for the increase in rate. It has been inferred, therefore, that the carbanion is not a real intermediate with difluorinated haloforms. Instead, Hine has suggested (*18*) that the removal of the hydrogen and the cleavage of the carbon-halogen bond are concerted processes:

$$\text{HO}^{\ominus} + \text{HCF}_2\text{X} \rightarrow \overset{\ominus}{\text{HO}} \ldots \text{H} \ldots \overset{\delta\ominus}{\text{CF}_2} \ldots \overset{\delta\ominus}{\text{X}} \rightarrow \text{H}_2\text{O} + :\text{CF}_2 + \text{X}^{\ominus} \quad (10)$$

"The loss of halide ion appears to add driving force to the proton removal . . . . Thus it is possible to go directly to what is probably the most stable of the dihalocarbenes and by-pass what would be a relatively unstable trihalomethyl anion" (*18*).

The kinetic isotope effect was measured by comparing the rates of the hydrolyses of $CHBrF_2$ and $CDBrF_2$. The observed value (2.02

± 0.14) is somewhat greater than those found in carbanion formation—
a fact which is also consistent with a concerted mechanism.

Replacement of the chlorine (or bromine) atom in difluorinated
haloforms by a sulfone groups results in a change of mechanism. Difluoromethyl phenyl sulfone (I) undergoes deuterium exchange at a rate
quite rapid as compared to its rate of basic hydrolysis (*31*). The intermediacy of difluorocarbene appears probable in view of the *base-
catalyzed* reaction with sodium thiophenoxide to give difluoromethyl
phenyl sulfide (II) (*31*). The formation of difluorocarbene from difluoromethyl phenyl sulfone is therefore a two-step process rather than a concerted reaction.

$$Ph—SO_2—CHF_2 + CH_3O^{\ominus} \rightleftharpoons Ph—SO_2—\overset{\ominus}{C}F_2 + CH_3OH$$

$$(I)$$

$$\Big\downarrow - Ph—SO_2^{\ominus} \quad (52\%) \tag{11}$$

$$Ph—S—CHF_2 \xleftarrow[PhS^{\ominus}]{} :CF_2 \xrightarrow[CH_3O^{\ominus}]{} CH_3O—CHF_2$$

$$(II) \qquad\qquad\qquad\qquad\qquad (38\%)$$

$$(22\%)$$

*c. Dihalocarbenes from Haloforms in Aprotic Media.* The basic
hydrolysis of haloforms discussed in the preceding paragraphs is excel-
lently suited for mechanistic studies. It has been seen, however, that the
reactions of the dihalocarbene intermediates with added nucleophiles
will, at best, compete with the attack on water, giving carbon monoxide
and formate ion. In order to achieve addition of dihalocarbenes to
nucleophiles (e.g., olefins) in good yields, aprotic media are required.
Potassium *tert*-butoxide has been the favored base, following the first
successful application of this technique by Doering and Hoffmann (*32*),
but sodium methoxide (*33–36*) and potassium isopropoxide (*37*) have
been applied occasionally. Any inert solvent, such as benzene, may be
used. Reactions with olefins have been frequently conducted in excess
olefin as the solvent. The yields of dichlorocarbene adducts are considerably improved by this procedure. The presence of *tert*-butanol may
be tolerated in some cases (*38*) but has been reported to be harmful in
others (*39*).

### 2. Decarboxylation of Trihaloacetates

The reaction of trichloroacetic acid to give chloroform and carbon
dioxide on heating with various bases was first observed by Silberstein
(*40*) in 1884. Detailed kinetic studies of the decarboxylation of various
trihaloacetic acids (*41–45*) revealed a first-order reaction of the car-

boxylate anion, forming carbon dioxide and a trihalomethyl anion. Subsequent protonation of the trihalocarbanion in protic solvents gives the haloform.

$$CX_3{-}CO_2^{\ominus} \rightarrow CO_2 + X_3C^{\ominus}$$

$$X_3C^{\ominus} + HB \xrightarrow[(k_{-1})]{} HCX_3 + B^{\ominus} \qquad (12)$$

$$X_3C^{\ominus} \xrightarrow[(k_2)]{} {:}CX_2 + X^{\ominus}$$

A linear correlation of the log $k$ values of carbanion formation by decarbocylation [Eq. (12)], and of carbanion formation from haloforms and alkali [Eqs. (2) and (6)] has been established (17). Stabilization of the trihalocarbanion appears to be the major factor determining the energy of activation in both reactions. In aqueous solution the haloform will be the only product of trihaloacetate decarboxylation if the protonation of the trihalocarbanion is fast as compared to the separation of a halide ion, $k_{-1} \gg k_2$ in Eq. (6). When, however, the two rates are comparable, some of the trihalocarbanions should hydrolyze via a dihalocarbene. This prediction has been verified in the decarboxylation of dichlorofluoroacetate (46). Analyses for the carbon monoxide and formate ion produced gave calculated yields of dichlorofluoromethane (69 ± 6%) reasonably near that found by direct analysis in one experiment (72%). This observation probably indicates that about 30% of the dichlorofluorocarbanions lose a chloride ion to give chlorofluorocarbene rather than being protonated by the solvent.

The decarboxylation of chlorodifluoroacetate ion (47) produces very little chlorodifluoromethane, but the yield increases on addition of chloride ion. Fluoride, bromide, and iodide bring about the formation of fluoroform, bromodifluoromethane, and difluoroiodomethane, respectively. It appears, therefore, that chlorodifluoroacetate ion decomposes by a concerted mechanism to give carbon dioxide, chloride ion, and difluorocarbene without any intermediate formation of the chlorodifluoromethyl anion:

$$CClF_2{-}CO_2^{\ominus} \rightarrow \overset{\delta\ominus}{Cl} \ldots CF_2 \ldots \overset{\delta\ominus}{CO_2} \rightarrow {:}CF_2 + Cl^{\ominus} + CO_2$$

$$\Big\downarrow F^{\ominus} \qquad\qquad\qquad\qquad\qquad X^{\ominus}\diagup\diagdown HO^{\ominus}, H_2O \qquad (13)$$

$$CF_3{-}CO_2^{\ominus} + Cl^{\ominus} \qquad\qquad CF_2X^{\ominus} \qquad CO \text{ and } HCO_2^{\ominus}$$

$$\Big\downarrow H_2O$$

$$HCF_2X \quad (X = F, Cl, Br, I)$$

Some $S_N2$ attack of fluoride ion on the chlorodifluoroacetate ion to give trifluoroacetate also occurs, but trifluoroacetate decarboxylates too slowly to yield a significant amount of fluoroform under the reaction conditions employed here. The rate of decarboxylation of chlorodifluoroacetate is about 40 times as large as would be expected from an interpolation of the data on trichloro-, dichlorofluoro-, and trifluoroacetates. The abnormal rate provides further evidence for the concerted character of the reaction (cf. Section I,A,1,b).

The decarboxylation of salts of trichloroacetic acid in an aprotic solvent is a convenient method to produce the trichloromethyl anion and dichlorocarbene, under neutral conditions (48, 49). 1,2-Dimethoxyethane is a suitable solvent; the decompositions in tetrahydrofuran and ethyl acetate are notably slower. The rates of decarboxylation of the alkali trichloroacetates are in the order K > Na > Li, but the sodium salt is more easily prepared in a dry state. The intermediacy of the trichlorocarbanion is shown by the addition to the carbonyl group of ketones, and by chlorine abstraction from various perchloro compounds to give carbon tetrachloride (50). In the presence of olefins, including some base-sensitive compounds, dichlorocyclopropanes are formed in good yields. Difluorocarbene, produced by the thermal breakdown of sodium chlorodifluoroacetate in diglyme, has been trapped by cyclohexene (51).

The thermal decarboxylation of sodium trichloroacetate in 1,2-dimethoxyethane without added acceptor leads to a variety of products, but has been shown to proceed by way of trichloroacetic anhydride (50). Trichloroacetic anhydride was also the major product of the decarboxylation of silver trichloroacetate (52). Trichloroacetyl chloride, arising by attack of dichlorocarbene on the trichloroacetate ion, is thought to be an intermediate in anhydride formation:

$$Cl_3C—CO_2^{\ominus} \; + \; :CCl_2 \rightarrow Cl_3C—CO—O—\overset{\ominus}{\underset{..}{C}}Cl_2$$
$$\rightarrow Cl_3C—CO—O—\underset{..}{C}Cl + Cl^{\ominus} \rightarrow Cl_3C—CO—Cl + CO \tag{14}$$

The treatment of trichloroacetic acid with concentrated aqueous silver nitrate afforded chloropicrin, $Cl_3C—NO_2$, as the major product, possibly arising from a sequence similar to Eq. (14) (53). Only minor amounts of dichloronorcarane could be obtained in the presence of cyclohexene.

### 3. Basic Cleavage of Alkyl Trichloroacetates and Related Compounds

The reaction of esters of trichloroacetic acid with alkoxide represents a convenient synthesis of dichlorocarbene (54, 55). The alkyl trichloroacetates undergo carbonate cleavage to give dialkyl carbonates and, presumably, the trichloromethyl anion. No attempts to trap the anion have been made, but the reactions of dichlorocarbene, arising from the trichlorocarbanion by loss of chloride ion, have been studied thoroughly.

$$Cl_3C-\overset{\overset{\displaystyle O}{\|}}{C}-OR + R'O^{\ominus} \rightarrow Cl_3C-\underset{\underset{\displaystyle OR'}{|}}{\overset{\overset{\displaystyle O^{\ominus}}{|}}{C}}-OR \rightarrow Cl_3C + RO-\overset{\overset{\displaystyle O}{\|}}{C}-OR'$$

$$Cl_3C^{\ominus} \rightarrow :CCl_2 + Cl^{\ominus} \tag{15}$$

The yields of dichlorocarbene, as estimated from the yields of dichlorocyclopropanes obtained in the presence of olefins, are excellent regardless of the base used (potassium tert-butoxide, sodium ethoxide, sodium methoxide). Excess olefin or pentane has been used as a solvent.

Dichlorocarbene is produced in much lower yield from tert-butyl dichloroacetate under similar conditions (54, 56) (13% of 1,1-dichloro-2,2-dimethylcyclopropane were obtained in the presence of isobutene, as compared to 86% from trichloroacetate). It has been proposed (56) that tert-butyl dichloroacetate is converted, in the presence of potassium tert-butoxide, into a mixture of tert-butyl chloroacetate and tert-butyl trichloroacetate, the latter giving dichlorocarbene and di-tert-butyl carbonate according to Eq. (15).

$$Cl_2CH-CO_2R + RO^{\ominus} \rightleftharpoons Cl\overset{\ominus}{C}H-CO_2R + ROCl$$

$$Cl\overset{\ominus}{C}H-CO_2R + ROH \rightleftharpoons ClCH_2-CO_2R + RO^{\ominus}$$

$$Cl_2CH-CO_2R + RO^{\ominus} \rightleftharpoons Cl_2\overset{\ominus}{C}-CO_2R + ROH \tag{16}$$

$$Cl_2\overset{\ominus}{C}-CO_2R + ROCl \rightarrow Cl_3C-CO_2R + RO^{\ominus}$$

The mechanism suggested for this disproportionation involves abstraction of positive chlorine as well as of hydrogen from the dichloroacetate by base. Whereas this step has not been substantiated, the reaction of dichloroacetate with tert-butyl hypochlorite in the presence of base has been shown to give dichlorocarbene and some tert-butyl trichloroacetate (*56*).  A similar disproportionation of dichloroacetonitril has been observed.

As in alkyl trichloroacetates, the carbonyl group of hexachloroacetone is highly reactive toward nucleophiles, thereby enabling the trichloromethyl anion to break away with the electron pair by which it was originally linked to the carbonyl group.  Hexachloroacetone readily yields dichlorocarbene in an aprotic medium on treatment with a base such as sodium methoxide (*57, 58*). The methyl trichloroacetate formed in the first step may react with sodium methoxide to give more dichlorocarbene according to Eq. (15).

$$Cl_3C-CO-CCl_3 + CH_3O^{\ominus} \rightarrow Cl_3C-CO-OCH_3 + Cl_3C^{\ominus}$$

$$Cl_3C^{\ominus} \rightarrow :CCl_2 + Cl^{\ominus} \tag{17}$$

In the presence of olefins, some reduction of hexachloroacetone to form hexachloroisopropanol occurs, the olefin probably being the source of hydrogen as no reduction was observed on addition of dichlorocyclopropanes (the reaction products) (*57*). *sym*-Difluorotetrachloroacetone and potassium *tert*-butoxide have been used as a convenient source of chlorofluorocarbene (*58a*).

The reactions of methyl trichloromethylsulfinate (III) and of trichloromethylsulfonyl chloride (IV) with alkoxide present a mechanistically similar situation (*59*).  The yields of dichlorocarbene addition to olefins are inferior to those obtained by reactions (15) and (17).

$$Cl_3C-SO_2CH_3 + RO^{\ominus} \rightarrow RO-SO_2CH_3 + Cl_3C^{\ominus} \rightarrow :CCl_2 + Cl^{\ominus}$$

(III)                                                              (18)

$$Cl_3C-SO_2Cl + 2RO^{\ominus} \rightarrow RO-SO_2OR + Cl_3C^{\ominus} \rightarrow :CCl_2 + Cl^{\ominus}$$

(IV)                                                              (19)

### 4. Halogen-Metal Exchange at Tetrahalomethanes

The attempted preparation of trifluoromethyllithium from trifluoroiodomethane by halogen-metal exchange led to the formation of tetrafluoroethylene in 43% yield (*60*).  This observation suggests the possible intermediacy of difluorocarbene, formed by decomposition of trifluoromethyllithium.  Dibromodifluoromethane appears to be better suited for the production of difluorocarbene because of the facile separation of bromide ion from the hypothetical intermediate, bromodifluoromethyllithium.  Franzen (*61–63*) has studied the dibromodifluoromethane and *n*-butyllithium system.

$$Br_2CF_2 + n\text{-BuLi} \rightarrow n\text{-BuBr} + [BrCF_2Li] \xrightarrow[-LiBr]{} :CF_2 \tag{20}$$

Difluorocarbene has been trapped by addition to olefins and to triphenylphosphine (61) and may also react with excess n-butyllithium (61, 62). The reaction, Eq. (20), has been conducted in a flow system in order to determine the lifetime of the various intermediates involved (63). On quenching the reaction with methanol after $10^{-4}$ sec. (the shortest reaction time possible with the equipment used), no alkali (LiOMe) was found, and it was concluded that bromodifluoromethyllithium had completely disappeared after $10^{-4}$ sec. Quenching by cyclohexene produced difluoronorcarane after reaction times of $1.2 \times 10^{-4}$ and $4.7 \times 10^{-4}$ sec., but not after $10^{-3}$ sec. (Tetrafluoroethylene was found in the latter experiment.) The half life of difluorocarbene thus appears to be about $5 \times 10^{-4}$ sec. under the conditions used by Franzen. (The formation of tetrafluoroethylene suggests that difluorocarbene disappears by some bimolecular reaction. Therefore its half life should depend strongly on concentration.)

When a variety of polyhalogenated methanes were treated with methyllithium or n-butyllithium in the presence of excess cyclohexene, olefin-carbene addition products were formed (64). Carbon tetrachloride gave low yields (the transfer of positive chlorine presenting difficulties), but bromotrichloromethane and trichloroiodomethane are well suited for the synthesis of dichlorocarbene. Attempts to produce dibromocarbene from carbon tetrabromide were less successful. The presence of trichloromethyllithium in reaction mixtures could not be shown by hydrolysis at $-60°$ (64), nor could the intermediacy of dichlorocarbene be established by use of a flow system (63).

Evidence has been obtained for the formation of the trichlorocarbanion and dichlorocarbene in the reaction of carbon tetrachloride and bromotrichloromethane with potassium tert-butoxide (64a).

$$t\text{-BuO}^{\ominus} + X\text{—CCl}_3 \rightarrow t\text{-BuO-X} + {}^{\ominus}:CCl_3 \rightarrow :CCl_2 + Cl^{\ominus}$$

The treatment of tetrahalomethanes with lithium metal (65) is mechanistically slightly different from the aforementioned reactions, since two halogen atoms are eliminated as halide ions. Dichlorocarbene was produced from carbon tetrachloride but also from chloroform where hydrogen in addition to chlorine appears to be replaced by lithium. While dichlorocarbene and chlorocarbene resulted in a ratio of about 2:1 from chloroform, bromoform gave mainly bromocarbene.

### 5. Thermal and Photochemical Reactions

In the first part of this section some reactions should be mentioned which are distinguished from the $\alpha$-eliminations, discussed above, by an increased stability of the organometallic intermediate. Thus trichloromethyltrichlorosilane (V) decomposes at 250° with the formation of tetrachlorosilane and dichlorocarbene, which has been added to cyclohexene (66). The decomposition of tribromomethyl phenyl mercury (VI) requires less vigorous conditions; dibromonorcarane was obtained in excellent yield from cyclohexene in refluxing benzene (67). The trichloro compound also decomposes at this temperature but needs prolonged heating.

$$Cl_3C-SiCl_3 \xrightarrow{250°} SiCl_4 + :CCl_2 \qquad (21)$$
$$(V)$$

$$Ph-Hg-CX_3 \xrightarrow{80°} Ph-Hg-X + :CX_2 \qquad (22)$$
$$(VI) \qquad\qquad (X = Cl, Br)$$

Some tetrafluoroethylene and perfluorocyclopropane were found in the thermal decomposition of tristrifluoromethylarsine and -stibine at 180°–220° (68). Perfluorocyclopropane resulted in almost quantitative yield from the pyrolysis of trimethyl-trifluoromethyl-tin (VII) at 150° (69). The authors agree in suggesting that the three-membered ring is produced by the addition of difluorocarbene to tetrafluoroethylene.

$$(CH_3)_3SnCF_3 \xrightarrow{150°} (CH_3)_3SnF + :CF_2 \rightarrow F_2C\underset{CF_2}{\diagup\diagdown}CF_2 \qquad (23)$$
$$(VII)$$

Several trifluoromethyl derivatives of pentavalent phosphorus proved to be valuable sources of difluorocarbene (69a):

$$
\begin{array}{ccc}
(CF_3)_3P + SF_4 & & (CF_3)_2PCl_3 + SbF_3 \\
\downarrow & & \downarrow \\
(CF_3)_3PF_2 & \rightleftharpoons & (CF_3)_2PF_3 + :CF_2 \\
(VIIa) & & \| \\
CF_3PCl_4 + SbF_3 & \longrightarrow & CF_3PF_4 + :CF_2 \\
& & \| \\
& & PF_5 + :CF_2
\end{array}
\qquad (23a)
$$

VIIa decomposed at 120° with formation of tetrafluoroethylene (10%), hexafluorocyclopropane (80%), and polytetrafluoroethylene (10%). At

200° the products were 80% of tetrafluoroethylene, 10% of hexafluoro-cyclopropane, and 10% of polytetrafluoroethylene (69a).

The UV absorption (70) and emission (71) bands of difluorocarbene were recorded during an electrical discharge through fluorocarbon vapor. The absorption spectrum of difluorocarbene was also observed when carbon tetrafluoride gas thermally decomposed in a graphite tube furnace (72). Analysis of the spectra indicates (71, 73) that difluoro-carbene is a nonlinear symmetrical molecule with a singlet ground state.

Perfluorocyclopropane was found among the products of irradiation of tetrafluoroethylene with pentafluoroiodoethane (74). Perfluorocyclo-propane was also produced in the irradiation of tetrafluoroethylene in the presence of mercury (75), and in the presence of nitrosyl fluoride (76). These observations may be explained in terms of a dissociation of tetrafluoroethylene to give difluorocarbene.

By using high intensity flash photolysis techniques, it was possible to follow the transient formation and slow decay of the absorption bands of difluorocarbene, produced from some halogenated ketones (77). The ketones included 1,3-dichloro-1,1,3,3-tetrafluoroacetone (VIII) and 1,1,3-trichloro-1,3,3-trifluoroacetone. The formation of difluorocarbene is thought to proceed via substituted acetonyl radicals (IX).

$$CF_2Cl—CO—CClF_2 \xrightarrow{h\nu} ClF_2C—CO— CF_2 \cdot + Cl \cdot$$
$$\text{(VIII)} \tag{24}$$

$$ClF_2C—CO—CF_2 \cdot \rightarrow ClF_2C \cdot + CO + :CF_2$$
$$\text{(IX)}$$

In the presence of oxygen, $ClO \cdot$ was detected, confirming the pro-duction of chlorine atoms. Under the experimental conditions used, the strongest absorption bands of difluorocarbene could be detected as long as 20 msec. after the flash, confirming the great stability of difluoro-carbene as compared with methylene (15 $\mu$sec.). The decay of difluoro-carbene absorption appears to be zero order, suggesting that difluoro-carbene is removed by diffusion to the walls of the reaction vessel.

The decomposition of carbon tetrachloride on pure tungsten gave rise to dichlorocarbene and chlorine (mass spectrometric analysis) (78). On carburized tungsten the results were essentially the same as were obtained with pure tungsten. It has been concluded that the reaction

$$CCl_4 + C \rightarrow 2 :CCl_2 \tag{25}$$

does not occur. A preliminary report (79) claiming that dichlorocarbene

had been obtained from reaction (25) as a liquid, stable at low temperatures, was not confirmed in a careful investigation (80).

The decomposition of chloroform at 485°–600° was studied without
carrier gas, and in a stream of toluene (81). The reaction was homogeneous and first order above 15 mm.; little, if any, radical abstraction
of hydrogen from toluene was observed. The reversible (?) formation
of dichlorocarbene and hydrogen chloride was suggested as the first step
in the thermal decomposition of chloroform (81).

## B. Reaction of Dihalocarbenes

### 1. Insertion Reactions

Few reactions of dihalocarbenes afford products arising by apparent
insertion of the carbenes into single bonds. Although the exact course
of these reactions has not been fully elucidated, it is obvious that they
scarcely, if ever, proceed by the direct (three-center) mechanism established for methylene.

The first instance of apparent carbon-hydrogen insertion of dichlorocarbene (produced from ethyl trichloroacetate and sodium methoxide)
was observed with 2-H-1-benzothiopyrane (X) (82). Two products, 2-
dichloromethyl-2-H-1-benzothiopyrane (XI) and 4-dichloromethyl-2-H-
1-benzothiopyran (XII) were obtained in a 2.4:1 ratio (1:1 if the dichlorocarbene was generated from sodium trichloroacetate). The distribution
of products in the allylic system suggests that an ambident ion (XIII)
is involved, and the reaction may occur as in Eq. (26).

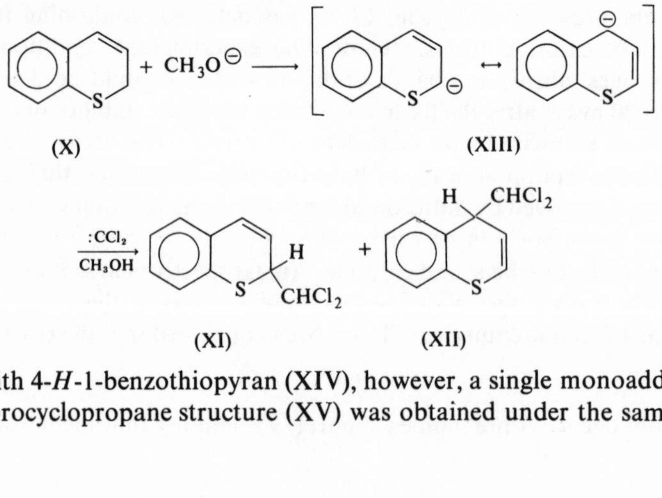

(26)

With 4-H-1-benzothiopyran (XIV), however, a single monoadduct of
dichlorocyclopropane structure (XV) was obtained under the same con-

ditions. The difference noted for the two isomeric benzothiopyrans suggests that a common intermediate ion is not involved. $3p$-Orbital interaction in XIV may activate the olefinic bond for reaction with the electrophilic carbene.

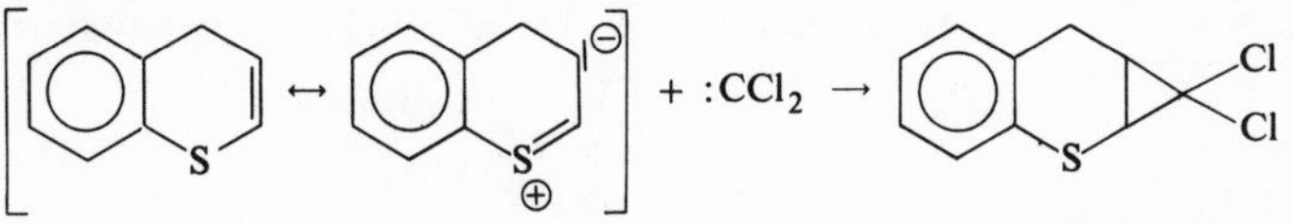

$$(27)$$

(XIV)                    (XV)

Dichlorocarbene, and dibromocarbene, afforded an insertion product as well as the normally expected adduct with 2,5-dihydrofuran (82a). The ratio of 6,6-dichloro-3-oxabicyclo[3.1.0]hexane (XVa) to 2-dichloromethyl-2,5-dihydrofuran (XVb) was 1.88 when dichlorocarbene was generated from ethyl trichloroacetate and sodium methoxide, and 1.12 with sodium trichloroacetate as the carbene precursor.

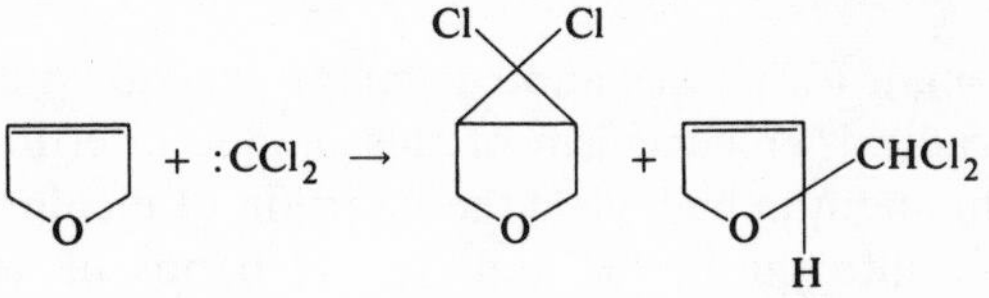

(XVa)        (XVb)

Dichlorocarbene has also been found to react with alkyl-substituted aromatic hydrocarbons with apparent insertion into the benzylic carbon-hydrogen bonds (83). The reaction with cumene to give $\beta$, $\beta$-dichloro-tert-butylbenzene (XVI) is typical

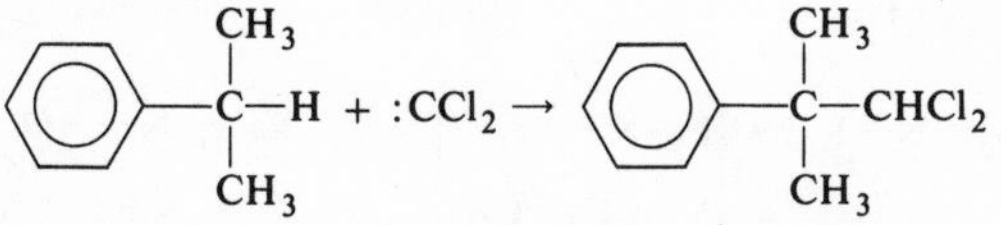

(33%)        $$(28)$$

(XVI)

Other hydrocarbons undergoing this reaction include $p$-diisopropylbenzene, tetralin, and diphenylmethane. Best yields resulted when dichlorocarbene was produced by thermal decomposition of sodium trichloroacetate. Only 0.5–5% of XVI were obtained from cumene by methods generating dichlorocarbene in alkaline media. It has been suggested that the additional thermal energy may be needed for the insertion reaction (83). The insertion mechanism is certainly not of the three-center type observed with methylene, since optically active *sec*-butyl-benzene was found to produce XVII with complete racemization (*84*).

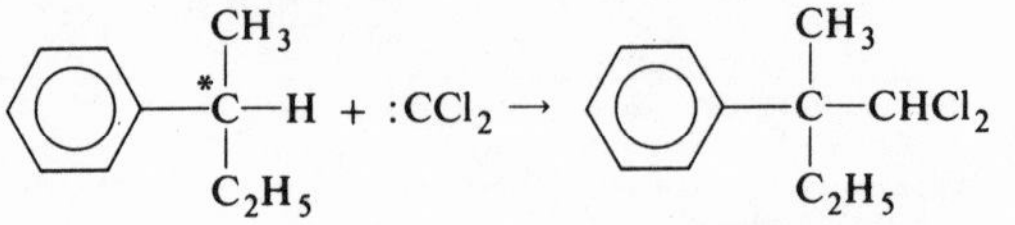

$$
\underset{\text{(XVII)}}{\overset{\displaystyle CH_3}{\underset{\displaystyle C_2H_5}{\overset{|}{\underset{|}{\overset{*}{C}}}}-H}} + :CCl_2 \rightarrow \underset{\text{(XVII)}}{\overset{\displaystyle CH_3}{\underset{\displaystyle C_2H_5}{\overset{|}{\underset{|}{C}}}-CHCl_2}} \quad \text{(inactive)} \qquad (29)
$$

Dichlorocarbene produced from bromodichloromethyl phenyl mercury [cf. Eq. (22)] was found to insert not only into the (benzylic) C—H bonds of ethylbenzene and cumene, but also into those of cyclohexane (*84a*).

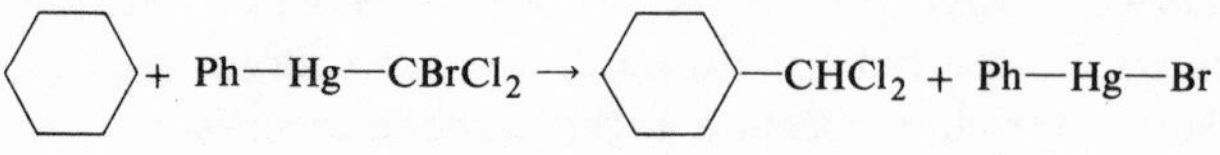

$$
\bigcirc + \text{Ph—Hg—CBrCl}_2 \rightarrow \bigcirc\text{—CHCl}_2 + \text{Ph—Hg—Br}
$$

$$32\%$$

Cyclohexyl bromide (22%) was another major product and may provide a clue to the (radical?) mechanism of this unique insertion. The same reagent brought about in high yield the insertion of dichlorocarbene and dibromocarbene into the Si—H and Ge—H bonds of various silanes and germanes (*84a*).

The formation of 2-trifluoromethyl-3,3,4,4-tetrafluorooxazetidine (XVIII) in the UV irradiation of a mixture of tetrafluoroethylene and nitrosyl fluoride (*76*) indicates that difluorocarbene is inserted into the N—F bond of either nitrosyl fluoride or the intermediate XIX. 2-Pentafluoroethyl-3,3,4,4-tetrafluorooxazetidine (XX) was the only product in the absence of UV light.

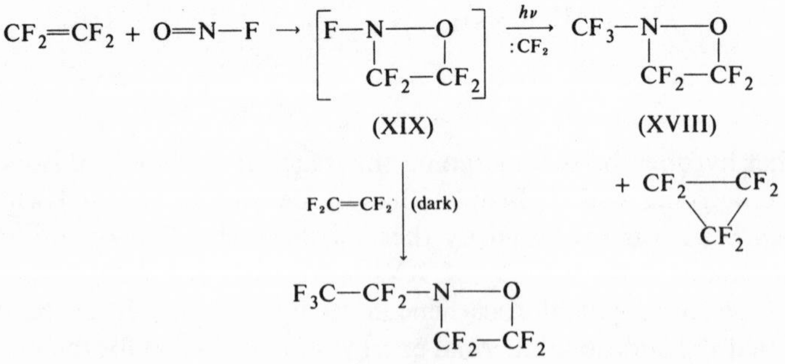

$$
\text{CF}_2{=}\text{CF}_2 + \text{O}{=}\text{N—F} \rightarrow \left[\underset{\underset{\text{(XIX)}}{\text{CF}_2{-}\text{CF}_2}}{\overset{\text{F—N}{-}\text{O}}{\underset{|\qquad\;|}{}}}\right] \xrightarrow[:\text{CF}_2]{h\nu} \underset{\underset{\text{(XVIII)}}{\text{CF}_2{-}\text{CF}_2}}{\overset{\text{CF}_3{-}\text{N}{-}\text{O}}{\underset{|\qquad\;|}{}}} \qquad (30)
$$

$$+ \underset{\text{CF}_2}{\overset{\text{CF}_2{-}\text{CF}_2}{\diagdown\diagup}}$$

$$\text{F}_2\text{C}{=}\text{CF}_2 \;\Big|\; \text{(dark)}$$

$$
\underset{\underset{\text{(XX)}}{\text{CF}_2{-}\text{CF}_2}}{\overset{\text{F}_3\text{C—CF}_2{-}\text{N}{-}\text{O}}{\underset{|\qquad\qquad|}{}}}
$$

The synthesis of aryl(trihalomethyl)-mercury compounds by reaction of an arylmercury halide with chloroform or bromoform and potassium *tert*-butoxide (*85*) was attributed to the insertion of a dihalocarbene into the mercury-halogen bond. Seyferth and Burlitch (*86*) have shown, however, that the reaction proceeds by simple nucleophilic displacement of a halide ion by the trihalomethyl anion. Thus phenylmercuric bromide with chloroform and potassium *tert*-butoxide gave only phenyl-(trichloromethyl)-mercury whereas bromodichloromethane afforded phenyl(bromodichloromethyl)-mercury.

$$X_3CH + B^\ominus \rightarrow BH + X_3C^\ominus \xrightarrow{\hspace{2cm}} :CX_2 + X^\ominus$$

$$\downarrow {\scriptstyle + \ Ph-HgY} \qquad\qquad \updownarrow {\scriptstyle + \ Ph-HgY} \qquad (31)$$

$$Ph-Hg-CX_3 + Y^\ominus \qquad Ph-Hg-CX_2Y$$

Similarly, $HgBr_2$ reacted with chloroform and potassium *tert*-butoxide to give, as the only organomercurial, trichloromethylmercuric bromide, $Br-Hg-CCl_3$ (1.2%). A 44% yield of this compound was obtained from mercuric bromide and sodium trichloroacetate (*86a*).

### 2. Reactions with Olefins

*a. Stereochemistry, Reactivity, and Mechanism.* Following the first report (*32*) of dihalocarbene addition to olefins (*32*), many authors have been engaged in this field, studying the mechanism of the reaction and extending its synthetic applications. The papers published on the present subject are exceeded in number only by those dealing with the chemistry of methylene itself. Two facts pertaining to the reaction mechanism have clearly emerged from these efforts: (1) The addition of dihalocarbenes to olefins proceeds stereospecifically *cis*; and (2) dihalocarbenes behave as strong electrophiles.

The products of dibromocarbene addition to *cis*- and *trans*-2-butene were shown by infrared (IR) spectroscopy not to be contaminated with each other (*87*); they were further converted to *cis*- and *trans*-1,2-dimethylcyclopropane by reduction with sodium in alcohol (*88*), thus establishing the *cis*-stereochemistry of the addition process.

The rate of addition of dihalocarbenes to olefins has been studied in competition experiments. If a mixture of olefins is employed in excess sufficient to prevent significant changes in concentration during the reaction, the ratio of the rate constants may be obtained directly from the ratio of products.

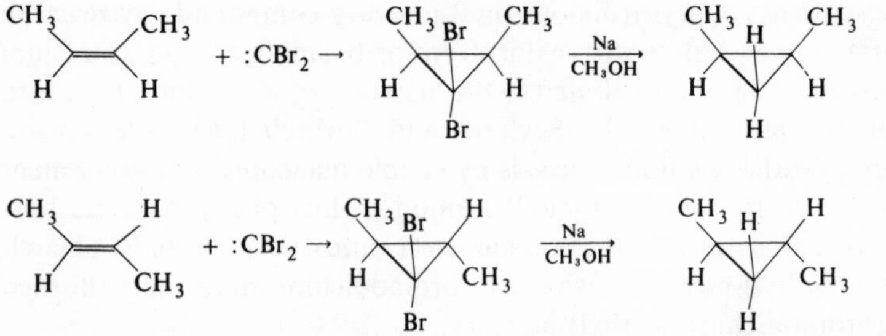

$$(32)$$

The results with dibromocarbene (89, 90) and dichlorocarbene (90) compare well with the relative rates of attack by other electrophiles such as bromine (91), and peracids (92) (Table II). An entirely different pattern of rate constants is observed for attack by trichloromethyl radicals (93). Dibromocarbene appears to be less selective than dichlorocarbene, a result which is consistent with the relative stabilities of dihalocarbenes derived previously (Section I,A,1,a).

Few data concerning steric effects in dihalocarbene addition reactions are available. Competition experiments with 1-substituted cyclohexenes afforded rate constants (relative to cyclohexene) for 1-methyl- and 1-phenylcyclohexene = 6, 1-cyclohexylcyclohexene = 1, and 1-α-naphthylcyclohexene = 0.5 (37). The obvious decrease in rate by bulky groups was attributed to steric hindrance.

TABLE II
RELATIVE REACTIVITIES OF OLEFINS (LOG $k$)

| Reactant:<br>Reference: | $:CCl_2$<br>(90) | $:CBr_2$<br>(89) | $:CBr_2$<br>(90) | $Br^{\oplus}$<br>(91) | $HO^{\oplus}$<br>(92) | $\cdot CCl_3$<br>(93) |
|---|---|---|---|---|---|---|
| 2,3-Dimethyl-2-butene | 1.73 | 0.94 | 0.84 | 1.15 | | |
| 2-Methyl-2-butene | 1.37 | 0.90 | 0.87 | 1.02 | 0.98 | 0.58 |
| Isobutene | 0.92 | 0.40 | 0.57 | 0.74 | −0.15 | 1.35 |
| 2-Methyl-1-butene | 0.74 | | | | | |
| 1,1-Diphenylethylene | | 0.30 | | | | |
| trans-2-Pentene | 0.33 | | | | | |
| Ethyl vinyl ether | 0.27 | | | | | |
| cis-2-Pentene | 0.21 | | | | | |
| Butadiene | | 0.09 | | | | 2.9 |
| Cyclohexene | 0.00 | 0.00 | 0.00 | 0.00 | 0.00 | 0.00 |
| Styrene | | 0.00 | | | | 2.6 |
| 1-Hexene | −0.73 | −0.76 | −0.71 | 0.31 | −1.42 | 0.62 |
| 1-Pentene | −0.86 | | −0.78 | | −1.48 | |
| Allylbenzene | | −1.30 | | | | 0.46 |

Hoberg (94) has recently suggested that the reactions commonly designated as "dihalocarbene additions to olefins" may actually be due to the intermediate trihalocarbanion. This alternative had been considered before (32, 87), and rejected, as carbanions or organometallic compounds are usually unreactive toward nonpolar double bonds. Since then the ability of organometallic compounds bearing $\alpha$-halogen, such as $XZnCH_2X$ (95) and $R_2AlCH_2X$ (94), to convert olefins to cyclopropanes has been discovered. Trihalomethyl anions might also display an increased reactivity toward double bonds, as compared to halogen-free carbanions. It appears appropriate, therefore, to summarize the arguments which support the intermediacy of dihalocarbenes in the formation of dihalocyclopropanes.

A two-step mechanism involving the addition of a trihalocarbanion to the olefin with *subsequent* elimination of halide ion [Eq. (33)] appears highly improbable. Such a mechanism does not explain the stereospecificity of the addition (the organometallic intermediate XXI may be configurationally stable with M = Zn or Al, but certainly not with M = Na or K), nor is it consistent with the function of the olefin as a *nucleophile* (Table II).

$$\begin{matrix} C \\ \| \\ C \end{matrix} + X_3C^\ominus \ M^\oplus \rightarrow \begin{matrix} -C-CX_3 \\ | \\ -C|^\ominus \ M^\oplus \end{matrix} \xrightarrow{-MX} \begin{matrix} -C \\ | \quad CX_2 \\ -C \end{matrix} \qquad (33)$$

(XXI)

One may consider, however, a one-step ($S_N2$) nucleophilic displacement of $X^\ominus$ from the trihalocarbanion by the olefin [Eq. (34)]. This mechanism attributes to the trihalomethyl anion the role of an *electrophile*, and it accounts for the stereospecificity as well.

$$\begin{matrix} C \\ \| \\ C \end{matrix} + X_3C^\ominus \rightarrow \left[ \begin{matrix} -C \\ | \quad CX_2 \text{---} X \\ -C \end{matrix} \right]^\ominus \rightarrow \begin{matrix} -C \\ | \quad CX_2 \\ -C \end{matrix} + X^\ominus \qquad (34)$$

Nucleophilic displacement of chloride by iodide indeed occurs easily with di(chloromethyl)zinc (96, 97) and ethyl chloromethyl mercury (98), but has not been observed with phenyl trichloromethyl mercury (86).

Thus it appears that the introduction of additional $\alpha$-halogen diminishes the rate of nucleophilic displacement, as it does with alkyl halides. It has been shown (Section I,A,1,*a*) that the base-catalyzed reactions of haloforms with nucleophiles proceed by addition to the dihalocarbenes, and not by displacement at the trihalocarbanion. By analogy olefins, taking the place of nucleophiles, may be expected to follow the same course. Furthermore, the kinetic studies by Franzen (*63*) show that formation of difluoronorcarane from the cyclohexene–dibromodifluoro-methane–*n*-butyllithium system takes place *after* all organometallic compounds have disappeared (cf. Section I,A,4). The evidence presented here, though not compelling, supports the addition mechanism, Eq. (32), rather than the displacement mechanism, Eq. (34). The latter may be more important with organometallic intermediates bearing only one or two $\alpha$-halogen atoms (cf. Chapters 2–4).

    *b. Synthesis of Dihalocyclopropanes.* The results obtained with some simple olefins are summarized in Table III. It serves to demonstrate the utility of various carbene precursors but does not cover all dihalocyclopropanes which have been prepared.

TABLE III
DIHALOCYCLOPROPANES FROM DIHALOCARBENE ADDITION TO OLEFINS

| Olefin | Carbene Precursor | Product | Yield (%) | Ref. |
|--------|-------------------|---------|-----------|------|
| 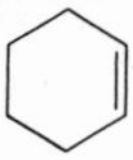 | $CHCl_3$ + KO—*t*-Bu | 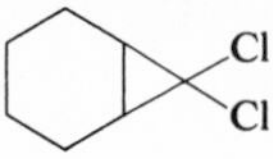 | 59 | *32* |
|  | $CHCl_3$ + NaOMe |  | 38 | *34* |
|  | $Cl_3C$—$CO_2Na$ |  | 65 | *48, 48* |
|  | $Cl_3C$—$CO_2Ag$ |  | 10 | *52, 53* |
|  | $Cl_3C$—$CO_2Et$ + NaOMe |  | 88 | *55* |
|  | $Cl_2CH$—$CO_2Et$ + NaOMe |  | 13 | *56* |
|  | $Cl_3C$—CO—$CCl_3$ + NaOMe |  | 43, 59 | *57, 58* |
|  | $Cl_3C$—$SO_2Me$ + KO—*t*-Bu |  | 48 | *59* |
|  | $Cl_3C$—$SO_2Cl$ + KO—*t*-Bu |  | 35 | *59* |
|  | $CCl_4$ + *n*-BuLi |  | 50 | *64* |
|  | $CBrCl_3$ + MeLi |  | 67 | *64* |
|  | $CBrCl_3$ + *n*-BuLi |  | 91 | *64* |
|  | $Cl_3C$—$SiCl_3$ |  | 60 | *66* |
| 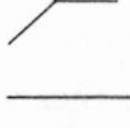 | $CHCl_3$ + KO—*t*-Bu | 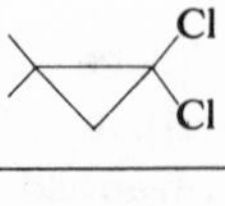 | 65 | *32* |

TABLE III (Continued)

| Olefin | Carbene Precursor | Product | Yield (%) | Ref. |
|---|---|---|---|---|
| | $Cl_3C$—$CO_2Na$ | | 60 | 49 |
| | $Cl_3C$—$CO_2Et$ + KO—$t$-Bu | | 86 | 55 |
| | $Cl_3C$—$SO_2Me$ + KO—$t$-Bu | | 15 | 59 |
| 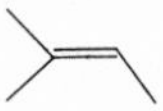 (isobutylene structure) | $CHCl_3$ + KO—$t$-Bu | 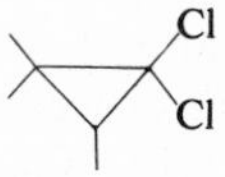 (dichlorocyclopropane with Cl, Cl) | 66 | 32 |
| | $Cl_3C$—CO—$CCl_3$ + NaOMe | | 23 | 57 |
| Ph—CH=$CH_2$ | $CHCl_3$ + KO—$t$-Bu | 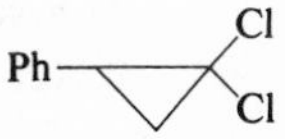 Ph (cyclopropane Cl, Cl) | 74 | 99 |
| Ph—C=$CH_2$ with $CH_3$ | $CHCl_3$ + KO—$t$-Bu | 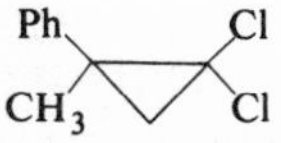 Ph, $CH_3$ (cyclopropane Cl, Cl) | 75 | 99 |
| 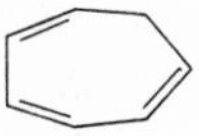 (cycloheptatriene) | $CHCl_3$ + NaOMe | 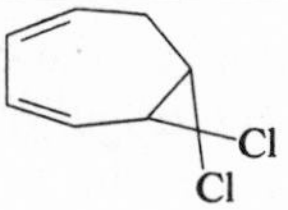 (bicyclic Cl, Cl) | 20 | 33 |
| | $Cl_3C$—$CO_2Na$ | | 46 | 48, 49 |
|  (cyclohexene) | $CHBr_3$ + KO—$t$-Bu | 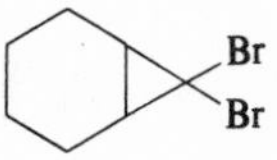 (bicyclic Br, Br) | 75 | 32 |
| | $CBr_4$ + $n$-BuLi | | 11 | 64 |
| | Ph—Hg—$CBr_3$ | | 88 | 67 |
| Ph—CH=$CH_2$ | $CHBr_3$ + KO—$t$-Bu | 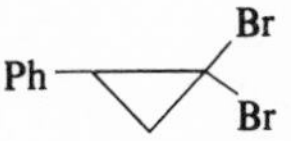 Ph (cyclopropane Br, Br) | 72 | 99 |
| Ph—C=$CH_2$ with $CH_3$ | $CHBr_3$ + KO—$t$-Bu | 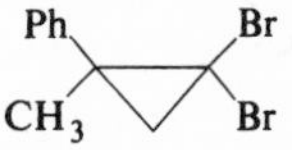 Ph, $CH_3$ (cyclopropane Br, Br) | 81 | 99 |
|  (cyclohexene) | $CF_2Cl$—$CO_2Na$ | 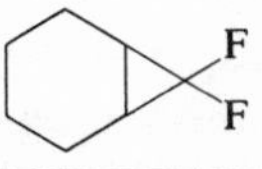 (bicyclic F, F) | 11 | 51 |
| | $CBr_2F_2$ + $n$-BuLi | | ? | 61, 63 |

Trihalomethyl mercurials appear to be particularly valuable carbene presursors when applied to olefins which are of low reactivity toward dihalocarbenes (*99a*). Thus, tetrachloroethylene afforded only 0.2–10% of hexachlorocyclopropane when treated with chloroform and base, or with sodium trichloroacetate (*99b–d*). Trichloroethylene and sodium

trichloroacetate afforded 25% of pentachlorocyclopropane (*99e*).   In
contrast, the reaction of Ph—Hg—CBrCl$_2$ with tetrachloroethylene at
90° produced hexachlorocyclopropane in 74% yield (*99a*).   Bromo-
pentachlorocyclopropane (48%) and 1,1-dibromotetrachlorocyclopro-
pane (26%) were prepared by means of Ph—Hg—CBr$_2$Cl and Ph—
Hg—CBr$_3$, respectively. The dihalocarbene adducts of ethylene, *cis*-
and *trans*-stilbene, and of several vinylsilances have also been obtained
in good yields by this procedure (*99a*).

Various olefins with functional groups have been converted to dihalocyclopropanes. Allyl chloride, a base-sensitive acceptor, afforded a
maximum yield of 59% of 1,1-dichloro-2(chloromethyl)-cyclopropane,
if dichlorocarbene was produced by decarboxylation of sodium trichloroacetate in 1,2-dimethoxyethane (*49*). Two products, 2,2-dichloro-
cyclopropyl acetate (XXII) and 1-trichloromethylethyl acetate (XXIII)
were obtained from vinyl acetate under the same conditions (*49*). The
1-trichloromethylethyl acetate (XXIII) might be formed by addition of
the trichlorocarbanion to the double bond, resulting in the primary
carbanion XXIV. The origin of the proton necessary to neutralize the
carbanion XXIV is not clear.

$$
\begin{array}{l}
\underset{\displaystyle CH_3\overset{\textstyle O}{\overset{\|}{C}}-O-CH=CH_2}{} \xrightarrow{Cl_3C^{\ominus}} CH_3\overset{\textstyle O}{\overset{\|}{C}}-O-\underset{\underset{CCl_3}{|}}{CH}-CH_2^{\ominus} \xrightarrow{H^{\oplus}} CH_3\overset{\textstyle O}{\overset{\|}{C}}-O-\underset{\underset{CCl_3}{|}}{CH}-CH_3
\end{array}
$$

$\downarrow$ :CCl$_2$                                            (XXIV)                              (XXIII)

$$
CH_3\overset{\textstyle O}{\overset{\|}{C}}-O-CH\underset{\underset{Cl \quad Cl}{C}}{\diagup \diagdown}CH_2
$$

(XXII)                                                                                                                                    (35)

Various 2,2-dichloro-1 steroidal cyclopropyl acetates have been prepared from the corresponding enol acetates by the same procedure (*99f*).

Vinyl and allyl ethers accept dichlorocarbene to give dichlorocyclo-
propyl and dichlorocyclopropylcarbinyl ethers, respectively (*99g*).

Cyclic vinyl ethers such as dihydropyran (*100*), 2-*H*-1-benzopyran,
and 4-*H*-1-benzopyran (*101*) were converted to dichlorocyclopropanes
in high yields, using ethyl trichloroacetate and sodium methoxide. Vinyl
sulfides reacted smoothly to give 2,2-dichlorocyclopropyl sulfides (*102*),
and addition of dichlorocarbene to unsaturated silanes has been reported
(*103*).

Dichlorocarbene and difluorocarbene (produced from sodium tri-chloroacetate and chlorodifluoroacetate, respectively) were added to steroids with $\Delta^2$, $\Delta^3$, and $\Delta^5$ unsaturation (104). Dichlorocarbene failed to add to the $\Delta^5$ double bond of XXV and similar structures, whereas difluorocarbene was less selective. The discrimination displayed by dichlorocarbene appears to be due to steric influences: The site of attack by dichlorocarbene changes from the $\Delta^3$ double bond in XXVI, R=CH$_3$, to the $\Delta^5$ double bond in XXVI, R=H. Both double bonds react with difluorocarbene.

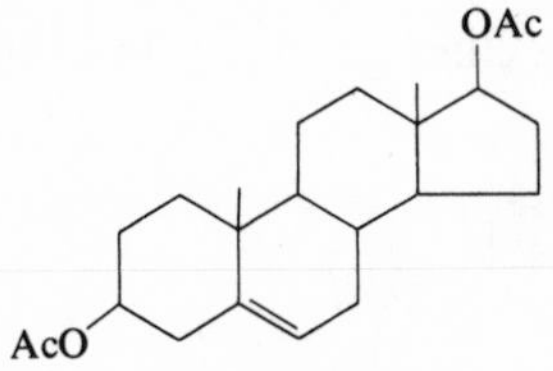

(XXV) 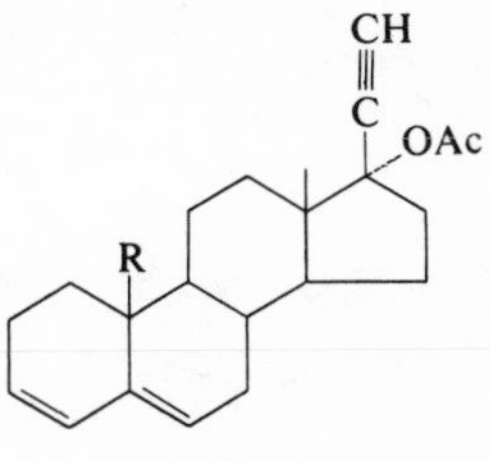                    (XXVI)

*c. Dihalocarbene Addition Accompanied by Rearrangement.* If di-chlorocarbene (from chloroform and base) is added to indene, a product of dichlorocyclopropane structure (XXVII) may be isolated which easily rearranges with loss of hydrogen chloride and ring expansion to give 2-chloronaphthalene (105–107). No cyclopropane intermediates have been isolated with dibromocarbene (106) and chlorobromocarbene (107); the latter affording a mixture of 2-bromo- and 2-chloronaph-thalene.

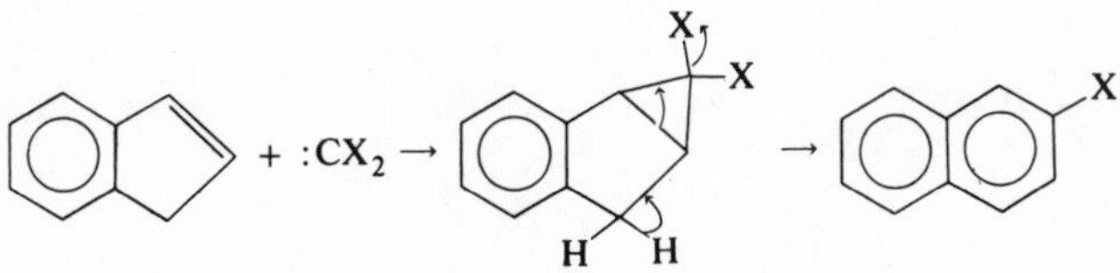

(XXVII)

Yields of 2-fluoronaphthalene (from dichlorofluoromethane, indene and base) are low (7–9%) (107). The reaction has been extended to 1-alkylindenes (106) and 2-alkylindenes (108), giving 1-alkyl-2-halo-naphthalenes and 2-halo-3-alkylnaphthalenes, respectively. The related conversion of pyrrole to 3-chloropyridine (109–111), and of indole to

3-chloroquinoline (*112, 113*) by chloroform and base has long been known and may proceed by a similar mechanism.

Benzofuran reacts with dichlorocarbene in hexane to form an adduct which is converted to bis[3-chloro-2(3-chromenyl)] ether (**XXVIIIc**) by hydrolysis with water. The ether is thought to form as shown in Eq. (36a) (*113a*). The product formed prior to addition of water (**XXVIIIa** or b) has not been identified. Benzothiophene does not react appreciably with dichlorocarbene.

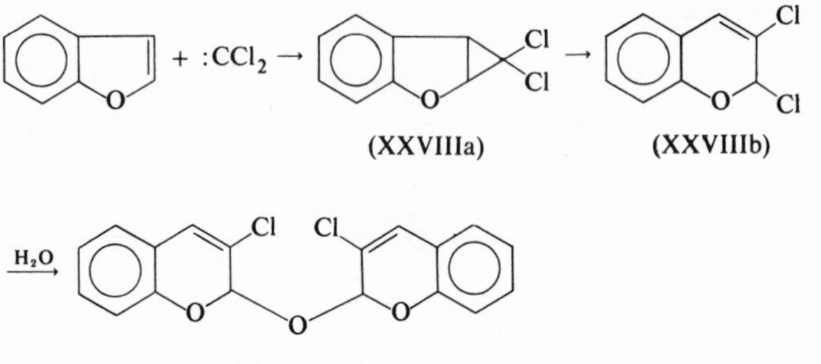

(XXVIIIa)                    (XXVIIIb)

(36a)

(XXVIIIc)

The dichlorocyclopropanes obtained by addition of dichlorocarbene to aliphatic ketene acetals rearrange at temperatures above 100° with elimination of alkyl chloride to give esters of α-chloroacrylic acids (*114*). Ethyl α-bromoacrylate was the only isolable product from ketene diethyl acetal and dibromocarbene (*115*). The hypothetical cyclopropane intermediate in the reaction of phenyl ketene acetals and dichlorocarbene eliminates hydrochloric acid and, with participation of the *tert*-butoxide used to produce the carbene, affords an *ortho*-ester of phenylpropiolic acid (**XXIX**) (*114*).

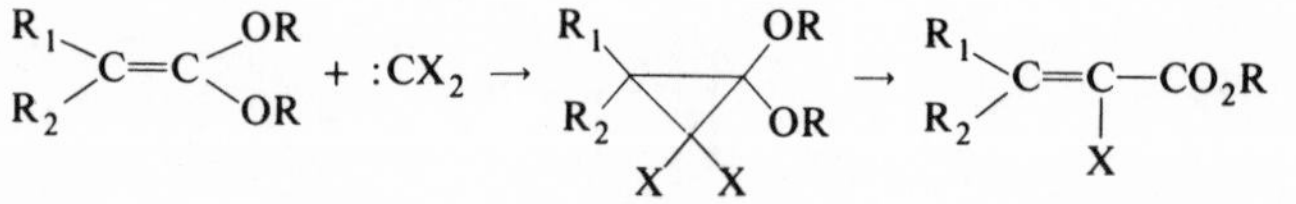

(37)

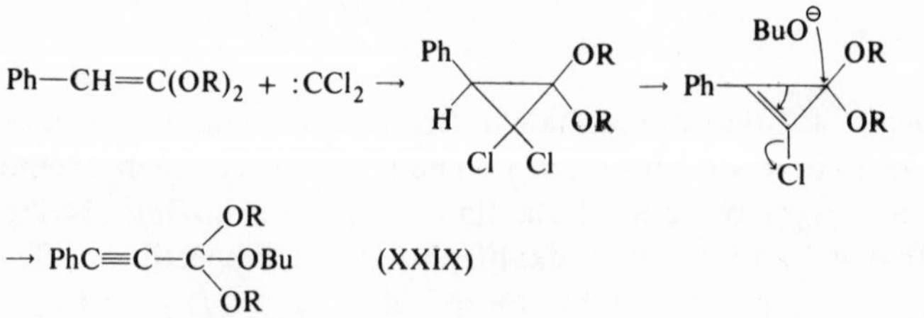

(38)

(XXIX)

The cyclopentene-dibromocarbene adduct (XXX), isolable at low temperatures, rearranges on distillation with the formation of 2,3-dibromocyclohexene (38). 2-Bromo-3-methylcyclohexene, reported by Moore and Ward (116) as arising from the action of methyllithium on XXX, appears to arise instead from the rearranged dibromide XXXI. The conversion of various dihalo-bicyclo[3.1.0]hexanes to 2-halo-3-hydroxycyclohexenes by aqueous silver nitrate (117) may also proceed via rearranged dihalides of cyclohexene structure.

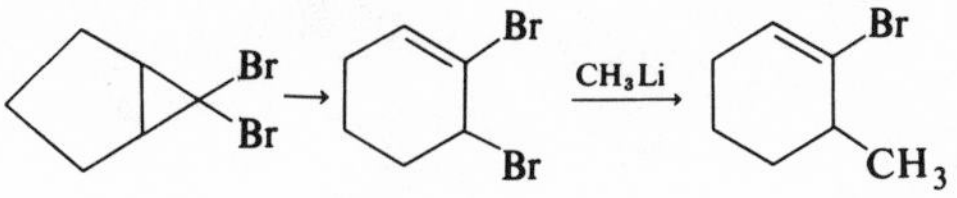

$$(39)$$

$$(XXX) \qquad (XXXI)$$

$$(36a)$$

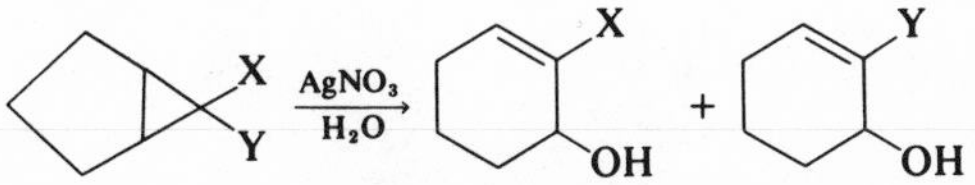

$$(40)$$

The same type of rearrangement has been observed with enamines derived from cyclic ketones.   1-Morpholinocyclopentene reacted with dichlorocarbene to give (after aqueous workup) 2-chloro-2-cyclohexenone (116a).   In contrast, 1-morpholinocyclohexene afforded a stable adduct.

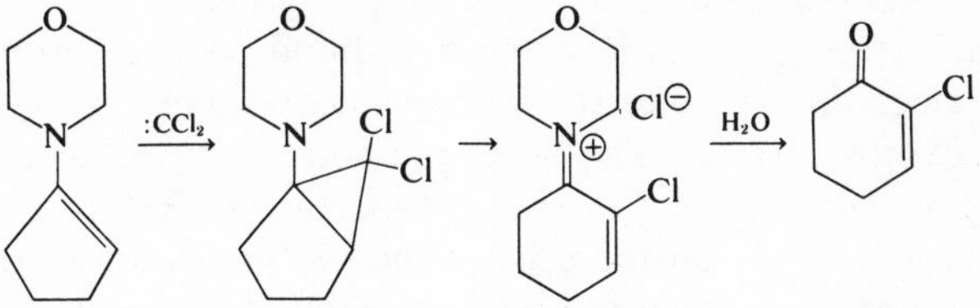

The addition of dihalocarbenes to norbornene has been studied by several research groups (117a–e).  Some authors (117c,d) were able to isolate the tricyclic dichlorocarbene adduct XXXIa (exo structure suggested by N.M.R. evidence) whereas others (117b,e) reported immediate formation of the rearranged product XXXIb.

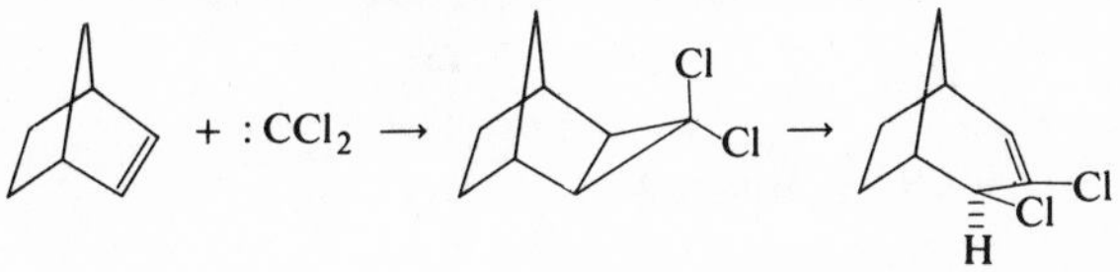

$$(XXXIa) \qquad (XXXIb)$$

Owing to the instability of the bromo analog of **XXXIa**, only 3,4-di-
bromobicyclo[3.2.1]oct-2-ene (**XXXIc**) could be obtained from dibromocarbene and norbornene (*117a,c*).  **XXXIb** and **XXXIc** were converted
to bicyclo[3.2.1]octan-3-one (**XXXId**).

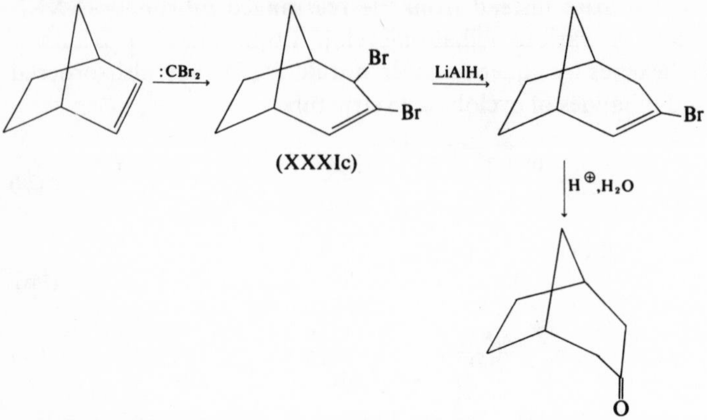

(40a)

d. *Conversions of Dihalocyclopropanes.*   The olefin-dihalocarbene
adducts have found many applications in synthetic organic chemistry.
Some typical examples are discussed in this paragraph.

   1,1-Dihalocyclopropanes have been reduced to cyclopropanes by
sodium in alcohol (*88*), catalytic hydrogenation (*118*), and by lithium
aluminum hydride (*119*).   The latter method was used to synthesize
various spiro compounds, e.g., the spirooctane **XXXII** from methyl-
enecyclohexane (*119*).   On the other hand, 7,7-dihalonorcaranes were
reduced smoothly by sodium in liquid ammonia, but gave low yields of
norcarane with lithium aluminum hydride (*119a*).   The two-step synthesis of cyclopropanes by dihalocarbene addition and reduction is preferred to the addition of methylene as no insertion products were formed.
It may be inferior, however, to the *catalyzed* reactions ($CuCl_2$, $ZnX_2$,
$R_2AlX$) of diazomethane with olefins (cf. Chapter 2, Section II,E,1,*b*).

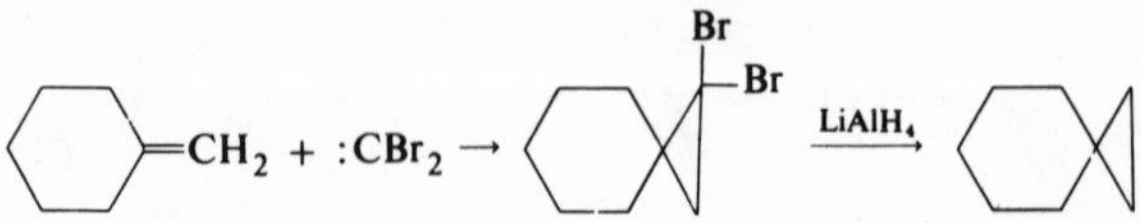

(41)

The two-step dihalocarbene procedure afforded a series of $2\alpha,3\alpha$-methylenecholestanes which were not accessible by the Simmons-Smith technique (*119b*). Phenylcyclopropane was also prepared via dibromo-carbene addition to styrene (*119a,c*).

Partial reduction of *gem.*-dihalocyclopropanes to monohalocyclo-propanes has been achieved in good yield with tri-*n*-butyltin hydride (*119d*).

1,1-Dihalocyclopropanes are converted to allenes by magnesium (*120, 121*), sodium on alumina (*120*), and lithium alkyls (*122*). The synthesis of the strained cyclic allene, 1,2-nonadiene (XXXIII), has been reported (*123*).

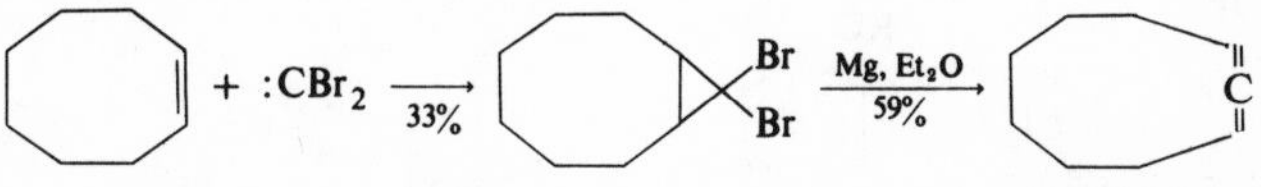

$$\text{(42)}$$

(XXXIII)

Some cases of spontaneous elimination of hydrogen chloride from dichlorocarbene adducts have been mentioned in the preceding paragraph. High temperatures are required to convert 7,7-dichloronorcarane to a mixture of toluene and cycloheptatriene (*34*), and the dichloro-carbene adduct of cycloheptatriene (XXXIV) to chloro-benzocyclo-butene (XXXV) [Eq. (43)] (*33*). The chloro-dihydrooxepine XXXVI has been synthesized from dihydropyran via addition of dichlorocarbene [Eq. (44)] (*100*), but the analogous synthesis of benzoxepines failed (*101*).

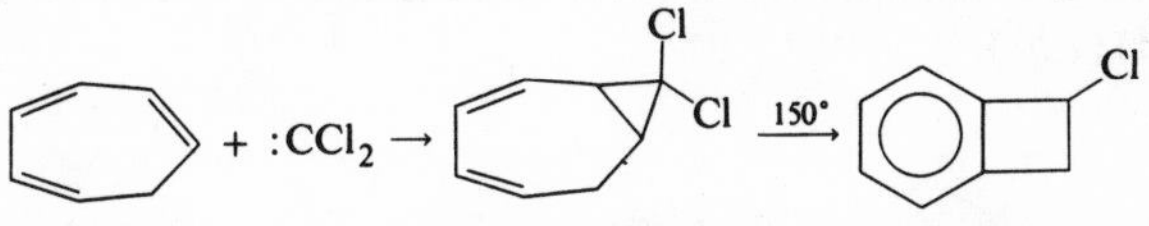

$$\text{(43)}$$

(XXXIV)      (XXXV)

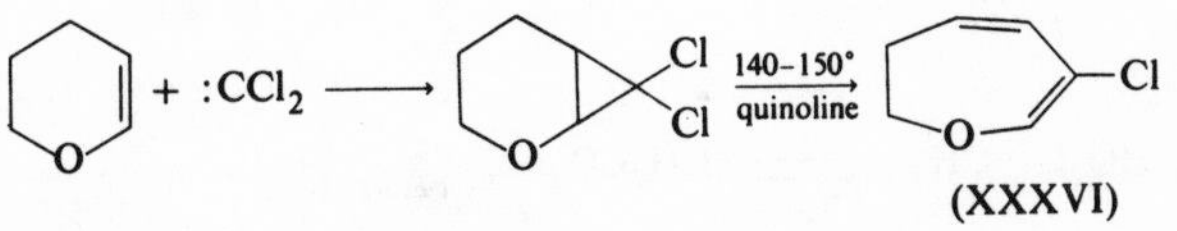

$$\text{(44)}$$

(XXXVI)

The addition of dichlorocarbene to enol ethers of cyclohexanone is involved in a synthesis of dihydrotropone (*124*) [Eq. (45)]. A similar reaction sequence, starting with methoxycyclohexadienes, affords tropone and substituted tropones [Eq. (46)] (*125*).

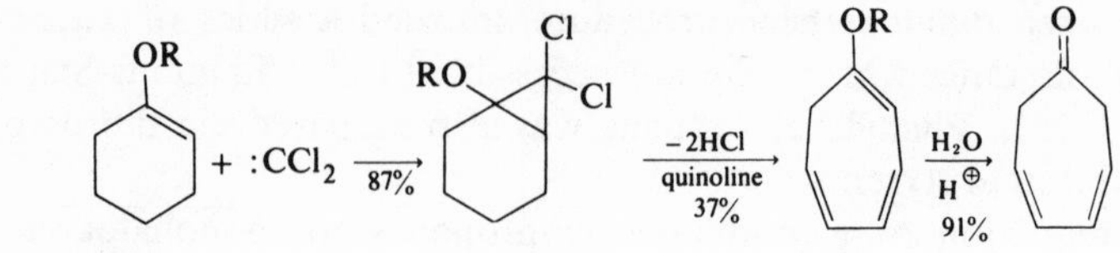

$$(45)$$

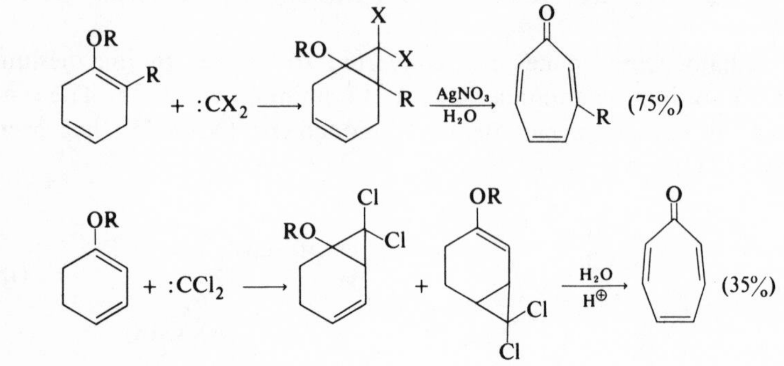

$$(46)$$

Application to 1,4- and 1,2-dihydro derivatives of estrone methyl ether afforded A-homo steroids in good yield (125a).

### 3. Reactions with Dienes

The reaction of dibromocarbene with 1,4-cyclohexadiene has been reported to proceed with mono- and (in smaller amount) di- addition (118, 126, 127). 7,7-Dibromo-4-norcarene was converted to cis-cyclopropane-1,2-diacetic acid (XXXVII) and further to dihydrosterculic acid (XXXVIII) (126).

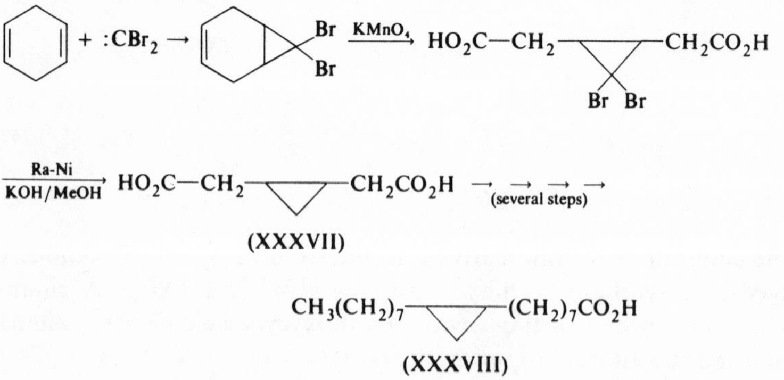

$$(47)$$

(XXXVII)

$$CH_3(CH_2)_7\text{—}\triangledown\text{—}(CH_2)_7CO_2H$$

(XXXVIII)

Dichlorocarbene and cycloocta-1,5-diene afforded the 1:1 adduct (59%) together with a little of the 2:1 adduct (*127a*). The bridged norcaradiene derivative **XXXVIIIa** has been synthesized from 4,7-dihydroindane in several steps, the first of which was addition of dibromocarbene (*127b*):

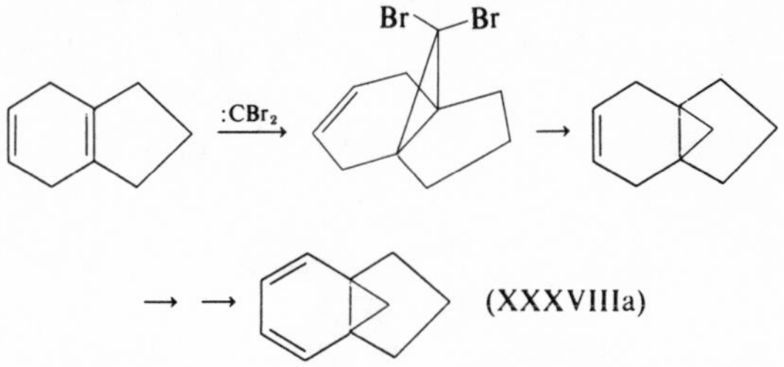

Br    Br

(XXXVIIIa)

1,6-Methanocyclodecapentaene (**XXXVIIIb**), an ingenious recent addition to the interesting series of conjugated, planar cyclopolyenes, has been prepared in a similar sequence from 1,4,5,8-tetrahydronaphthalene (*127c*). Both syntheses utilize the preferential addition of dihalocarbenes to the more highly substituted double bonds.

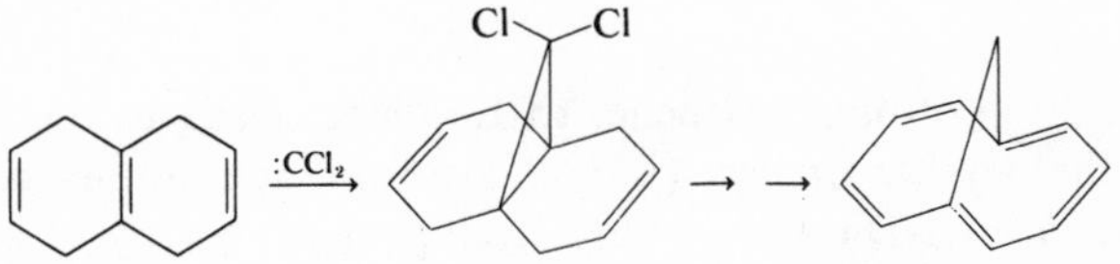

Cl    Cl

(XXXVIIIb)

The unique tricyclo[3.3.2.0$^{4,6}$]deca-2,7,9-triene ("bullvalene") (**XXXVIIIc**) which, owing to a rapidly reversible, degenerate Cope rearrangement, shows only a single H-N.M.R. signal at 100°, has been converted to a less "degenerate" derivative of homotropilidene by additio of dichlorocarbene (*127d*).

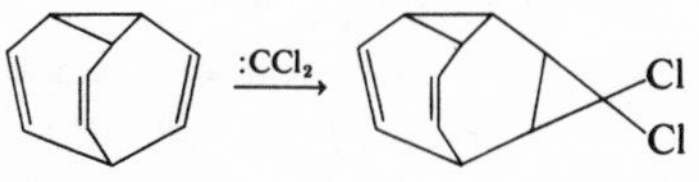

(XXXVIIIc)

Dihalocarbenes add smoothly to allenes. Various allenes of structure **XXXIX** were reported to give dibromocyclopropanes of structure **XL** exclusively (*128*). The same orientation has been observed with dibromocarbene and allenes having terminal methylene groups (XLI) whereas the two possible adducts (XLII and XLIII) occasionally result from dichlorocarbene addition (*129*).

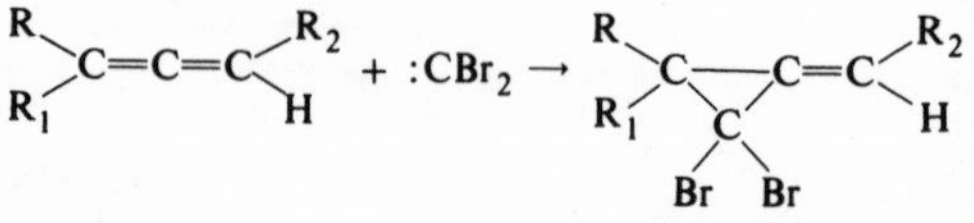

$$\underset{R_1}{\overset{R}{>}}C{=}C{=}\underset{H}{\overset{R_2}{C{<}}} + :CBr_2 \rightarrow \underset{R_1}{\overset{R}{>}}C{-}\underset{\underset{Br\quad Br}{\overset{|}{C}}}{C}{-}C{=}\underset{H}{\overset{R_2}{C{<}}} \tag{48}$$

(XXXIX)                                 (XL)

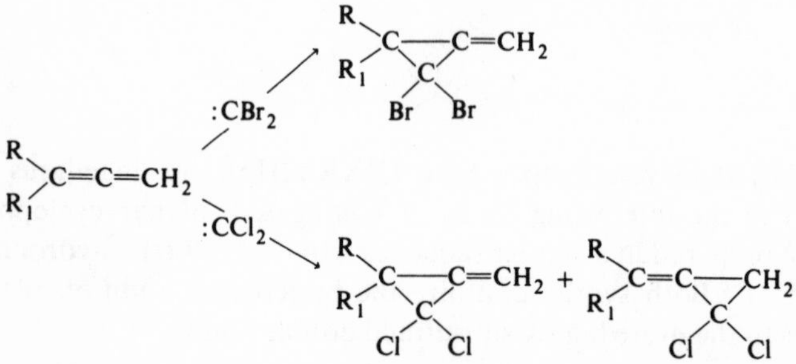

$$\underset{R_1}{\overset{R}{>}}C{=}C{=}CH_2 \quad\begin{cases} \overset{:CBr_2}{\nearrow} & \underset{R_1}{\overset{R}{>}}C{-}\underset{\underset{Br\quad Br}{\overset{|}{C}}}{C}{=}CH_2 \\ \\ \underset{\searrow}{:CCl_2} & \underset{R_1}{\overset{R}{>}}C{-}\underset{\underset{Cl\quad Cl}{\overset{|}{C}}}{C}{=}CH_2 + \underset{R_1}{\overset{R}{>}}C{=}C{-}\underset{\underset{Cl\quad Cl}{\overset{|}{C}}}{C}H_2 \end{cases} \tag{49}$$

(XLI)                    (XLII)              (XLIII)

The addition of dihalocarbenes to 1,3-dienes leads to the formation of vinyl-dihalocyclopropanes (*130*). Twofold addition is difficult to achieve (*131*). 1,1-Dichloro-2-vinyl-cyclopropane on pyrolysis affords a mixture of chloroolefins among which 1-chlorocyclopentadiene predominates (*132*). The preferred site of reaction in isoprene is the methyl-substituted double bond (*131, 133, 134*), a result which may be expected if the relative reactivities of different olefins (Table II) apply also to intramolecular competition. It is surprising, however, that chloroprene appears to follow a similar course (*135*), Eq. (51).

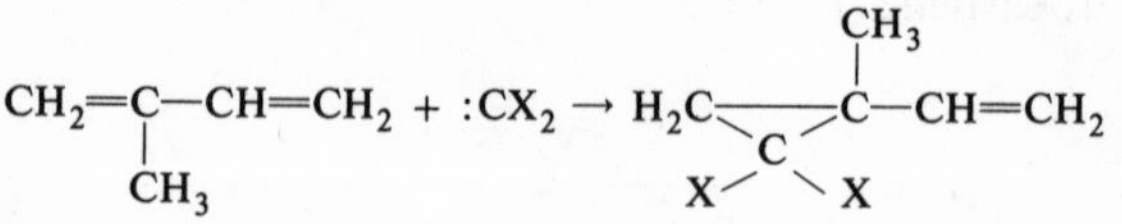

$$CH_2{=}\underset{\underset{CH_3}{|}}{C}{-}CH{=}CH_2 + :CX_2 \rightarrow H_2C{-}\underset{\underset{X\quad X}{\overset{|}{C}}}{C}{-}\overset{CH_3}{\overset{|}{C}}{-}CH{=}CH_2 \tag{50}$$

$$CH_2{=}\underset{\underset{Cl}{|}}{C}{-}CH{=}CH_2 + :CCl_2 \rightarrow H_2C{-}\underset{\underset{Cl\quad Cl}{\overset{|}{C}}}{C}{-}\overset{Cl}{\overset{|}{C}}{-}CH{=}CH_2 \xrightarrow{Ox.} H_2C{-}\underset{\underset{Cl\quad Cl}{\overset{|}{C}}}{C}{-}\overset{Cl}{\overset{|}{C}}{-}CO_2H \tag{51}$$

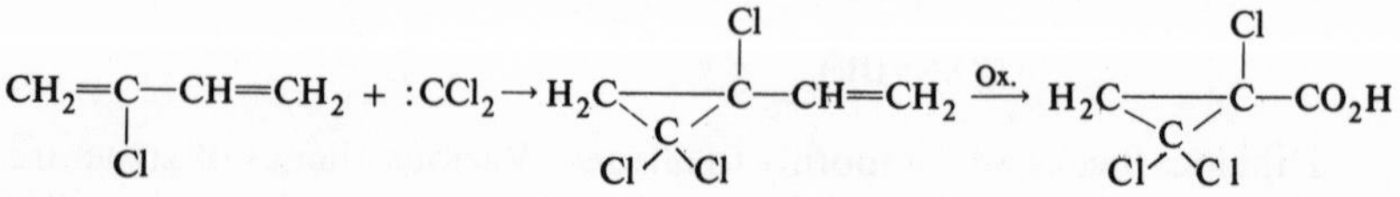

## 4. Reactions with Acetylenes

Acetylenes are much less reactive toward dihalocarbenes than olefins. If both double and triple bonds are present within the same molecule, reaction at the olefinic site takes place in good yields without any attack on the acetylene (136, 137). It does not matter whether the acetylenic bond (136) or the olefinic bond (137) occupies the terminal position.

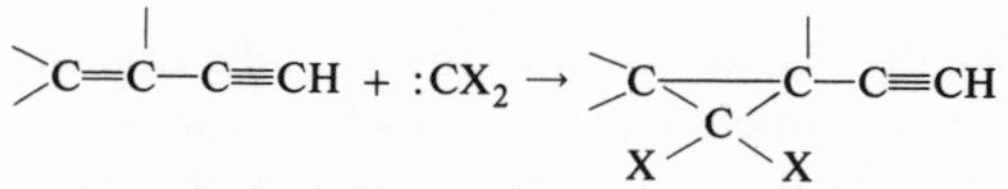

$$\text{>C=C-C≡CH} + :CX_2 \rightarrow \text{>C} \underset{X \quad X}{\overset{C}{\diagup \diagdown}} \text{C-C≡CH} \tag{52}$$

$$CH_3-C≡C-\underset{\underset{CH_3}{|}}{C}=CH_2 + :CCl_2 \rightarrow CH_3-C≡C-\underset{\underset{Cl \quad Cl}{C}}{\overset{\overset{CH_3}{|}}{C}}CH_2 \tag{53}$$

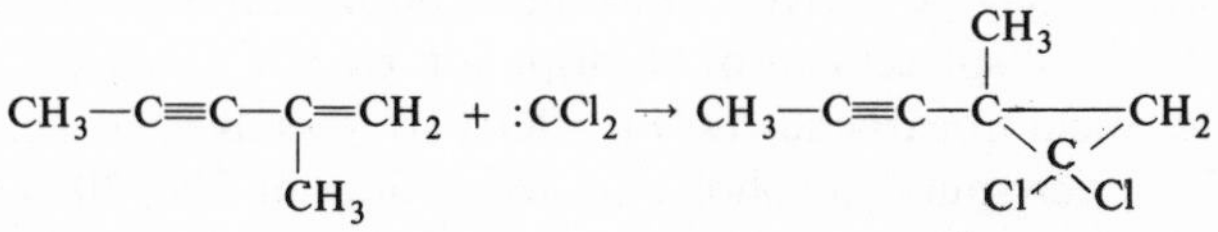

Addition of dihalocarbenes to acetylenes has been achieved with diphenylacetylene (138) and di-n-propylacetylene (139). The dihalocyclopropene intermediates (XLIV), presumably very unstable, were hydrolyzed to give cyclopropenones (XLV) the isolation of which is facilitated by their unique properties (solubility in aqueous acids, due to the formation of cyclopropenium ions). (Yield of di-n-propyl-cyclopropenone: 5%.)

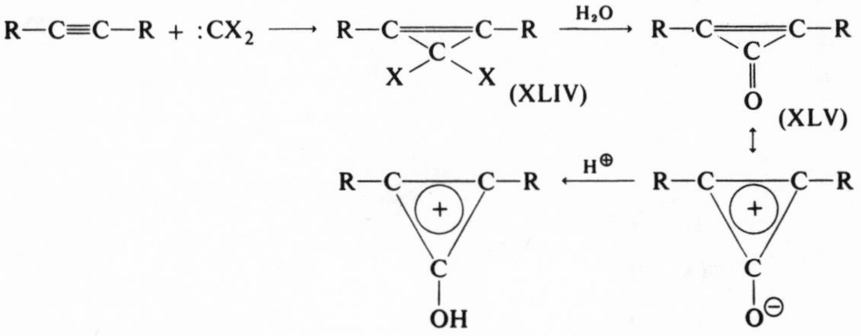

$$R-C≡C-R + :CX_2 \longrightarrow R-C\underset{\underset{X \quad X}{C}}{=}C-R \overset{H_2O}{\longrightarrow} R-C\underset{\underset{\overset{||}{O}}{C}}{=}C-R \tag{(XLIV)} \tag{(XLV)}$$

$$R-C\underset{\underset{OH}{C}}{\overset{+}{\diagup \diagdown}}C-R \overset{H^{\oplus}}{\longleftarrow} R-C\underset{\underset{O^{\ominus}}{C}}{\overset{+}{\diagup \diagdown}}C-R \tag{54}$$

Difluorocarbene [generated by pyrolysis of $(CF_3)_3PF_2$ at $100°$] was added to hexafluoro-2-butyne in the gas phase to give 1,2-bis(trifluoromethyl)-3,3-difluorocyclopropene (XLVI). A second molecule of difluorocarbene could be added to XLVI with the formation of 1,3-bis-(trifluoromethyl)-1,1,4,4-tetrafluorobicyclobutane (XLVII) (140).

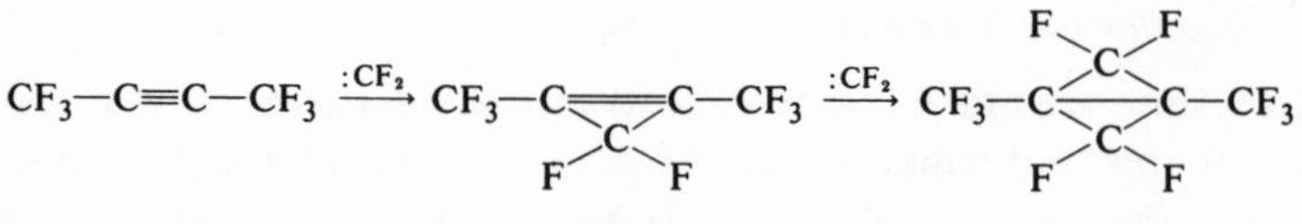

$$CF_3-C\equiv C-CF_3 \xrightarrow{\;:CF_2\;} CF_3-C \overset{\displaystyle =\!\!=}{\underset{\underset{\displaystyle F \quad F}{\diagdown C \diagup}}{\phantom{=}}} C-CF_3 \xrightarrow{\;:CF_2\;} CF_3-C \overset{\overset{\displaystyle F \searrow C \swarrow F}{}}{\underset{\underset{\displaystyle F \quad F}{\diagdown C \diagup}}{\phantom{=}}} C-CF_3$$

$$\text{(XLVI)} \qquad\qquad\qquad \text{(XLVII)}$$

### 5. Reactions with Aromatic Compounds

Most benzene derivatives are inert toward dihalocarbenes, but some aromatic compounds which approach "olefinic character" were found susceptible to attack by dichlorocarbene. Anthracene afforded a product (XLVIII) which may be derived from the hypothetical dichlorocarbene-adduct XLIX by displacement of chloride ion by *tert*-butoxide (used to produce the dichlorocarbene) (*141*). XLVIII dissolves in acids with elimination of *tert*-butyl alcohol and formation of the 10-chloro-di-benzotropylium ion (L).

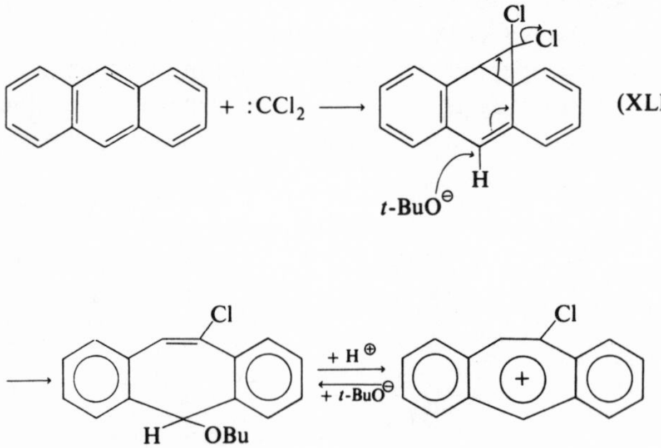

$$(55)$$

(XLVIII)                                (L)

1- and 2-Methoxynaphthalene are converted to the chlorobenzotro-pones LI and LII, respectively, by dichlorocarbene (*142*). Whereas the hypothetical intermediates LIII and LIV decompose spontaneously with loss of methyl chloride, the dichlorocarbene adduct of 9-methoxy-phenanthrene (LV) has been obtained in 52% yield, and has been pyro-lyzed to give the chloro-dibenzotropone LVI (*142*).

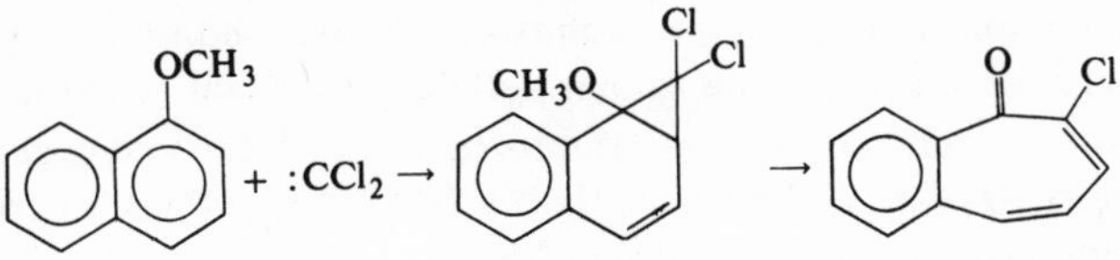

(LIII) (LI)

(56)

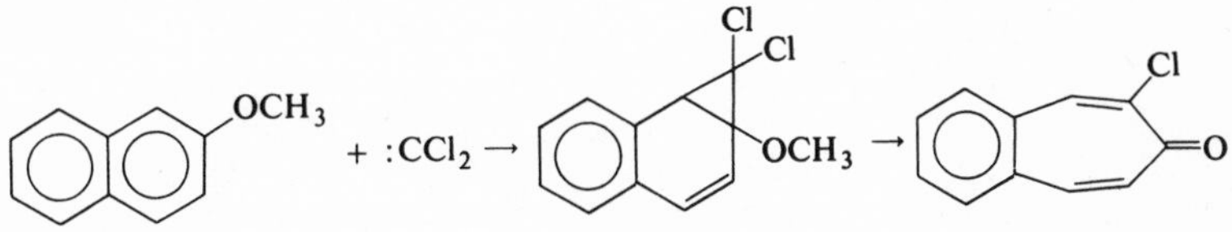

(LIV) (LII)

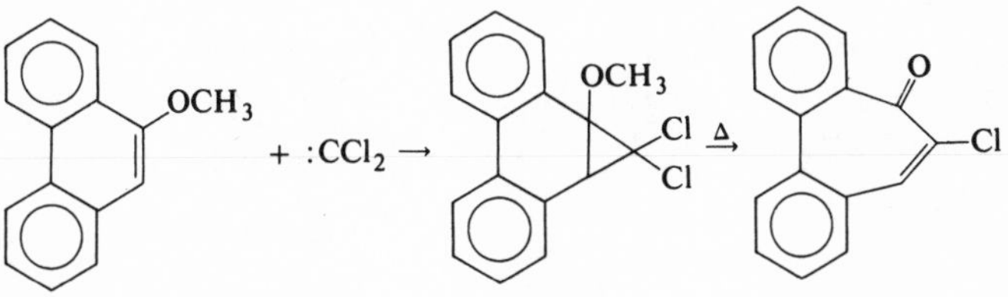

(LV) (LVI)

## 6. *Reactions with Amines and Phosphines*

Addition of dichlorocarbene to the carbon-nitrogen double bond of benzalaniline has been described (*35*, *57*). This reaction has been extended to other imines (LVII), giving 1,3-diaryl-2,2-dichloroaziridines (LVIII) in good yields, regardless of the *p*-substituent in the amine part of LVII (*143*). Hydrolysis of the aziridines LVIII proceeds with rearrangement to give the corresponding $\alpha$-chloro-$\alpha$-phenylacetanilides (LIX) in almost quantitative yields (*35*, *143*).

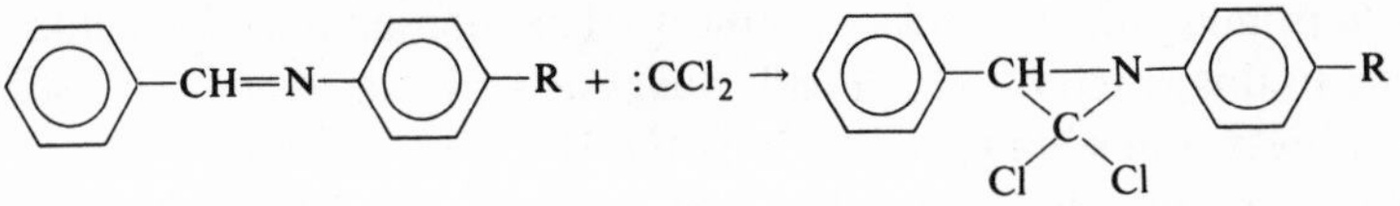

(LVII) (LVIII) (57)

R = H, OEt, Cl

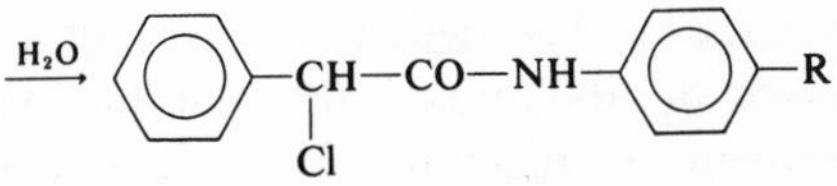

(LIX)

Reaction of an iminium salt, 1-cyclohexenyl-$N$-pyrrolidinium per-chlorate (LX), with dichlorocarbene (generated from sodium trichloro-acetate) led to the formation of $N$-(1-trichloroacetoxy-1-carboxycyclo-hexyl)pyrrolidine (LXI) (*143*). LXI is probably formed by attack of tri-chloroacetate ion on the intermediate imine LXII.

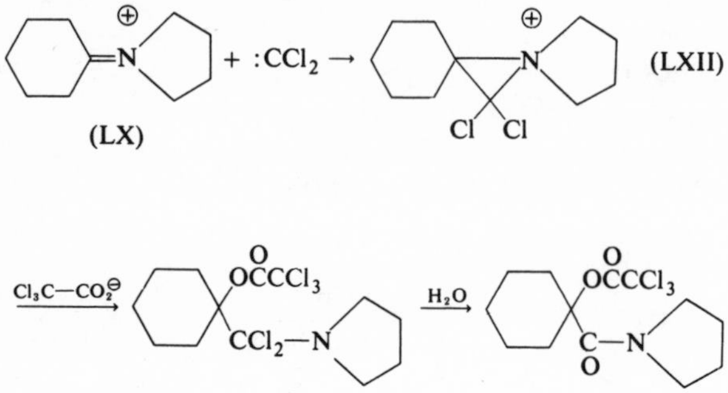

(58)

The conversion of haloforms to cyanide ion by alkali amides in liquid ammonia has long been known (*143a*). The same reaction can be brought about by a variety of other bases, such as alkali hydroxides, alkoxides (*143b*), and alkali diphenylmethides (*143c*) in liquid ammonia. Under these conditions the addition of trihalocarbanions to the carbonyl group of ketones has been achieved in excellent yields (*143b*), but it has not been possible to trap dihalocarbenes by addition to olefins (*143b, c*).

The action of alkali on a mixture of chloroform and a primary amine was first studied by Hoffmann (*144*) in 1867, and has been widely used in synthesis [for literature references see (*145*)] and analysis (to distinguish between primary and secondary amines). The intermediacy of dichloro-carbene in this reaction was already suggested by Nef (*146*), and some recent observations support this hypothesis. The formation of form-amides during the Hoffman isocyanide synthesis has been found to be simultaneous with and not subsequent to isocyanide formation (*145*), and can be accounted for by hydrolysis of the intermediate R—NH —CHCl$_2$. The decarboxylation of sodium trichloroacetate in the pre-sence of arylamines afforded fair yields of isocyanides (*147*). The sequence of reactions, Eq. (59), is consistent with the present evidence concerning the mechanism of the Hoffmann isocyanide synthesis.

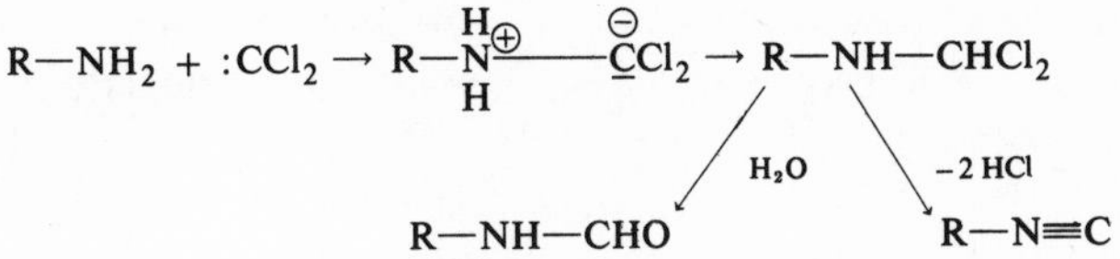

$$R—NH_2 + :CCl_2 \rightarrow R—\overset{H}{\underset{H}{\overset{\oplus}{N}}}—\overset{\ominus}{\underset{}{C}}Cl_2 \rightarrow R—NH—CHCl_2$$

$$\swarrow H_2O \qquad \searrow -2\,HCl \qquad (59)$$

$$R—NH—CHO \qquad\qquad R—N\equiv C$$

Dialkylformamides were the major products (30–60% yields) obtained from secondary amines, chloroform, and a base (*148–150*). The formamides are thought to arise by hydrolysis of the intermediate amidodichlorides which have not been isolated despite precautions taken to exclude water during the reaction. If hydrogen sulfide was introduced into the reaction mixture, thioformamides instead of formamides were produced (*36*). Piperidine reacts with chloroform to yield piperidine hydrochloride and dichloromethylpiperidine (readily hydrolyzed to *N*-formylpiperidine), but the reaction is very slow in the absence of a strong base (*151*).

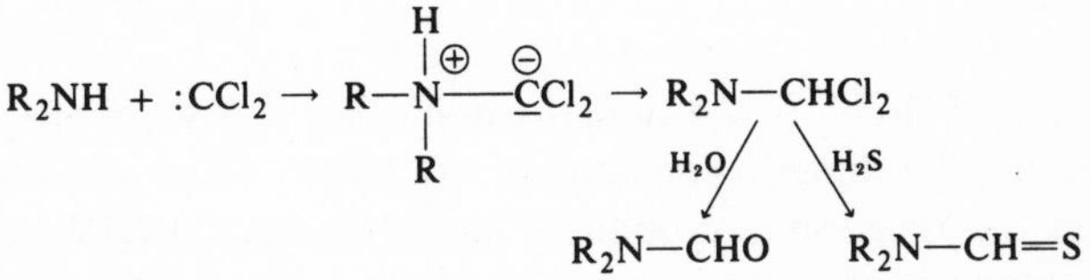

$$R_2NH + :CCl_2 \rightarrow R—\overset{H}{\underset{R}{\overset{\oplus}{N}}}—\overset{\ominus}{\underset{}{C}}Cl_2 \rightarrow R_2N—CHCl_2 \qquad (60)$$

$$\qquad\qquad H_2O \swarrow \qquad \searrow H_2S$$

$$R_2N—CHO \qquad R_2N—CH{=}S$$

Decarboxylation of sodium trichloroacetate in the presence of methylaniline led to the formation of an orthoformamide, *N, N′, N′*-trimethyl-*N, N′, N″*-triphenyl-triaminomethane (LXIII) (*152*). If the first step in this reaction is analogous to Eq. (60), the intermediate amidodichloride must undergo further displacement rather than hydrolysis.

$$Cl_3C—CO_2Na + Ph—NH—CH_3 \rightarrow (Ph—\underset{CH_3}{\overset{}{N}}—)_3CH \quad (20\%) \qquad (61)$$

$$(LXIII)$$

The interaction of pyrrole with dihalocarbenes proceeds with ring expansion to give 3-halopyridines [Eq. (62)] (*153, 154*). Thus the behavior of pyrrole resembles that of indene (cf. Section I,B,2,*c*) rather than that of secondary amines. Some disubstituted indoles accept dichlorocarbene and dibromocarbene with the formation of indolenines (LXIV) instead of (or in addition to) ring expansion [Eq. (63)] (*155, 156*).

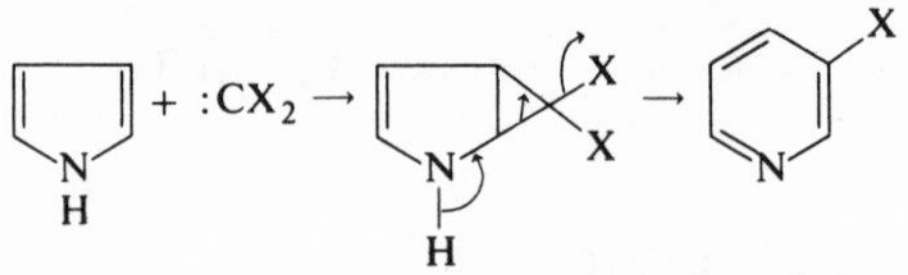

$$(10-12\%) \qquad (62)$$

$$(X = Cl, Br)$$

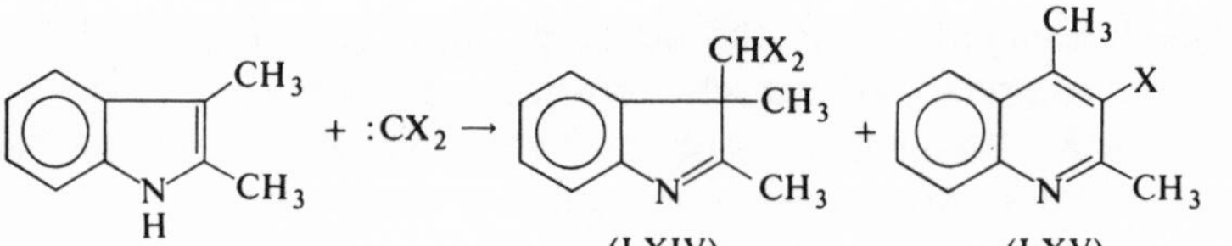

$$(63)$$

(LXIV)          (LXV)

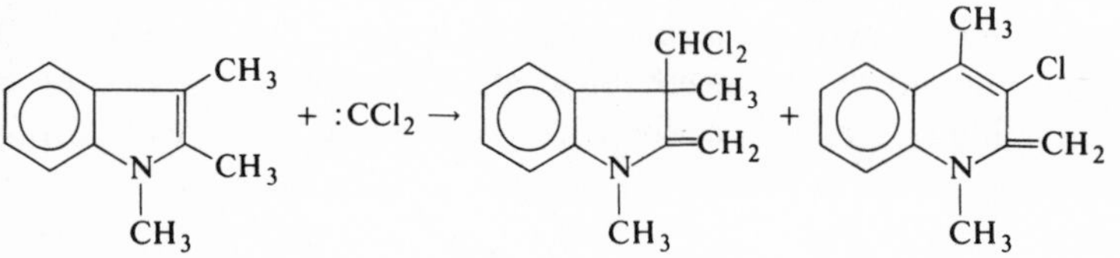

The ratio of 3-chloro-2,4-dimethylquinoline (LXV, X = Cl) to 3-dichloromethyl-2,3-dimethylindolenine (LXIV, X = Cl) depends strongly on the reaction conditions. The ratio LXV:LXIV equals 0.4 when dichlorocarbene is produced from ethyl trichloroacetate and potassium *tert*-butoxide, but changes to 2.6 if sodium trichloroacetate is decomposed in refluxing 1,2-dimethoxyethane (*156*). The figures for dibromocarbene are 1.15 (CHBr$_3$ and EtONa) and 6.4 (Br$_3$C—CO$_2$Na). The variation in product ratio is regarded as strong evidence that the two types of product arise by different pathways. The quinoline (LXV) is thought to form via the 2,3-carbene adduct which decomposes exclusively with loss of halide ion and ring expansion [cf. Eq. (62)]. The indolenine (LXIV) may arise by electrophilic attack of the dihalocarbene at position 3 of the ambident indolyl ion (present in higher concentration in strongly alkaline media).

A variety of products was obtained from tertiary amines and dichlorocarbene, depending on the structure of the amine used (*150*). Benzyldimethylamine reacted to give *N*, *N*-dimethyl-phenylacetamide (LXVI) and dibenzyl. Formation of LXVI is most likely due to a Stevens rearrangement of the benzyl group in the ylide LXVII, formed by addition of dichlorocarbene to benzyldimethylamine. The formation of dibenzyl may be explained by elimination of a benzyl anion from the ylide LXVII, which can be benzylated by the quaternary salt resulting from protonation of the ylide (*150*).

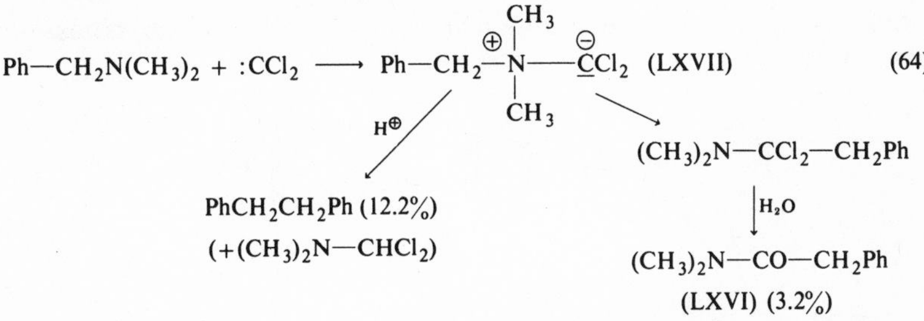

$$Ph—CH_2N(CH_3)_2 + :CCl_2 \longrightarrow Ph—CH_2—\overset{\oplus}{\underset{\underset{CH_3}{|}}{\overset{\overset{CH_3}{|}}{N}}}—\overset{\ominus}{C}Cl_2 \quad (LXVII) \tag{64}$$

$$(CH_3)_2N—CCl_2—CH_2Ph$$

PhCH$_2$CH$_2$Ph (12.2%)
(+(CH$_3$)$_2$N—CHCl$_2$)

$\Big\downarrow$ H$_2$O

$$(CH_3)_2N—CO—CH_2Ph$$
$$(LXVI) \ (3.2\%)$$

When triethylamine was treated with chloroform and potassium *tert*-butoxide, diethylformamide (15.2%) and *N*, *N*-diethyl-α-chloropropionamide (LXVIII) (12%) were obtained (*150*). Diethylformamide probably arises by β-elimination in the initially formed ylide LXIX, followed by hydrolysis. LXVIII is the expected result of a Stevens rearrangement where the product has been chlorinated. A similar chlorinated product, α, α, β-trichloroethyldimethylamine (LXX), was formed from trimethylamine and dichlorocarbene (*150*). The source of the extra chlorine may well be *tert*-butyl hypochlorite [cf. (*56*)] but no final conclusion can be drawn.

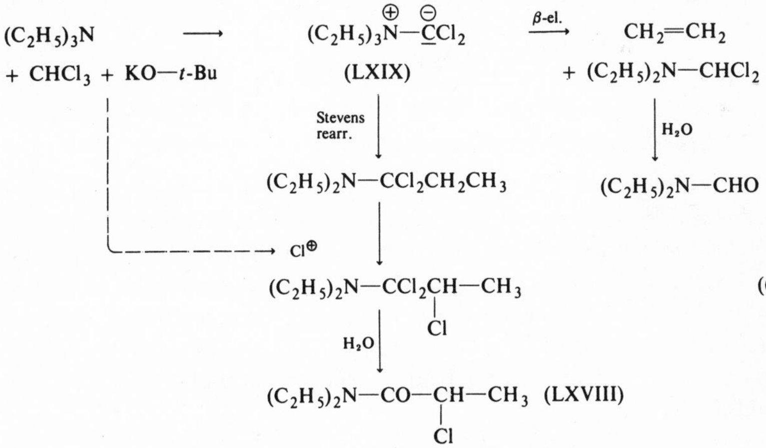

$$(C_2H_5)_3N \longrightarrow (C_2H_5)_3\overset{\oplus}{N}—\overset{\ominus}{C}Cl_2 \overset{\beta\text{-el.}}{\longrightarrow} CH_2=CH_2$$
$$+ CHCl_3 + KO—t\text{-Bu} \qquad (LXIX) \qquad\qquad + (C_2H_5)_2N—CHCl_2$$

Stevens rearr. $\Big\downarrow$        $\Big\downarrow$ H$_2$O

$$(C_2H_5)_2N—CCl_2CH_2CH_3 \qquad\qquad (C_2H_5)_2N—CHO$$

$$\text{Cl}^{\oplus} \qquad \Big\downarrow$$

$$(C_2H_5)_2N—CCl_2\overset{|}{\underset{Cl}{C}H}—CH_3 \tag{65}$$

H$_2$O $\Big\downarrow$

$$(C_2H_5)_2N—CO—\overset{|}{\underset{Cl}{C}H}—CH_3 \quad (LXVIII)$$

$$(CH_3)_3N + CHCl_3 + KO—t\text{-Bu} \longrightarrow (CH_3)_2N—CCl_2CH_2Cl \tag{66}$$
$$(LXX)$$

A novel deoxygenation reaction for pyridine-$N$-oxide using dichloro-carbene has been reported ($156a$). Both Ph—Hg—CCl$_3$ and sodium trichloroacetate were useful as carbene precursors whereas only trace amounts of pyridine were obtained with chloroform and potassium *tert*-butoxide.

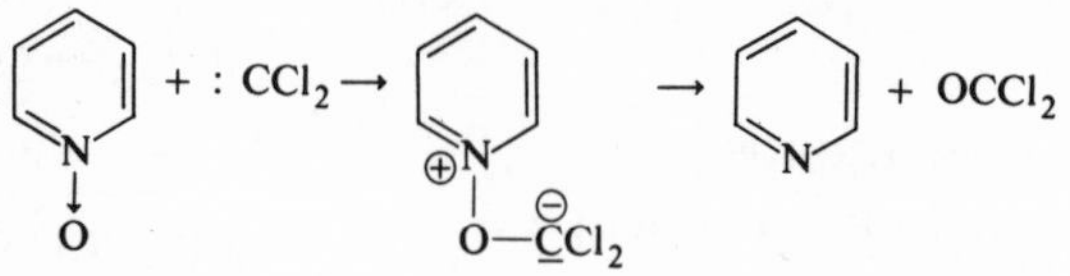

Dichlorocarbene and dibromocarbene have been added to triphenyl-phosphine ($39$, $157$). No isolation of the resulting ylides (LXXI) was attempted; they were used to convert a variety of aldehydes and ketones to 1,1-dihaloolefins (Wittig reaction). Yields were in the range of 30–80%, and generally better with aldehydes than with ketones.

$$Ph_3P + :CX_2 \rightarrow \left[ Ph_3\overset{\oplus}{P}-\overset{\ominus}{\underline{C}}X_2 \leftrightarrow Ph_3P=CX_2 \right] \xrightarrow{R_2C=O} R_2C=CX_2 \qquad (67)$$

$$(LXXI)$$

Phosphorus ylides were found to react with halocarbenes to give olefins according to Eq. (67a) ($157a$):

$$\underset{R}{\overset{R'}{\diagdown}}\overset{\ominus}{C}-\overset{\oplus}{P}R''_3 + :CXY \rightarrow \underset{R}{\overset{R'}{\diagdown}}C=C\overset{X}{\underset{Y}{\diagup}} + PR''_3 \qquad (67a)$$

### 7. Reaction with Diazo Compounds

Photolyses and pyrolyses of diazo compounds frequently afford olefins which are apparent dimers of the carbenes involved. Attack of the carbene on excess diazo compound, rather than actual dimerization, has been considered the most probable path to these products. Evidence supporting this mechanism was provided when dihalocarbenes were produced from haloforms in the presence of diphenyldiazomethane or di-azofluorene. The expected 1,1-dihaloolefins were obtained in 20–85% yields ($158$).

$$R_2CN_2 + :CXY \rightarrow N_2 + R_2C=CXY \qquad (68)$$
$$X = F,Cl,Br$$
$$Y = Cl,Br,Ph$$

In order to exclude the possible intervention of trihalocarbanions in Eq. (68), the competition of diphenyldiazomethane and tetramethylethylene for dichlorcarbene has been studied. The two components were found to react with a common intermediate and proved to be comparable "carbenophiles" (ratio of rate constants = 1.14) (*158*).

### 8. Reactions with Anions

The nucleophiles considered until now as reactants of dihalocarbenes were neutral molecules. This section is devoted to some ionic or highly polar species. The addition of halide ions to dihalocarbenes was an important point in the mechanistic discussion of Section I,A,1,*a*. The addition of halide ions to dihalocarbenes cannot be observed unless the resulting trihalocarbanions revert to haloforms by protonation. Under aprotic conditions halide ions have little influence on the course of dihalocarbene reactions.

The fast hydrolytic reactions converting dihalocarbenes to carbon monoxide and formate ion have not been discussed in Section I,A,1. It has been shown by studying the kinetics in a sealed tube that carbon monoxide and formate ion are not produced simultaneously. Rather, formate ion arises in a slow subsequent reaction from carbon monoxide and hydroxide ion (*159*). Competition experiments with added anions indicate that dichlorocarbene reacts preferentially with water and not with hydroxide ion (*2, 3, 159*). The hydrolysis of dichlorocarbene probably proceeds as represented by Eq. (69).

$$:CCl_2 + H_2O \rightarrow H_2\overset{\oplus}{O}-\overset{\ominus}{C}Cl_2 \xrightarrow{-H^{\oplus}} HO-\overset{\ominus}{C}Cl_2 \xrightarrow{-Cl^{\ominus}} HO-\underset{|}{C}-Cl$$

$$\rightarrow H^{\oplus} + Cl^{\ominus} + CO \xrightarrow[\text{slow}]{HO^{\ominus}} HCO_2^{\ominus}$$

(69)

A similar sequence may be expected for the reaction of dihalocarbenes with alkoxides in alcoholic solution. The evolution of ethylene and carbon monoxide from a refluxing mixture of ethanol, potassium hydroxide, and bromoform was observed as early as 1855 (*160*). The results were duplicated with chloroform (*161*), and the composition of the gas was shown to be independent of the hydroxide ion concentration (*162, 163*). There was some disagreement, however, whether the ethylene was derived from the ethanol (*160*) or from the haloform (*146*). Hine *et al.* (*164*) studied this reaction in various alcohols and obtained the olefins corresponding to the alcohols used. The formation of rearranged and cyclic products (essentially the same as those obtained by nitrous acid deamination of amines) suggests a carbonium ion mechanism (*165*).

$$RO^{\ominus} + :CX_2 \rightarrow X^{\ominus} + R-O-\overset{..}{C}-X \rightarrow R^{\oplus} + CO + X^{\ominus} \qquad (70)$$

If X is fluorine, the intermediate $RO-\overset{..}{C}-F$ does not release fluoride ion but instead adds alcohol to give an alkyl orthoformate as the only product (*166*).

The reaction, Eq. (70), may involve a concerted transition state (LXXII) or a very short-lived carbonium ion. The "deoxidation" of optically active neopentyl alcohol-1-*d* proceeds with predominant formation of *optically active* 2-methyl-1-butene-3-*d* (LXXIII), which is the thermodynamically less stable olefin (*167*).

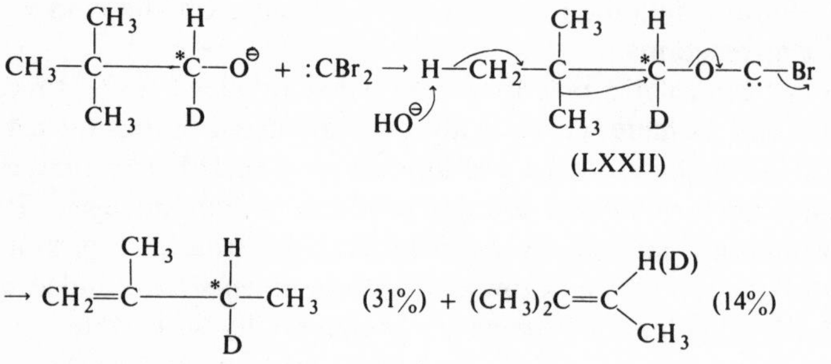

(LXXII)

(71)

(LXXIII)

The familiar Reimer-Tiemann synthesis of phenolic aldehydes (*168, 169*) involves the attack of dichlorocarbene on the *o*- and *p*-positions of phenoxide ions (*170*). Chloroform reacts with aqueous sodium phenoxide only very slowly, but in the presence of sodium hydroxide it reacts rapidly to give *o*- and *p*-hydroxybenzaldehyde (*171*). (The *o*-:*p*-ratio is 1.9 under these conditions, i.e., attack on the *p*-position is slightly favored. In the usual synthetic procedure the *o*-:*p*-ratio is strongly affected by ion-pair formation.) It may be concluded (cf. Section A,1,*a*) that the Reimer-Tiemann reaction is *not* initiated by the nucleophilic attack of phenoxide ion on chloroform. Instead, dichlorocarbene reacts with phenoxide ion. In aqueous solution, water and phenoxide compete for dichlorocarbene. Competition constants $k_{Ph}/k_w$ have been determined for some phenols (*159*): phenol 102, *p*-methoxyphenol 110, guajacol 140, and $\beta$-naphthol 251.

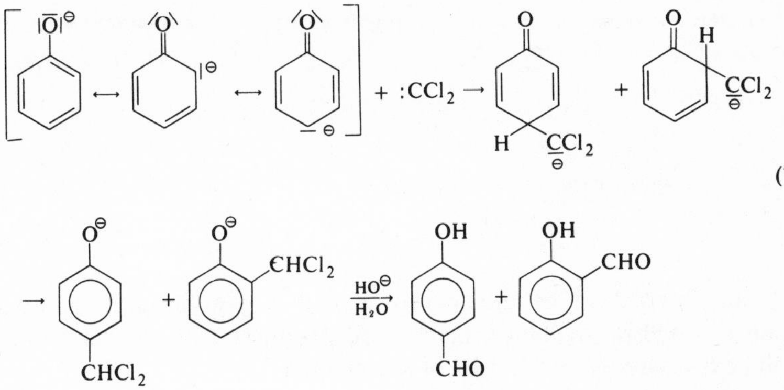

(72)

The reaction of dihalocarbenes with various carbanions derived from (substituted) malonic esters has been studied. Introduction of a difluoromethyl group has been achieved by treating alkyl- and arylmalonic esters, and diphenylacetonitril, with chlorodifluoromethane in the presence of sodium *tert*-butoxide (*172*). Because of the slow $S_N2$ reactions of chlorodifluoromethane, and the strong influence of *tert*-butoxide, difluorocarbene has been suggested as an intermediate in this reaction.

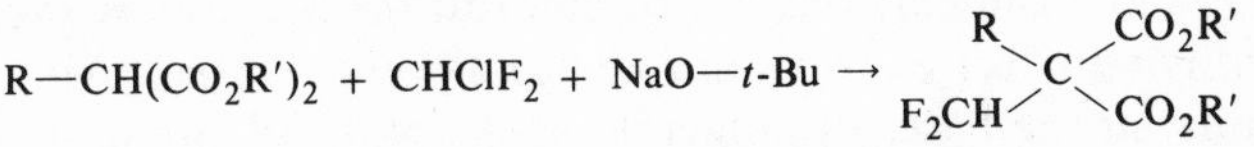

$$R—CH(CO_2R')_2 + CHClF_2 + NaO—t\text{-}Bu \rightarrow \begin{matrix} R \\ F_2CH \end{matrix} C \begin{matrix} CO_2R' \\ CO_2R' \end{matrix} \qquad (73)$$

The analogous dichloromethylation (*173*) and dibromomethylation (*174*) of ethyl methylmalonate is brought about by treatment with haloform and base. The product, LXXIV (X=Cl), was also obtained by decarboxylation of sodium trichloroacetate in the presence of sodium ethyl methylmalonate (*174*). This observation supports the intermediacy of dichlorocarbene. Sodium ethyl malonate is converted to ethyl propene-1,1,3,3-tetracarboxylate (LXXV), a reaction known since 1882 (*175*). A variety of dihalocarbene precursors has been tried recently, and the sequence of reactions [Eq. (75)] has been proposed to account for the formation of LXXV (*176*).

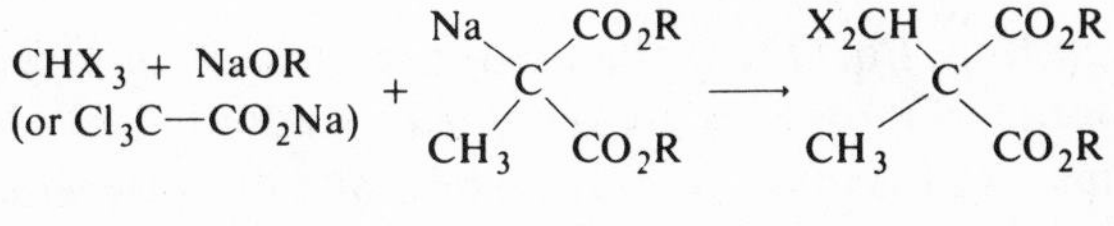

$$\begin{matrix} CHX_3 + NaOR \\ (\text{or } Cl_3C—CO_2Na) \end{matrix} + \begin{matrix} Na \\ CH_3 \end{matrix} C \begin{matrix} CO_2R \\ CO_2R \end{matrix} \longrightarrow \begin{matrix} X_2CH \\ CH_3 \end{matrix} C \begin{matrix} CO_2R \\ CO_2R \end{matrix} \qquad (74)$$

(LXXIV) (X = Cl, Br)

$$NaCH(CO_2R)_2 + :CCl_2 \rightarrow Cl_2\overset{\ominus}{\underset{}{C}}-CH(CO_2R)_2 \rightarrow Cl_2CH-\overset{\ominus}{\underset{}{C}}(CO_2R)_2$$

$$\xrightarrow{-Cl^{\ominus}} \underset{H}{\overset{Cl}{\diagdown}}C=C(CO_2R)_2 \xrightarrow[\text{(Michael)}]{+\,\overset{\ominus}{C}H(CO_2R)_2} (RO_2C)_2CH-\overset{Cl}{\underset{H}{\overset{|}{\underset{|}{C}}}}-\overset{\ominus}{\underset{}{C}}(CO_2R)_2$$

$$\longrightarrow (RO_2C)_2CH-CH=C(CO_2R)_2 \qquad\qquad (75)$$
$$\text{(LXXV)}$$

The interaction of dihalocarbens and organolithium compounds leads to alkyl (aryl) halocarbenes, and products derived therefrom. It will be discussed in Section III of this chapter.

## II. CHLOROCARBENE

Chlorocarbene is the only (mono)halocarbene that has been thoroughly studied so far; most of the work being due to G. L. Closs and his associates. Bromocarbene has not attracted more than occasional interest, and fluorocarbene is still unknown.

Elimination was the most promising route, and for some years the only one, to chlorocarbene. The removal of a proton from methylene chloride is more difficult than from chloroform because of the diminished acidifying effect of two chlorine atoms versus three. Alkyllithium compounds, strong bases of moderate nucleophilicity, are best suited to produce chlorocarbene from methylene chloride (177, 178); low yields have been obtained by use of potassium tert-butoxide (179). Chlorocarbene has been obtained by treatment of chloroform with lithium in tetrahydrofuran (65), but dichlorocarbene is also formed in this process. The reaction of lithium with bromoform appears to give bromocarbene exclusively (65).

$$CH_2Cl_2 + R-Li \rightarrow R-H + [CHCl_2Li] \rightarrow LiCl + :CHCl \qquad (76)$$

$$CHCl_3 + 2\,Li \begin{cases} \nearrow :CHCl + 2\,LiCl \\ \searrow :CCl_2 + LiCl + 1/2\,H_2 \end{cases} \qquad (77)$$

$$CHBr_3 + 2\,Li \rightarrow :CHBr + 2\,LiBr \qquad (78)$$

If the reaction, Eq. (76), is run in the presence of an excess of various olefins, chlorocyclopropanes are obtained by addition of chlorocarbene to the olefins. Yields range from 25 to 67% and increase with the nucleophilic character of the olefin. The addition proceeds strictly cis, but chlorocarbene displays considerable steric discrimination whenever two isomers can be formed (*178*), e.g.:

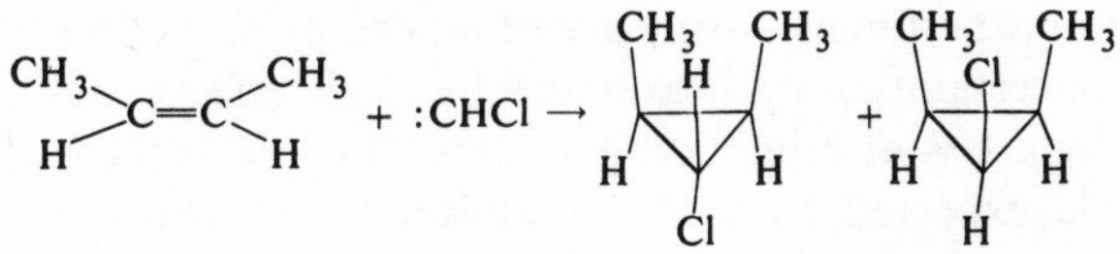

$$(79)$$

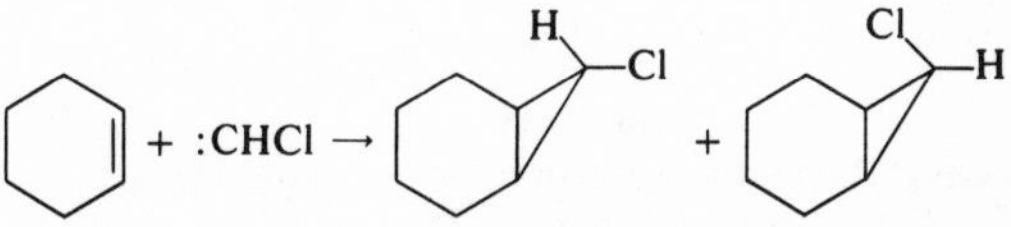

$$(80)$$

Observed isomer ratios were: 2-methyl-2-butene 1.6; 1-pentene 3.4; cyclohexene 3.2; and *cis*-2-butene 5.5. The original assignment of configuration to the stereoisomers (*178*), based on the predictable non-bonded interactions in the transition state, turned out to be in error and has recently been reversed (*178a*). The two adducts of chlorocarbene to 1-butene, LXXVI and LXXVII, were synthesized from *cis*- and *trans*-1-chloro-1-butene via the stereospecific Simmons-Smith reaction (methylene iodide and zinc-copper couple). The product obtained from *trans*-1-chloro-1-butene was identical with the *minor* adduct of the chlorocarbene reaction (LXXVII), and vice versa. It is clearly established, therefore, that the major product of chlorocarbene addition has *cis*-orientation.

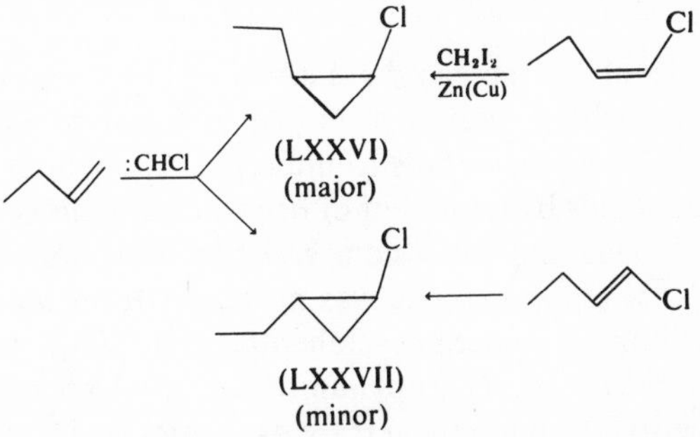

$$(80a)$$

Predominant formation of the more hindered products has also been observed in the addition of other carbenes to olefins (cf. Chapters 5 and 9). It may be explained in terms of a transition state which involves considerable charge separation (*178a*), but the possible incorporation of a molecule of lithium halide in the transition state also deserves consideration.

The reactivity of chlorocarbene in its additions to olefins was studied in competition experiments, using a tenfold excess of olefin (180) (Table IV). Some uncertainties are introduced by steric effects, but chlorocarbene is clearly a less discriminating species than dichlorocarbene. This result may be expected from the diminished stabilizing effect of one versus two chlorine atoms.

TABLE IV
RELATIVE RATES OF ADDITION OF CHLOROCARBENE
AND DICHLOROCARBENE TO OLEFINS (180)

| | $\text{Log}\,(k/k_0)_{:CHCl}$ (corr.) | $\text{Log}\,(k/k_0)_{:CCl_2}$ |
|---|---|---|
| 2,3-Dimethyl-2-butene | 0.45 | 0.81 |
| 2-Methyl-2-butene | | 0.45 |
| cis | 0.34 | |
| trans | 0.14 | |
| Isobutene | 0.00 | 0.00 |
| Cyclohexene | | −0.92 |
| cis | −0.04 | |
| trans | −0.55 | |
| 1-Pentene | | −1.78 |
| cis | −0.45 | |
| trans | −1.00 | |

More evidence of the increased reactivity of chlorocarbene, as compared to dichlorocarbene, comes from the addition to benzene, a reaction which dichlorocarbene fails to undergo. Tropylium halides were obtained in small yields by treatment of benzene with methylene chloride (bromide and iodide) and potassium tert-butoxide, followed by acid extraction (179). If chlorocarbene was produced from methylene chloride and methyllithium, 7-methylcycloheptatriene (20%) was the major product, probably formed via tropylium chloride which escapes further reaction with methyllithium only in trace quantities (< 1%) (181).

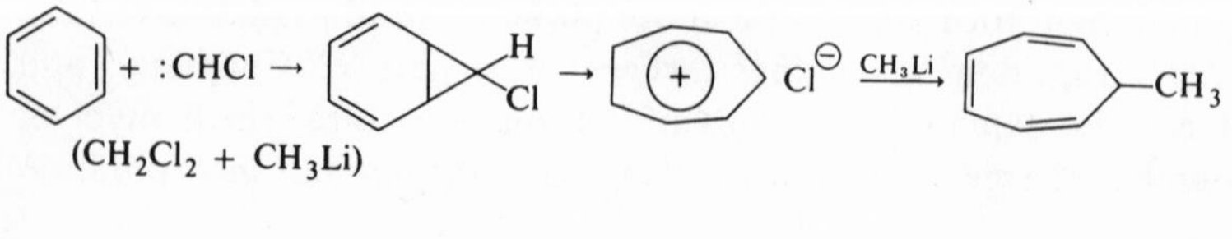

$(CH_2Cl_2 + CH_3Li)$

(81)

Phenoxide ions are more susceptible to electrophilic attack than benzene. Reaction with chlorocarbene, produced from methylene chloride and methyllithium, leads to 2-methyldihydrotropone (LXXVIII) and methyltropylium ion (LXXIX), both of which result from the intermediate tropone by further reaction with methyllithium (*182*). The intermediacy of a tropone is clearly shown with 2,6-di-*tert*-butylphenoxide where bulky *ortho*-substituents prevent the addition of methyllithium (*182*).

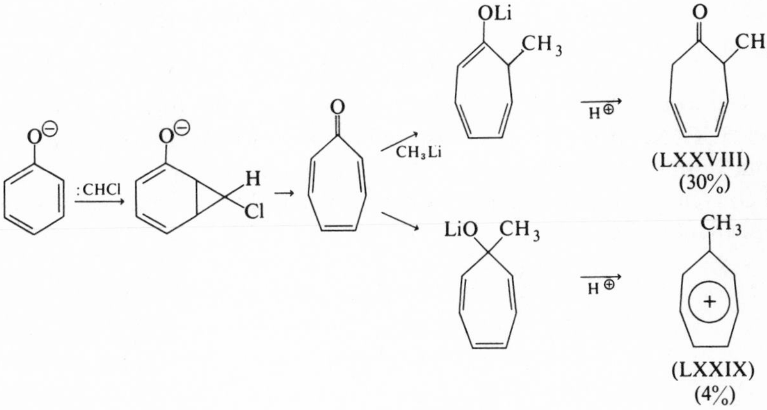

$$(82)$$

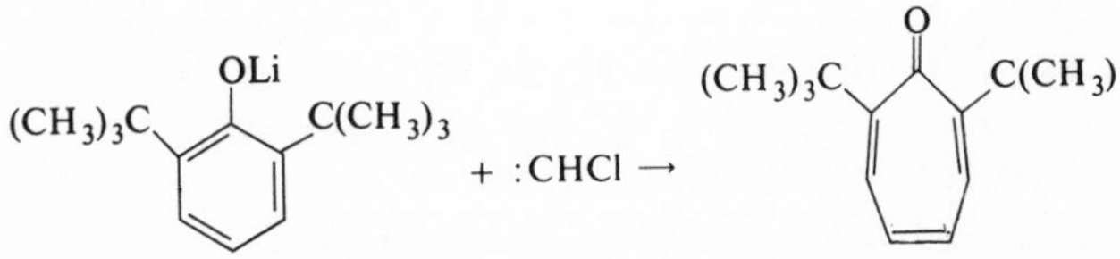

$$(83)$$

The reactions of chlorocarbene with pyrrole and indole proceed with ring expansion to give pyridine (32%) and quinoline (13%), respectively (*183*):

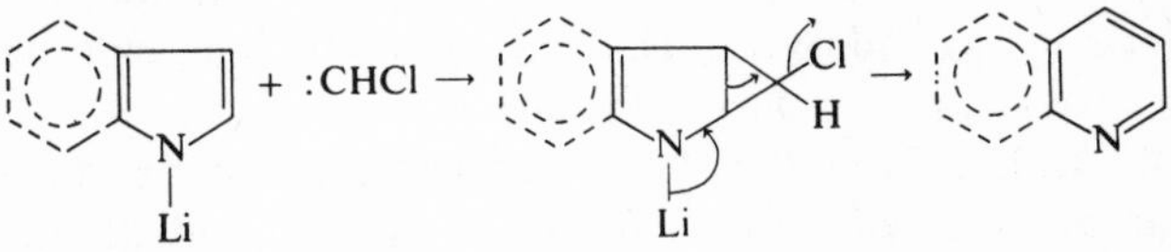

$$(84)$$

The reaction of cyclooctatetraene with methylene chloride and methyllithium led to a 3:1 mixture of *syn*- and *anti*-9-chlorobicyclo-[6.1.0]nona-2,4,6-triene (LXXIXa) (*183a*). LXXIXa was also obtained from dipotassium cyclooctatetraenide and chloroform (*183b*). The latter reaction may well proceed by way of chlorocarbene and cyclooctate-traene, formed in analogy to Eq. (77). Methylene chloride and dipotas-sium cyclooctatetraenide afforded bicyclo[6.1.0]nona-2,4,6-triene (*183b*).

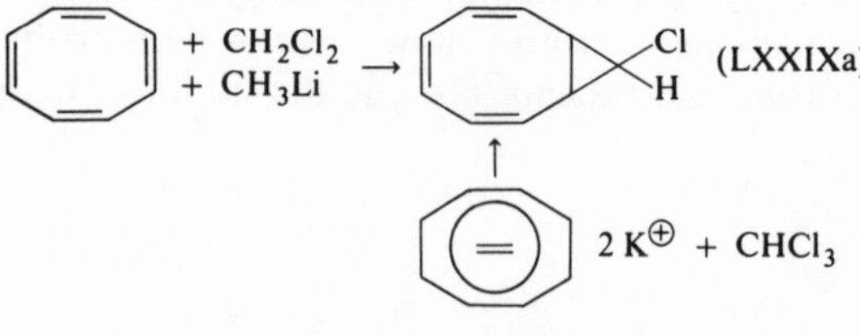

Chlorocarbene adds to triphenylphosphine with formation of the ylide LXXX. This ylide has been used in the synthesis of 1-chloroolefins from ketones (Wittig reaction) (*184*, *185*), and has further been identified by conversion to phosphonium salts (LXXXI) which are accessible by in-dependent routes (*184*).

$$Ph_3P + :CHCl \rightarrow Ph_3P{=}CHCl \quad \begin{array}{l} \xrightarrow{R_2CO} R_2C{=}CHCl + Ph_3PO \\ \\ \xrightarrow{HA} Ph_3\overset{\oplus}{P}{-}CH_2Cl\ A^{\ominus} \end{array} \qquad (85)$$

$$\text{(LXXX)} \qquad\qquad\qquad \text{(LXXXI)}$$

Recently, Closs and Coyle (*186*) have succeeded in preparing chloro-diazomethane in solution by reaction of diazomethane with *tert*-butyl hypochlorite at $-100°C$. Photolysis ($-80°$) and pyrolysis ($-20°$) of these solutions produced highly reactive chlorocarbene. *cis*-2-Butene gave the two epimeric 1-chloro-*cis*-2,3-dimethylcyclopropanes [cf. Eq. (79)] in equal quantities. Both 7-chloronorcaranes [cf. Eq. (80)] were formed from cyclohexene in a 1:1 ratio. Chlorocarbene generated from chlorodiazomethane inserted into the carbon-hydrogen bonds of *n*-pentane with the formation of chloroalkanes. The ratio of insertion into primary versus secondary C—H bonds was 0.05, i.e., chlorocarbene is very selective as compared to methylene.

In the authors' opinion "the remarkable reactivity differences of chlorocarbene derived from the diazo compound and of the formally identical intermediate from methylene chloride . . . suggests that in the $\alpha$-elimination a truly free carbene might be bypassed" (*186*). It should be remembered, however, that the excited singlet state is held responsible for the insertion reactions of methylene. Similarly, excited states may be involved in the decomposition of chlorodiazomethane and may account for the reactivity differences observed.

## III. ALKYL- AND ARYLHALOCARBENES

Alkylhalocarbenes have been produced by the $\alpha$-elimination of hydrogen chloride from 1,1-dichloroalkanes (187), and by interaction of dihalocarbenes with lithium alkyls or Grignard reagents (62, 187).

$$R\text{—}CHCl_2 + R'Li \rightarrow R'H + [R\text{—}CCl_2Li] \rightarrow LiCl + R\text{—}\underset{\cdot}{C}\text{—}Cl \qquad (86)$$

$$R\text{—}M + :CX_2 \rightarrow [R\text{—}CX_2M] \rightarrow MX + R\text{—}\underset{\cdot}{C}\text{—}X \qquad (87)$$

In the reaction, Eq. (87), the dihalocarbene intermediate may be generated either from the organometallic compound (R—M) and a haloform (elimination of hydrogen halide) (187), or from the organometallic compound and a tetrahalomethane (elimination of halogen, initiated by halogen-metal interconversion). Various alkylfluorocarbenes were produced by the latter procedure, using dibromodifluoromethane or bromotrifluoromethane (62).

Under the conditions of their formation alkylhalocarbenes undergo two principal reactions: First, intramolecular shift of hydrogen or other groups to give haloolefins (LXXXII), and, second, reaction with excess organometallic reagent to give olefins (LXXXIII). The mechanism of the second reaction is discussed in Chapter 3. With alkylchlorocarbenes the two reactions, Eqs. (88a) and (88b), are comparable in rate if the carbene contains secondary hydrogen adjacent to the electron-deficient carbon atom. No vinyl chloride, however, results from methylchlorocarbene which adds exclusively to the lithium alkyls present (187). It may be concluded that the hydrogen shift in alkylchlorocarbenes involves considerable discrimination in favor of secondary hydrogen.

$$
\begin{array}{l}
R\text{—}CH_2\text{—}\underset{\cdot}{C}\text{—}X \\
\qquad + R\text{—}CH_2M
\end{array}
\quad
\begin{array}{l}
a \longrightarrow R\text{—}CH=CHX \qquad \text{(LXXXII)} \\
b \searrow R\text{—}CH=CH\text{—}CH_2R \quad \text{(LXXXIII)}
\end{array}
\qquad (88)
$$

Alkylfluorocarbenes produced from n-alkyl organometallics give olefins (LXXXIII) in fair yields, whereas 1-fluoroolefins (LXXXII, X=F) are obtained from sec-alkyl organometallics (62). It appears, therefore, that alkylfluorocarbenes are slightly less reactive than alkylchlorocarbenes, intramolecular shift of hydrogen [Eq. (88a)] taking place only when tertiary hydrogen is available.

The ratio of *cis-*:*trans*-1-chloropropene equals 9 regardless whether the olefin is obtained from 1,1-dichloropropane and methyllithium according to Eq. (86), or from chloroform and ethyllithium according to Eq. (87) (*187*). This observation may be taken as additional evidence of a common intermediate, ethylchlorocarbene.

An alkylchlorocarbene of neophylic structure (LXXXIV) was found to undergo phenyl shift [Eq. (89)] (*187*). Halogenated alkylfluorocarbenes, which are probably involved in the decomposition of the alkyltrichlorosilanes LXXXV and LXXXVI, rearrange with migration of chlorine rather than fluorine or hydrogen [Eq. (90)] (*188*).

$$
\underset{\underset{\text{(LXXXIV)}}{}}{
\begin{array}{c}
\text{CH}_3 \\
| \\
\text{Ph}-\text{C}-\text{CHCl}_2 \\
| \\
\text{CH}_3
\end{array}}
\xrightarrow{\text{CH}_3\text{Li}}
\begin{array}{c}
\text{CH}_3 \\
| \\
\text{Ph}-\text{C}-\underset{\cdot\cdot}{\text{C}}-\text{Cl} \\
| \\
\text{CH}_3
\end{array}
\rightarrow
(\text{CH}_3)_2\text{C}{=}\text{C}\underset{\text{Cl}}{\overset{\text{Ph}}{\diagdown}}
\qquad (89)
$$

$$
\underset{\text{(LXXXV)}}{\text{CHClF}-\text{CF}_2-\text{SiCl}_3} \xrightarrow{250°} \text{CHClF}-\underset{\cdot\cdot}{\text{C}}-\text{F} \rightarrow \text{FHC}{=}\text{CClF}
\qquad (90)
$$

$$
\underset{\text{(LXXXVI)}}{\text{CCl}_2\text{F}-\text{CF}_2-\text{SiCl}_3} \rightarrow \text{CCl}_2\text{F}-\underset{\cdot\cdot}{\text{C}}-\text{F} \rightarrow \text{ClFC}{=}\text{CClF}
$$

The $\alpha$-hydrogen of benzal chloride is sufficiently acidic to permit proton abstraction by potassium *tert*-butoxide as well as by methyllithium. Phenylchlorocarbene and *p*-tolylchlorocarbene thus produced have been added to a variety of olefins to give cyclopropanes in 20–70% yields [Eq. (91)] (*189*).

$$
\text{R}-\hexagon-\text{CHCl}_2 + \text{KO}-t\text{-Bu} \rightarrow \text{R}-\hexagon-\underset{\cdot\cdot}{\text{C}}-\text{Cl} \xrightarrow{\parallel} \text{(cyclopropane product)}
\qquad (91)
$$
$$
(+\ \text{CH}_3\text{Li})
$$

Addition of arylchlorocarbenes to diarylacetylenes, followed by treatment with acid, affords triarylcyclopropenium salts (LXXXVII) (*190*). 1,2-Diphenylcyclopropenium bromide (LXXXVIII) results from phenylacetylene via 1,2-diphenylcyclopropenyl ether (LXXXIX) (*191*), and diphenylcyclopropenone (XCI) from phenylketene diethyl acetal (XC) (*192*).

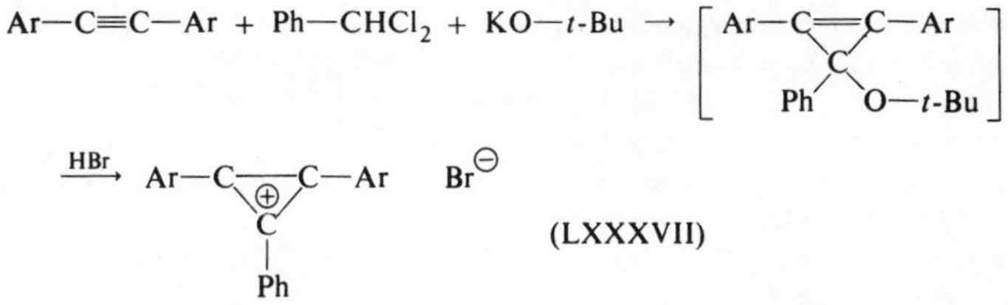

$$Ar—C\equiv C—Ar + Ph—CHCl_2 + KO—t\text{-}Bu \rightarrow \left[ \begin{array}{c} Ar—C{=}C—Ar \\ \diagdown C \diagup \\ Ph \quad\; O—t\text{-}Bu \end{array} \right]$$

(92)

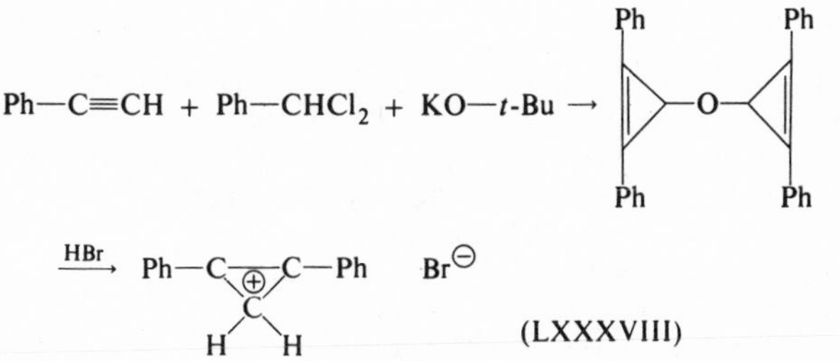

$$\xrightarrow{HBr,} \quad Ar—C{\overset{\oplus}{—}}C—Ar \quad Br^{\ominus}$$
$$\underset{Ph}{|}\;C$$

(LXXXVII)

$$Ph—C\equiv CH + Ph—CHCl_2 + KO—t\text{-}Bu \rightarrow$$

$$\begin{array}{cc} Ph & Ph \\ \triangleright\!\!—O—\!\!\triangleleft \\ Ph & Ph \end{array} \qquad \text{(LXXXIX)}$$

(93)

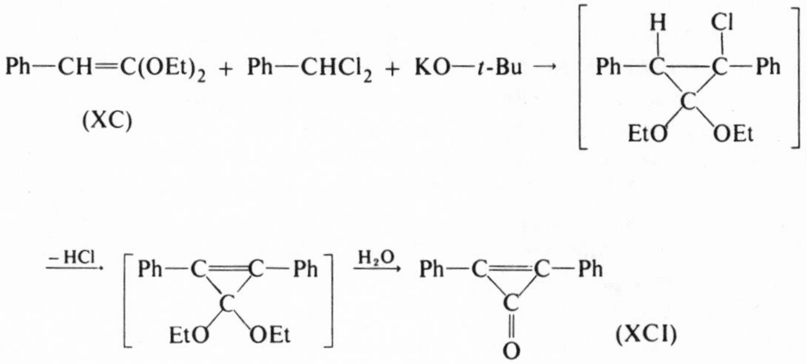

$$\xrightarrow{HBr,} \quad Ph—C{\overset{\oplus}{—}}C—Ph \quad Br^{\ominus}$$
$$\underset{H \quad H}{C}$$

(LXXXVIII)

$$Ph—CH{=}C(OEt)_2 + Ph—CHCl_2 + KO—t\text{-}Bu \rightarrow \left[ \begin{array}{c} H \quad\; Cl \\ Ph—C—C—Ph \\ \diagdown C \diagup \\ EtO \quad OEt \end{array} \right]$$

(XC)

(94)

$$\xrightarrow{-HCl,} \left[ \begin{array}{c} Ph—C{=}C—Ph \\ \diagdown C \diagup \\ EtO \quad OEt \end{array} \right] \xrightarrow{H_2O} \begin{array}{c} Ph—C{=}C—Ph \\ \diagdown C \diagup \\ \| \\ O \end{array} \quad \text{(XCI)}$$

## REFERENCES

1. A. Geuther, *Ann.* **123**, 121 (1862).
2. J. Hine, *J. Am. Chem. Soc.* **72**, 2438 (1950).
3. J. Hine and A. M. Dowell, Jr., *J. Am. Chem. Soc.* **76**, 2688 (1954).
4. P. Petrenko-Kritschenko and V. Opotsky, *Ber. deut. chem. Ges.* **59**, *B*, 2131 (1926).
5. J. Hine, A. M. Dowell, Jr., and J. E. Singley, Jr., *J. Am. Chem. Soc.* **78**, 479 (1956).
6. J. Hine, C. H. Thomas, and S. J. Ehrenson, *J. Am. Chem. Soc.* **77**, 3886 (1955).
7. C. Willgerodt, *Ber. deut. chem. Ges.* **14**, 2451 (1881).
8. J. B. Ekeley and C. J. Klemme, *J. Am. Chem. Soc.* **46**, 1252 (1924).
9. Ch. Weizmann, E. Bergmann, and M. Sulzbacher, *J. Am. Chem. Soc.* **70**, 1189 (1948).

10. E. D. Bergmann, D. Ginsburg, and D. Lavie, *J. Am. Chem. Soc.* **72**, 5012 (1950).
11. R. Lombard and R. Boesch, *Bull. soc. chim. France* **1953**, 733, 1050.
12. W. M. Dehn, *J. Am. Chem. Soc.* **31**, 1220 (1909).
13. R. P. Bell and M. H. Ford-Smith, *J. Chem. Soc.* **1961**, 1413.
14. Y. Sakamoto, *J. Chem. Soc. Japan* **57**, 1169 (1936); *Bull. Chem. Soc. Japan* **11**, 627 (1936); *Chem. Abstr.* **31**, 931, 4189 (1937).
15. J. Hine, R. C. Peek, Jr., and B. D. Oakes, *J. Am. Chem. Soc.* **76**, 827 (1954).
16. J. Hine and N. W. Burske, *J. Am. Chem. Soc.* **78**, 3337 (1956).
17. J. Hine, N. W. Burske, M. Hine, and P. B. Langford, *J. Am. Chem. Soc.* **79**, 1406 (1957).
18. J. Hine and P. B. Langford, *J. Am. Chem. Soc.* **79**, 5497 (1957).
19. J. Hine, R. Butterworth, and P. B. Langford, *J. Am. Chem. Soc.* **80**, 819 (1958).
20. W. v. E. Doering and L. K. Levy, *J. Am. Chem. Soc.* **77**, 509 (1955).
21. W. v. E. Doering and K. C. Schreiber, *J. Am. Chem. Soc.* **77**, 514 (1955).
22. W. v. E. Doering and A. K. Hoffmann, *J. Am. Chem. Soc.* **77**, 521 (1955).
23. S. H. Maron and V. K. LaMer, *J. Am. Chem. Soc.* **60**, 2588 (1938).
24. C. G. Swain and C. B. Scott, *J. Am. Chem. Soc.* **75**, 141 (1953).
25. J. Hine and S. J. Ehrenson, *J. Am. Chem. Soc.* **80**, 824 (1958).
26. J. Hine and F. P. Prosser, *J. Am. Chem. Soc.* **80**, 4282 (1958).
27. E. A. Moelwyn-Hughes, *Proc. Roy. Soc.* **A196**, 540 (1949).
28. J. Hine, S. J. Ehrenson, and W. H. Brader, *J. Am. Chem. Soc.* **78**, 2282 (1956).
29. J. Hine and J. J. Porter, *J. Am. Chem. Soc.* **79**, 5493 (1957).
30. J. Hine and A. D. Ketley, *J. Org. Chem.* **25**, 606 (1960).
31. J. Hine and J. J. Porter, *J. Am. Chem. Soc.* **82**, 6178 (1960).
32. W. v. E. Doering and A. K. Hoffmann, *J. Am. Chem. Soc.* **76**, 6162 (1954).
33. A. P. terBorg and A. F. Bickel, *Proc. Chem. Soc.* **1958**, 283.
34. H. E. Winberg, *J. Org. Chem.* **24**, 264 (1959).
35. E. K. Fields and J. M. Sandri, *Chem. & Ind. (London)* **1959**, 1216.
36. W. Walter and G. Maerten, *Angew. Chem.* **73**, 755 (1961).
37. O. M. Nefedov, M. N. Manakov, and A. A. Ivaschenko, *Izvest. Akad. Nauk S.S.S.R., Otdel. Khim. Nauk.* **1962**, 1242.
38. J. Sonnenberg and S. Winstein, *J. Org. Chem.* **27**, 748 (1962).
39. A. J. Speziale and K. W. Ratts, *J. Am. Chem. Soc.* **84**, 854 (1962).
40. H. Silberstein, *Ber. deut. chem. Ges.* **17**, 2664 (1884).
41. F. H. Verhoek *et al.*, *J. Am. Chem. Soc.* **56**, 571 (1934); **67**, 1062 (1945); **69**, 613, 2987 (1947); **72**, 299 (1950).
42. R. A. Fairclough, *J. Chem. Soc.* **1938**, 1186.
43. L. H. Sutherland and J. G. Aston, *J. Am. Chem. Soc.* **61**, 241 (1939).
44. J. Bigeleisen and T. L. Allen, *J. Chem. Phys.* **19**, 760 (1951).
45. L. W. Clark, *J. Phys. Chem.* **63**, 99 (1959); **64**, 917, 1758 (1960).
46. J. Hine and D. C. Duffey, *J. Am. Chem. Soc.* **81**, 1129 (1959).
47. J. Hine and D. C. Duffey, *J. Am. Chem. Soc.* **81**, 1131 (1959).
48. W. M. Wagner, *Proc. Chem. Soc.* **1959**, 229.
49. W. M. Wagner, H. Kloosterziel, and S. van der Ven, *Rec. trav. chim.* **80**, 740 (1961).
50. W. M. Wagner, H. Kloosterziel, and A. F. Bickel, *Rec. trav. chim.* **81**, 925, 933 (1962).
51. J. M. Birchall, G. W. Cross, and R. N. Haszeldine, *Proc. Chem. Soc.* **1960**, 81.

52. V. Joan, F. Badea, E. Corianescu, and C. D. Nenitzescu, *Angew. Chem.* **72,** 416 (1960).
53. F. Badea and C. D. Nenitzescu, *Angew. Chem.* **72,** 415 (1960).
54. W. E. Parham and F. C. Loew, *J. Org. Chem.* **23,** 1705 (1958).
55. W. E. Parham and E. E. Schweizer, *J. Org. Chem.* **24,** 1733 (1959).
56. W. E. Parham, F. C. Loew, and E. E. Schweizer, *J. Org. Chem.* **24,** 1900 (1959).
57. P. K. Kadaba and J. O. Edwards, *J. Org. Chem.* **25,** 1431 (1960).
58. F. W. Grant and W. B. Cassic, *J. Org. Chem.* **25,** 1433 (1960).
58a. B. Farah and S. Horensky, *J. Org. Chem.* **28,** 2494 (1963).
59. U. Schöllkopf and P. Hilbert, *Angew. Chem.* **74,** 431 (1962).
60. O. R. Pierce, E. T. McBee, and G. F. Judd, *J. Am. Chem. Soc.* **76,** 474 (1954).
61. V. Franzen, *Angew. Chem.* **72,** 566 (1960).
62. V. Franzen and L. Fikentscher, *Chem. Ber.* **95,** 1958 (1962).
63. V. Franzen, *Chem. Ber.* **95,** 1964 (1962).
64. W. Miller and C. S. Y. Kim, *J. Am. Chem. Soc.* **81,** 5008 (1959).
64a. W. G. Kofron, F. B. Kirby, and Ch. R. Hauser, *J. Org. Chem.* **28,** 873 (1963).
65. O. M. Nefedov, A. A. Ivaschenko, M. N. Manakov, W. I. Sherjajev, and A. D. Petrov, *Izvest. Akad. Nauk. S.S.S.R., Otdel. Khim. Nauk.* **1962,** 367.
66. W. I. Bevan, R. N. Haszeldine, and J. C. Young, *Chem. & Ind. (London)* **1961,** 789.
67. D. Seyferth, J. M. Burlitch, and J. K. Heeren, *J. Org. Chem.* **27,** 1491 (1962).
68. P. B. Ayscough and H. J. Emeleus, *J. Chem. Soc.* **1954,** 3381.
69. H. C. Clark and C. J. Willis, *J. Am. Chem. Soc.* **82,** 1888 (1960).
69a. W. Mahler, *Inorg. Chem.* **2,** 230 (1963).
70. R. K. Laird, E. B. Andrews, and R. F. Barrow, *Trans. Faraday Soc.* **46,** 803 (1950).
71. P. Venkateswarlu, *Phys. Rev.* **77,** 676 (1950).
72. J. L. Margrave and K. Wieland, *J. Chem. Phys.* **21,** 1552 (1953).
73. J. Duchesne and L. Burnelle, *J. Chem. Phys.* **21,** 2005 (1953).
74. R. N. Haszeldine, *J. Chem. Soc.* **1953,** 3761.
75. E. Atkinson, *J. Chem. Soc.* **1952,** 2684.
76. S. Andreades, *Chem. & Ind. (London)* **1962,** 782.
77. J. P. Simons and A. J. Yarwood, *Nature* **187,** 316 (1960).
78. L. P. Blanchard and P. LeGoff, *Can. J. Chem.* **35,** 89 (1957).
79. M. Schmeisser and N. H. Schröder, *Angew. Chem.,* **72,** 349 (1960).
80. M. Schmeisser, H. Schröter, and H. Schilder, *Chem. Ber.* **95,** 1648 (1962).
81. A. E. Shilov and R. D. Sabirova, *Zhur. Fiz. Khim.* **34,** 860 (1960); *Russian J. Phys. Chem. (English Transl.)* **4,** 408 (1960).
82. W. E. Parham and E. Koncos, *J. Am. Chem. Soc.* **83,** 4034 (1961).
82a. J. C. Anderson and C. B. Reese, *Chem. & Ind. (London)* **1963,** 575.
83. E. K. Fields, *J. Am. Chem. Soc.* **84,** 1744 (1962).
84. V. Franzen, unpublished results (1962).
84a. D. Seyferth and J. M. Burlitch, *J. Am. Chem. Soc.* **85,** 2667 (1963).
85. O. A. Reutov and A. N. Lovtsova, *Izvest. Akad. Nauk S.S.S.R., Otdel. Khim. Nauk* **1960,** 1716; *Doklady Akad. Nauk S.S.S.R.* **139,** 622 (1961).
86. D. Seyferth and J. M. Burlitch, *J. Am. Chem. Soc.* **84,** 1757 (1962).
86a. T. J. Logan, *J. Org. Chem.* **28,** 1129 (1963).
87. P. S. Skell and A. Y. Garner, *J. Am. Chem. Soc.* **78,** 3409 (1956).

88. W. v. E. Doering and P. LaFlamme, *J. Am. Chem. Soc.* **78**, 5447 (1956).
89. P. S. Skell and A. Y. Garner, *J. Am. Chem. Soc.* **78**, 5430 (1956).
90. W. v. E. Doering and W. A. Henderson, Jr., *J. Am. Chem. Soc.* **80**, 5274 (1958).
91. S. V. Anantakrishnan and R. Venkataraman, *Chem. Revs.* **33**, 27 (1943).
92. D. Swern, *Chem. Revs.* **45**, 1 (1949).
93. M. S. Kharasch *et al., J. Org. Chem.* **14**, 239, 537 (1949); **18**, 328 (1953).
94. H. Hoberg, *Ann.* **656**, 1 (1962).
95. G. Wittig and K. Schwarzenbach, *Angew. Chem.* **71**, 652 (1959); *Ann.* **650**, 1 (1962).
96. H. Hoberg, *Ann.* **656**, 15 (1962).
97. G. Wittig and F. Wingler, *Ann.* **656**, 18 (1962).
98. A. Ledwith and L. Phillips, *J. Chem. Soc.* **1962**, 3796.
99. W. J. Dale and P. E. Schwartzentruber, *J. Org. Chem.* **24**, 955 (1959).
99a. D. Seyferth, R. J. Minasz, A. J. H. Treiber, J. M. Burlitch, and S. R. Dowd, *J. Org. Chem.* **28**, 1163 (1963).
99b. W. R. Moore, S. E. Krikorian, and J. E. LaPrade, *J. Org. Chem.* **28**, 1404 (1963).
99c. E. K. Fields and S. Meyerson, *J. Org. Chem.* **28**, 1915 (1963).
99d. S. W. Tobey and R. West, *J. Am. Chem. Soc.* **86**, 56 (1964).
99e. S. W. Tobey and R. West, *Tetrahedron Letters* **1963**, 1179.
99f. C. E. Cook and M. E. Wall, *Chem. & Ind.* (*London*) **1963**, 1927.
99g. H. A. Bruson and T. P. O'Day (Olin Mathieson Corp.) U. S. Patent 3,047,633 (1962).
100. E. E. Schweizer and W. E. Parham, *J. Am. Chem. Soc.* **82**, 4085 (1960).
101. W. E. Parham and L. D. Huestis, *J. Am. Chem. Soc.* **84**, 813 (1962).
102. E. P. Prilezaeva, N. P. Petuchova, and M. F. Shostakovskij, *Doklady Akad. Nauk S.S.S.R.* **144**, 1059 (1962).
103. J. Cudlin and V. Chvalovsky, *Collection Czech. Communs.* **27**, 1658 (1962).
104. L. H. Knox, E. V. Velarde, S. M. Berger, and D. H. Cuadriello, *Chem. & Ind.* (*London*) **1962**, 860; *J. Am. Chem. Soc.* **85**, 1851 (1963).
105. W. E. Parham and H. E. Reiff, *J. Am. Chem. Soc.* **77**, 1177 (1955).
106. W. E. Parham, H. E. Reiff, and P. Schwartzentruber, *J. Am. Chem. Soc.* **78**, 1437 (1956).
107. W. E. Parham and R. E. Twelves, *J. Org. Chem.* **22**, 730 (1957).
108. W. E. Parham and C. D. Wright, *J. Org. Chem.* **22**, 1473 (1957).
109. G. L. Ciamician and M. Dennstedt, *Ber. deut. chem. Ges.* **14**, 1153 (1881); **15**, 1172 (1882).
110. O. Bocchi, *Gazz. chim. ital.* **30**, I, 89 (1900).
111. G. Plancher and U. Ponti, *Atti accad. nazl. Lincei* [5] **18**, II, 473 (1909).
112. G. Magnanini, *Gazz. chim. ital.* **17**, 249 (1887).
113. G. Plancher and O. Carrasco, *Atti accad. nazl. Lincei* [5] **13**, I, 575 (1904).
113a. W. E. Parham, Ch. G. Fritz, R. W. Soeder, and R. M. Dodson, *J. Org. Chem.* **28**, 577 (1963).
114. S. M. McElvain and Ph. L. Weyna, *J. Am. Chem. Soc.* **81**, 2579 (1959).
115. M. F. Dull and P. G. Abend, *J. Am. Chem. Soc.* **81**, 2588 (1959).
116. W. R. Moore and H. R. Ward, *Chem. & Ind.* (*London*) **1961**, 594.
116a. M. Ohno, *Tetrahedron Letters* **1963**, 1753.
117. P. S. Skell and S. R. Sandler, *J. Am. Chem. Soc.* **80**, 2024 (1958).

117a. C. W. Jefford, *Proc. Chem. Soc.* **1963**, 64.

117b. L. Ghosez and P. Laroche, *Proc. Chem. Soc.* **1963**, 90.

117c. W. R. Moore, W. R. Moser, and J. E. LaPrade, *J. Org. Chem.* **28**, 2200 (1963).

117d. R. C. DeSelms and Ch. M. Combs, *J. Org. Chem.* **28**, 2206 (1963).

117e. E. Bergman, *J. Org. Chem.* **28**, 2210 (1963).

118. K. Hofmann, S. F. Orochena, S. M. Sax, and G. A. Jeffrey, *J. Am. Chem. Soc.* **81**, 992 (1959).

119. E. Funakubo, I. Moritani, S. Murahashi, and T. Tuji, *Tetrahedron Letters* **1962**, 539.

119a. O. M. Nefedov, N. N. Novickaja, and A. D. Petrov, *Doklady Akad. Nauk S.S.S.R.* **152**, 629 (1963).

119b. R. C. Cookson, D. P. G. Hamon, and J. Hudec, *J. Chem. Soc.* **1963**, 5782.

119c. R. Ketcham, R. Cavestri, and D. Jambotkar, *J. Org. Chem.* **28**, 2139 (1963).

119d. D. Seyferth, H. Yamazaki, and D. L. Alleston, *J. Org. Chem.* **28**, 703 (1963).

120. W. v. E. Doering and P. LaFlamme, *Tetrahedron* **2**, 75 (1958).

121. T. J. Logan, *Tetrahedron Letters* **1961**, 173.

122. L. Skatteböl, *Tetrahedron Letters* **1961**, 167.

123. P. D. Gardner and M. Narayana, *J. Org. Chem.* **26**, 3518 (1961).

124. W. E. Parham, R. W. Soeder, and R. M. Dodson, *J. Am. Chem. Soc.* **84**, 1755 (1962).

125. A. J. Birch and J. M. H. Graves, *Proc. Chem. Soc.* **1962**, 282.

125a. A. J. Birch, J. M. H. Graves, and J. B. Siddall, *J. Chem. Soc.* **1963**, 4234.

126. K. Hofmann, S. F. Orochena, and C. W. Yoko, *J. Am. Chem. Soc.* **79**, 3608 (1957).

127. S. Winstein and J. Sonnenberg, *J. Am. Chem. Soc.* **83**, 3235 (1961).

127a. G. I. Fray, *J. Chem. Soc.* **1963**, 4284.

127b. E. Vogel, W. Wiedemann, H. Kiefer, and W. F. Harrison, *Tetrahedron Letters* **1963**, 673.

127c. E. Vogel and H. D. Roth, *Angew. Chem.* **76**, 145 (1964).

127d. G. Schröder, *Angew. Chem.* **75**, 722 (1963).

128. W. J. Ball and S. R. Landor, *Proc. Chem. Soc.* **1961**, 246.

129. A. Bézaguet, *Compt. rend.* **254**, 3371 (1962).

130. R. C. Woodworth and P. S. Skell, *J. Am. Chem. Soc.* **79**, 2542 (1957).

131. E. C. Herrick and M. Orchin, *J. Org. Chem.* **24**, 139 (1959).

132. N. P. Neureiter, *J. Org. Chem.* **24**, 2044 (1959).

133. A. Ledwith and R. M. Bell, *Chem. & Ind. (London)* **1959**, 459.

134. T. Shono and R. Oda, *J. Chem. Soc. Japan* **80**, 1200 (1959); *Chem. Abstr.* **55**, 4381 (1961).

135. I. A. Dyakonov, T. V. Nisovkina, and T. A. Kornilova, *Zhur. Obshchei Khim.* **32**, 664 (1962).

136. L. Vo-Quang and P. Cadiot, *Compt. rend.* **252**, 3827 (1961).

137. I. A. Dyakonov and L. P. Danilkina, *Zhur. Obshchei Khim.* **32**, 1008 (1962).

138. M. E. Volpin, Y. D. Koreshkov, and N. D. Kursanov, *Izvest. Akad. Nauk S.S.S.R., Otdel Khim. Nauk* **1959**, 560.

139. R. Breslow and R. Peterson, *J. Am. Chem. Soc.* **82**, 4426 (1960).

140. W. Mahler, *J. Am. Chem. Soc.* **84**, 4600 (1962).

141. R. W. Murray, *Tetrahedron Letters No.* **7**, 27 (1960).

142. W. E. Parham, D. A. Bolon, and E. E. Schweizer, *J. Am. Chem. Soc.* **83**, 603 (1961).

143. A. G. Cook and E. K. Fields, *J. Org. Chem.* **27**, 3686 (1962).

143a. F. B. Dains and R. Q. Brewster, *J. Am. Chem. Soc.* **42**, 1573 (1920).

143b. H. G. Viehe, E. Franchimont, and P. Valange, *Chem. Ber.* **96**, 420, 426 (1963).

143c. Ch. R. Hauser, W. G. Kofron, W. R. Dunnavant, and W. F. Owens, *J. Org. Chem.* **26**, 2627 (1961).

144. A. Hoffmann, *Ann.* **144**, 114 (1867); **146**, 107 (1868).

145. P. A. S. Smith and N. W. Kalenda, *J. Org. Chem.* **23**, 1599 (1958); cf. also T. Shingaki and M. Takebayashi, *Bull. Chem. Soc. Japan* **36**, 617 (1963).

146. J. U. Nef, *Ann.* **298**, 368 (1897).

147. A. P. Krapcho, *J. Org. Chem.* **27**, 1089 (1962).

148. M. Saunders and R. W. Murray, *Tetrahedron* **6**, 88 (1959).

149. M. B. Frankel, H. Feuer, and J. Bank, *Tetrahedron Letters No.* **7**, 5 (1959).

150. M. Saunders and R. W. Murray, *Tetrahedron* **11**, 1 (1960).

151. A. Pierce and M. M. Joullié, *J. Org. Chem.* **27**, 2220 (1962).

152. D. H. Clemens, E. Y. Shropshire, and W. D. Emmons, *J. Org. Chem.* **27**, 3664 (1962).

153. G. Ciamician and M. Dennstedt, *Ber. deut. chem. Ges.* **14**, 1153 (1881); **15**, 1172 (1882).

154. E. R. Alexander, A. B. Herrick, and Th. M. Roder, *J. Am. Chem. Soc.* **72**, 2760 (1950).

155. B. Robinson, *Tetrahedron Letters* **1962**, 139.

156. C. W. Rees and C. E. Smithen, *Chem. & Ind. (London)* **1962**, 1022.

156a. E. E. Schweizer and G. J. O'Neill, *J. Org. Chem.* **28**, 2460 (1963).

157. A. J. Speziale, G. J. Marco, and K. W. Ratts, *J. Am. Chem. Soc.* **82**, 1260 (1960).

157a. R. Oda, Y. Ito, and M. Okano, *Tetrahedron Letters* **1964**, 7.

158. H. Reimlinger, *Angew. Chem.* **74**, 153 (1962); *Chem. Ber.* **97**, 339 (1964).

159. E. A. Robinson, *J. Chem. Soc.* **1961**, 1663.

160. M. Hermann, *Ann.* **95**, 211 (1855).

161. H. Bassett, *Ann.* **132**, 54 (1864).

162. H. Long, *Ann.* **194**, 23 (1878).

163. G. Mossler, *Monatsh. Chem.* **29**, 373 (1903).

164. J. Hine, E. L. Pollitzer, and H. Wagner, *J. Am. Chem. Soc.* **75**, 5607 (1953).

165. P. S. Skell and I. Starrer, *J. Am. Chem. Soc.* **81**, 4117 (1959).

166. J. Hine, A. D. Ketley, and K. Tanabe, *J. Am. Chem. Soc.* **82**, 1398 (1960).

167. W. A. Sanderson and S. H. Mosher, *J. Am. Chem. Soc.* **83**, 5033 (1961).

168. K. Reimer, *Ber. deut. chem. Ges.* **9**, 423 (1876).

169. K. Reimer and F. Tiemann, *Ber. deut. chem. Ges.* **9**, 824, 1285 (1876).

170. H. Wynberg, *J. Am. Chem. Soc.* **76**, 4998 (1954).

171. J. Hine and J. M. van der Veen, *J. Am. Chem. Soc.* **81**, 6447 (1959).

172. T. Y. Shen, S. Lucas, and L. H. Sarett, *Tetrahedron Letters* **1961**, 43.

173. A. Kötz and W. Zörnig, *J. prakt. Chem.* [2] **74**, 425 (1906).

174. A. P. Krapcho, *J. Org. Chem.* **27**, 2375 (1962).

175. M. Conrad and M. Guthzeit, *Ber. deut. chem. Ges.* **15**, 2841 (1882).

176. A. P. Krapcho, P. S. Huyffer, and I. Starrer, *J. Org. Chem.* **27**, 3096 (1962).

177. G. L. Closs and L. E. Closs, *J. Am. Chem. Soc.* **81**, 4996 (1959).

178. G. L. Closs and L. E. Closs, *J. Am. Chem. Soc.* **82**, 5723 (1960).

178a. G. L. Closs, R. A. Moss, and J. J. Coyle, *J. Am. Chem. Soc.* **84**, 4985 (1962).

179. M. E. Volpin, D. N. Kursanov, and V. G. Dulova, *Tetrahedron* **8**, 33 (1960).

180. G. L. Closs and G. M. Schwartz, *J. Am. Chem. Soc.* **82**, 5729 (1960).

181.  G. L. Closs and L. E. Closs, *Tetrahedron Letters No.* **10,** 38 (1960).

182.  G. L. Closs and L. E. Closs, *J. Am. Chem. Soc.* **83,** 599 (1961).

183.  G. L. Closs and G. M. Schwartz, *J. Org. Chem.* **26,** 2609 (1961).

183a.  E. A. LaLancette and R. E. Benson, *J. Am. Chem. Soc.* **85,** 2853 (1963).

183b.  T. J. Katz and P. J. Garratt, *J. Am. Chem. Soc.* **85,** 2852 (1963).

184.  D. Seyferth, S. O. Grim, and T. O. Read, *J. Am. Chem. Soc.* **82,** 1510 (1960); **83,** 1617 (1961).

185.  G. Wittig and M. Schlosser, *Angew. Chem.* **72,** 324 (1960).

186.  G. L. Closs and J. J. Coyle, *J. Am. Chem. Soc.* **84,** 4350 (1962).

187.  W. Kirmse and B. v. Bülow, *Chem. Ber.* **96,** 3316, 3323 (1963).

188.  R. N. Haszeldine and J. C. Young, *Proc. Chem. Soc.* **1959,** 394.

189.  R. A. Moss, *J. Org. Chem.* **27,** 2683 (1962).

190.  R. Breslow and H. W. Chang, *J. Am. Chem. Soc.* **83,** 2367 (1961).

191.  R. Breslow, J. Lockhart, and H. W. Chang, *J. Am. Chem. Soc.* **83,** 2375 (1961).

192.  R. Breslow, R. Haynie, and J. Mirra, *J. Am. Chem. Soc.* **81,** 247 (1959).

# CHAPTER 9

# Carbenes Containing $\alpha$-Hetero Atoms

THE CONTENTS OF this chapter are restricted to structures which contain nitrogen, oxygen, sulfur, or selenium attached directly to the carbene carbon. Resonance between the electron-deficient carbene carbon and the electron-rich hetero atoms profoundly influences the reactivity of such carbenes. If the hetero atoms are doubly bonded to "divalent" carbon, the resonance interaction is sufficient to make isonitriles (I), fulminic acid derivatives (II), and carbon monoxide (III) stable compounds which display no electrophilic reactivity but behave more or less actively as nucleophiles.

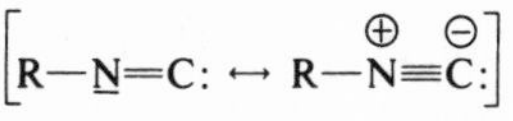

$$\left[ R-\underset{..}{N}=C: \;\leftrightarrow\; R-\overset{\oplus}{N}\equiv\overset{\ominus}{C:} \right] \qquad \left[ R-O-\underset{..}{N}=C: \;\leftrightarrow\; R-O-\overset{\oplus}{N}\equiv\overset{\ominus}{C:} \right]$$
$$\text{(I)} \qquad\qquad\qquad\qquad \text{(II)}$$

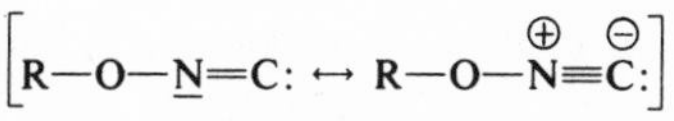

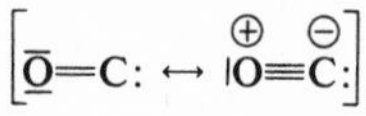

$$\left[ \overset{..}{\underset{..}{O}}=C: \;\leftrightarrow\; I\overset{\oplus}{O}\equiv\overset{\ominus}{C:} \right]$$
$$\text{(III)}$$

In contrast to carbon monoxide, carbon monosulfide is capable of only transitory existence when produced in a high-frequency discharge through carbon disulfide, or by photolysis of carbon disulfide. The spectrum of CS has been observed by various workers both in emission (1–3) and absorption (4–6). The lifetime (up to 30 min.) was found to depend on the surface of the vessel (7). These observations show that CS is removed by a heterogeneous reaction, and suggest that in the gas phase CS exhibits the stability of a normal molecule.

The study of carbenes with singly bonded $\alpha$-hetero atoms has been more rewarding, and various features will be discussed in the following paragraphs.

## I. AMINOCARBENES

The olefin IV has been synthesized from $N,N'$-diphenyl-1,2-diamino-ethane and chloral ($8$) or ethyl orthoformate ($9$). Molecular weight determinations indicate a reversible dissociation of IV to give the reso-nance-stabilized carbene V ($8, 10$). Phenyl has been replaced by various aryl groups without appreciable effect on the dissociation of IV ($9a$).

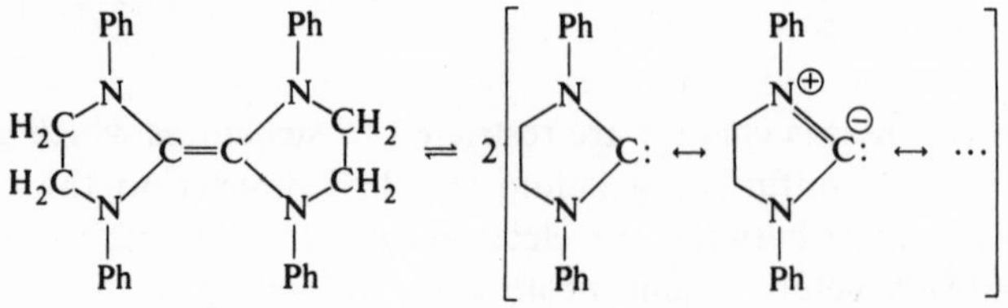

    (IV)                (V)

V behaves as a nucleophile and resembles an isonitrile rather than a typical carbene. Reaction with acids produces amidinium salts (VI) which hydrolyze to $N$-formyl-1,2-dianilinoethane (VII) ($10$), but revert to IV on treatment with base ($11$). V does not add to olefins, with the exception of tetracyanoethylene. Acylation of the central carbon atom is brought about by aldehydes, a reaction which is thought to proceed by addition of V to the carbonyl group [Eq. (2)] ($10$). C-Alkylation [Eq. (3)] occurs with various "C—H acidic" compounds (CH$_3$Y, Y = NO$_2$ > SO$_2$CH$_3$ > CN > CO$_2$R > CO—R) ($10, 10a$).

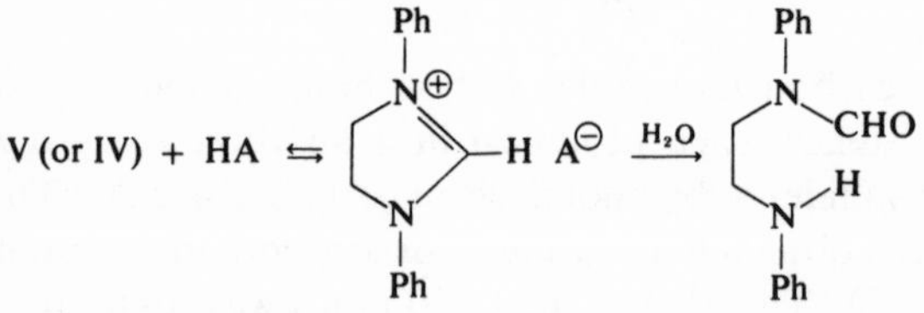

$$\text{V (or IV)} + HA \rightleftharpoons \text{(VI)} \xrightarrow{H_2O} \text{(VII)} \tag{1}$$

             (VI)             (VII)

$$\text{V (or IV)} + R—CH{=}O \rightarrow \quad\rightarrow \tag{2}$$

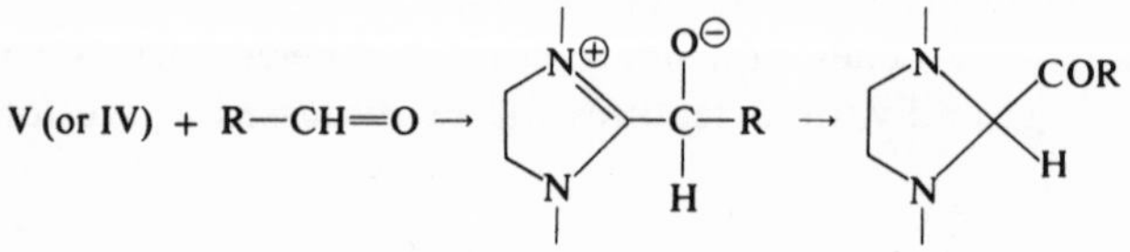

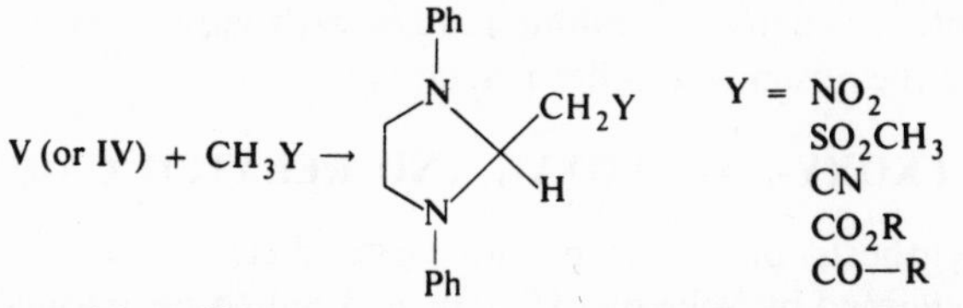

$$V \text{ (or IV)} + CH_3Y \rightarrow \underset{\underset{Ph}{|}}{\overset{\overset{Ph}{|}}{}} \quad \begin{array}{l} Y = NO_2 \\ \quad\quad SO_2CH_3 \\ \quad\quad CN \\ \quad\quad CO_2R \\ \quad\quad CO\text{---}R \end{array} \tag{3}$$

IV reacts with sulfur even at room temperature to give the thione VIII (*10a*). Diazo compounds are attacked at elevated temperatures, with reaction at the terminal nitrogen leading to azines[Eq. (3a)] (*10a*). This behavior is in contrast with that of electrophilic carbenes (e.g., dihalocarbenes, cf. Chapter 8, Section I,B,7), which attack the electron-rich carbon atom of diazo compounds to form olefins.

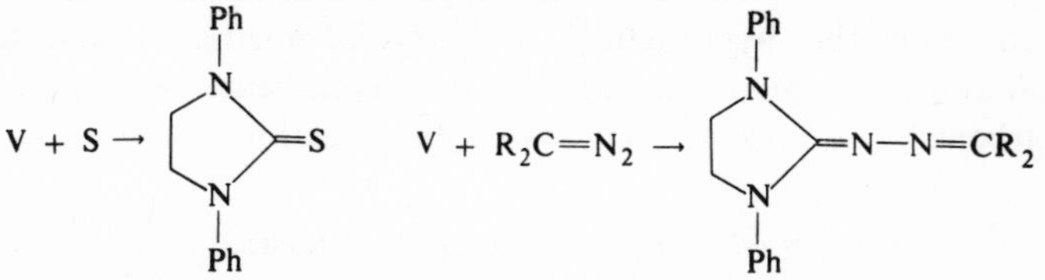

$$V + S \rightarrow \quad\quad\quad V + R_2C{=}N_2 \rightarrow \tag{3a}$$

(VIII)

The intermediacy of V is not certain in all cases; some of the reactions may be attributed to the dimer IV as well as to V. Oxidation was recently shown to start with IV and to proceed via radical cations [Eq. (4)] (*11*).

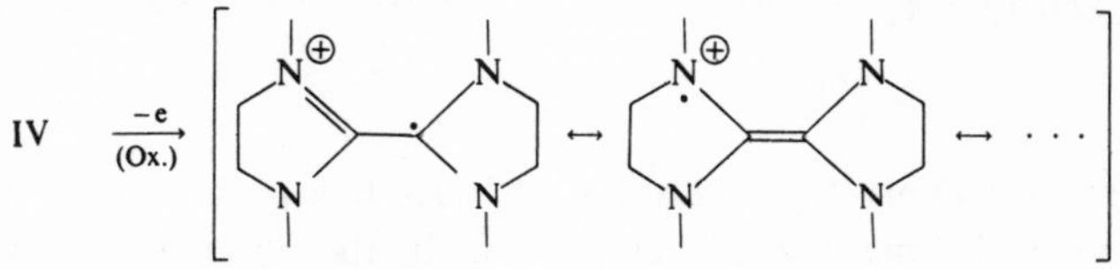

$$IV \xrightarrow[\text{(Ox.)}]{-e} \left[ \quad\quad\quad \leftrightarrow \quad\quad\quad \leftrightarrow \cdots \right] \tag{4}$$

The properties of tetrakis(dimethylamino)ethylene do not indicate a dissociation to give bis(dimethylamino)carbene (*11a, b*).

The hybrid structure VIIIa has been attributed to crystalline, moderately stable compounds obtained from *N*-alkylbenzthiazolium halides by treatment with base (*11c*):

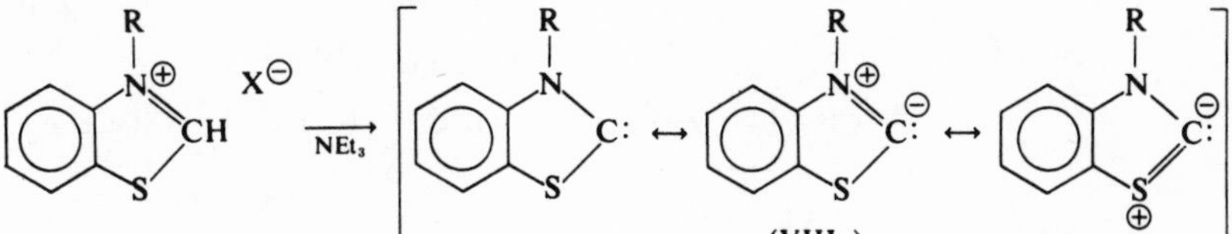

(VIIIa)

These stable "carbenes" combine readily with various electrophiles and dimerize in the absence of other reactants.

## II. ALKOXY-, ARYLOXY-, AND RELATED CARBENES

The synthesis of "carbon monoxide diethylacetal" (= diethoxycarbene), claimed by Scheiblei (*12*), turned out to be erroneous (*13–15*). In fact, carbenes containing α-oxygen appear to be unstable, reactive species, and tetraethoxyethylene does not dissociate up to 200°C. (*16*).

More promising routes to dialkoxycarbenes have been explored recently. Thermal decomposition of the sodium salt of *N'*-(diethoxymethylene)toluene-*p*-sulfonylhydrazine (VIIIb) appears to follow the usual pattern (78% yield of sodium toluene-*p*-sulfinate). The products derived from the hypothetical diethoxydiazomethane indicate both radical and polar decomposition of diethoxycarbene. Attempts to trap the carbene by addition to olefins were unsuccessful (*16a*).

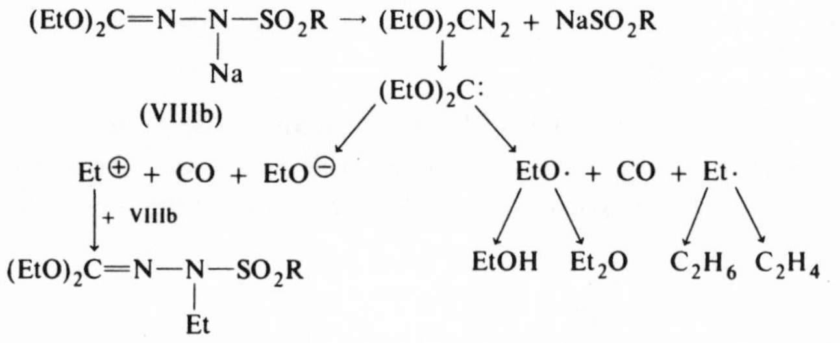

(EtO)2C=N—N—SO2R → (EtO)2CN2 + NaSO2R
Na
(VIIIb)
(EtO)2C:
Et⊕ + CO + EtO⊖
+ VIIIb
(EtO)2C=N—N—SO2R
Et
EtO· + CO + Et·
EtOH Et2O C2H6 C2H4

The reverse Diels-Alder reaction of VIIIc has been studied as a possible source of dimethoxycarbene (*16b*). In the absence of oxygen and moisture, the apparent dimer of the carbene, tetramethoxyethylene, has been isolated in 50% yield. Methyl orthoformate (27%) was obtained by pyrolysis of VIIIc in methanol, and some dimethyl carbonate was produced in the presence of oxygen.

CH3O OCH3
Cl
Cl
Ph
Cl Cl
Cl Cl
Cl
Ph
Cl H
+ (CH3O)2C:
CH3OH
HC(OCH3)3
(CH3O)2C=C(OCH3)2
O2
(CH3O)2CO

(VIIIc)

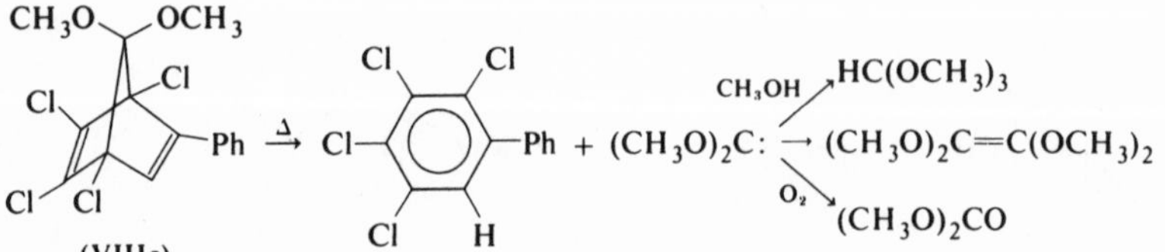

A cyclic dialkoxycarbene intermediate has been postulated in the reaction of cyclic thionocarbonates with trialkylphosphites which comprises the second step of a stereospecific synthesis of olefins from 1,2-glycols (*16c*):

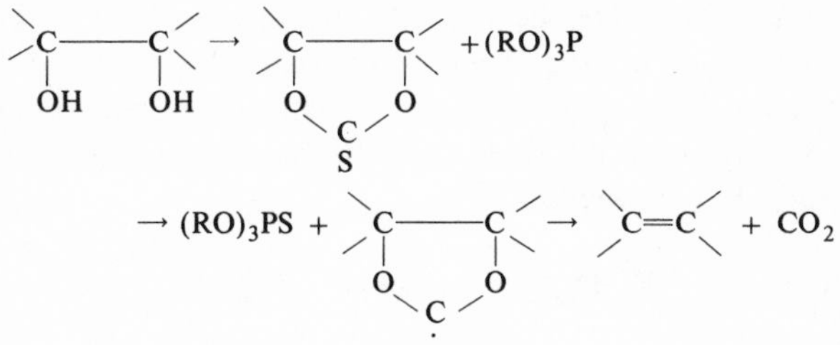

Phenoxycarbene and various alkoxycarbenes have been produced from the corresponding chloroethers by $\alpha$-elimination of hydrogen chloride (*16*, *17*). Because $\alpha$-chloroethers undergo $S_N2$ displacement very readily, *tert*-butyllithium was the only suitable base to effect $\alpha$-elimination in many cases. Treatment of dichlormethyl alkyl ethers with methyllithium in the presence of lithium iodide proved to be a convenient modification which probably involves displacement of one chlorine by iodine and, subsequently, by lithium (*17a*). The aryloxy- and alkoxycarbenes thus obtained added to olefins in fair yields. The *trans-*:*cis-* ratios of the 7-alkoxynorcaranes (IX) resulting from cyclohexene are interesting. The variation with the size of the alkyl group may be attributed to steric factors. The small *trans-*:*cis-* ratio observed with phenoxycarbene indicates a higher reactivity of this carbene, possibly due to resonance interaction of the oxygen with the aromatic ring (*17*). In contrast to the behavior of cyclohexene, *cis*-2-butene accepts phenoxycarbene with predominant formation of the more hindered *cis*-product.

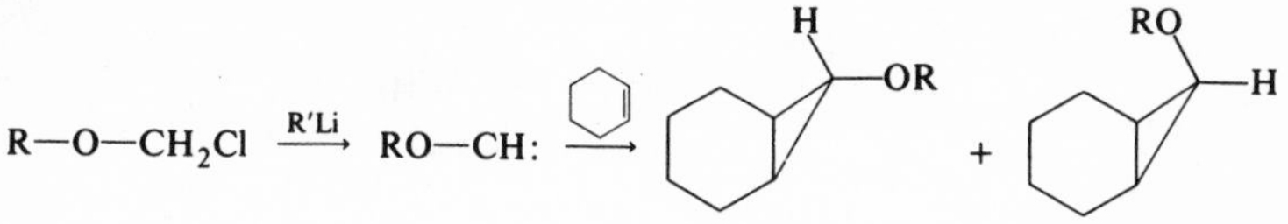

| R | *trans-*:*cis-* |
|---|---|
| phenyl | 1.8 |
| methyl | 4.5 |
| *n*-butyl | 4.5 |
| isopropyl | 7 |

Triphenylphosphine-$n$-butoxymethylene (X) undergoes the familiar Wittig reaction with carbonyl compounds at low temperatures. Above $-10°$C. X decomposes with formation of triphenylphosphine and a variety of products among which 1,2-di-$n$-butoxyethylene (XI) and 1-$n$-butoxy-1-pentene (XII) are the most interesting ones (18). These products are pictured as arising from $n$-butoxycarbene in Eq. (6), but attempts to trap the carbene by addition to olefins have been unsuccessful. Analogs of XI have been obtained from triphenylphosphine-$tert$-butoxymethylene and -diphenoxymethylene.

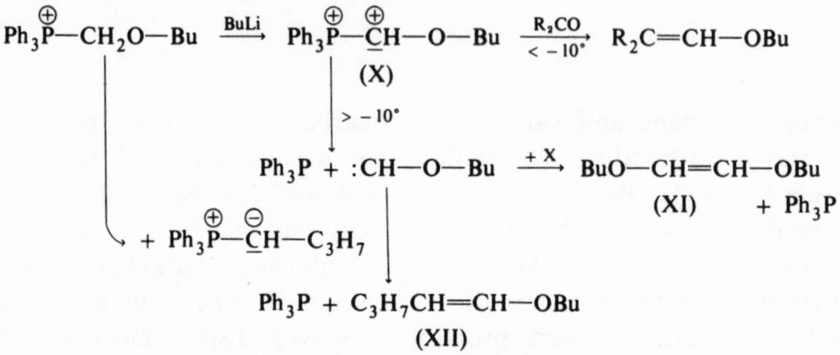

$$\overset{\oplus}{Ph_3P}-CH_2O-Bu \xrightarrow{\text{BuLi}} \overset{\oplus}{Ph_3P}-\overset{\oplus}{\underset{\text{(X)}}{C}H}-O-Bu \xrightarrow[<-10°]{R_2CO} R_2C=CH-OBu$$

$$\Big\downarrow >-10°$$  (6)

$$Ph_3P + :CH-O-Bu \xrightarrow{+X} \underset{\text{(XI)}}{BuO-CH=CH-OBu} + Ph_3P$$

$$\searrow + \overset{\oplus}{Ph_3P}-\overset{\ominus}{C}H-C_3H_7$$

$$Ph_3P + \underset{\text{(XII)}}{C_3H_7CH=CH-OBu}$$

Various alkoxychlorocarbenes have been postulated as intermediates by Hine $et\ al$. The reaction of chlorodifluoromethane with isopropoxide ion in isopropyl alcohol affords isopropyl difluoromethyl ether (XIII) and isopropyl orthoformate (XIV) (19). As XIII is not attacked by isopropoxide under the reaction conditions used, XIV is thought to arise via isopropoxyfluorocarbene:

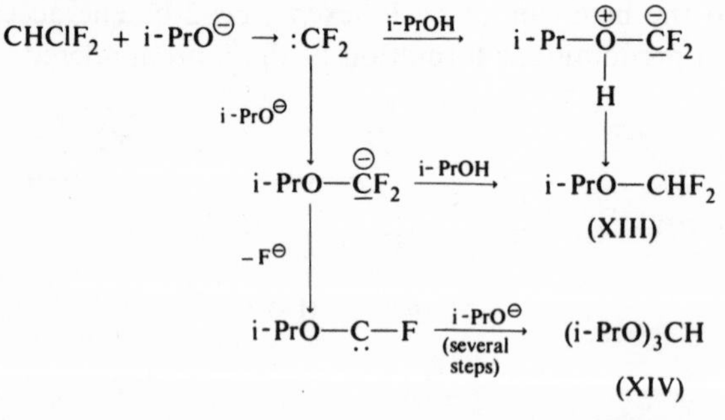

$$CHClF_2 + i\text{-}PrO^{\ominus} \rightarrow :CF_2 \xrightarrow{i\text{-}PrOH} i\text{-}Pr-\overset{\oplus}{O}-\overset{\ominus}{C}F_2$$

$$\Big\downarrow i\text{-}PrO^{\ominus} \qquad\qquad\qquad\qquad \Big| H$$

$$i\text{-}PrO-\overset{\ominus}{C}F_2 \xrightarrow{i\text{-}PrOH} \underset{\text{(XIII)}}{i\text{-}PrO-CHF_2}$$  (7)

$$\Big\downarrow -F^{\ominus}$$

$$i\text{-}PrO-\overset{\cdot\cdot}{C}-F \xrightarrow[\substack{\text{(several)}\\ \text{steps}}]{i\text{-}PrO^{\ominus}} \underset{\text{(XIV)}}{(i\text{-}PrO)_3CH}$$

Remarkably, alkoxyfluorocarbenes do not decompose to give carbon monoxide, halide ions, and carbonium ions, as alkoxychlorocarbenes do (cf. Chapter 8, Section I,B,8). The reaction of methyl dichloromethyl ether with alkoxides displays a considerable isotope effect ($k_H/k_D = 5.4 \pm 2.2$ with isopropoxide), which is neither consistent with a $S_N2$ displacement nor with the reversible formation of an anion. The reaction has therefore been postulated to involve the concerted $\alpha$-elimination of hydrogen chloride to give methoxychlorocarbene (20).

The unique acyloxycarbene XV is held responsible for the formation of the phthalide XVI from phthalic anhydride and triethyl phosphite (21). Added diethyl phosphite captures the intermediate XV, but no reaction with olefins has been observed.

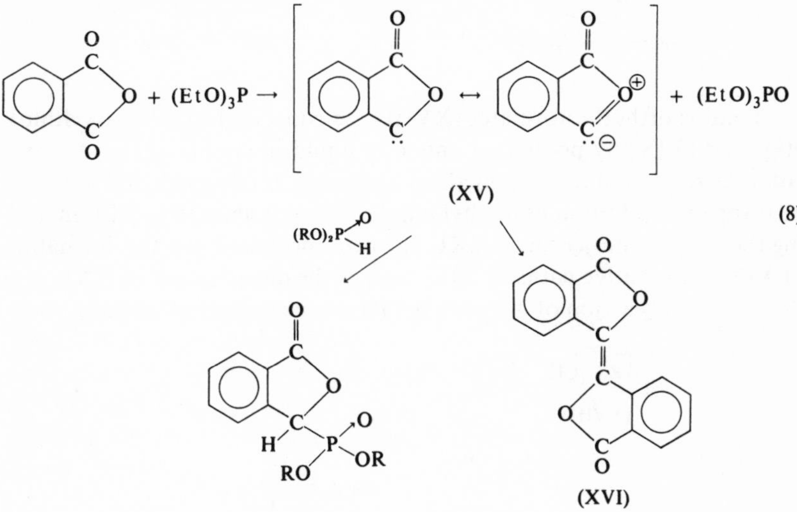

(8)

(XV)

(XVI)

## III. ALKYLTHIO- AND ARYLTHIOCARBENES

The $\alpha$-elimination of hydrogen chloride from $\alpha$-chlorothioanisol (XVII) appears to be easier than from the corresponding oxygen compound. Potassium tert-butoxide at $-15°$ is sufficient to effect this elimination, and yields up to 90% of phenylthiocarbene-olefin adducts have been obtained (22).

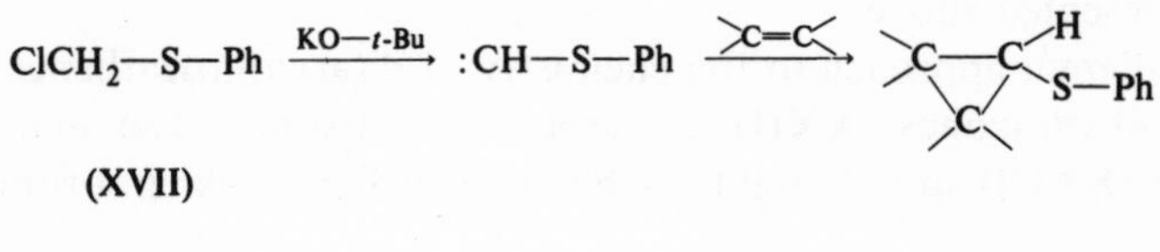

(9)

(XVII)

The stereochemistry of the two cyclohexene adducts, formed in a 2:1 ratio, has been established not only by N.M.R. (nuclear magnetic resonance) measurements, but also by oxidation to the sulfones. These may be equilibrated by alkali, and the thermodynamically more stable one (most probably *trans-*) was obtained from the *minor* phenylthio-carbene adduct (*22a*). 1,3-Cyclohexadiene has been used as an acceptor with no indication of 1,4-addition. With *cis*-2-butene and phenylthio-carbene, the *cis*-:*trans*- ratio was 3.6 whereas the *cis* adduct was the only product obtained from *cis*-1,2-di(phenylthio)ethylene (*22a*):

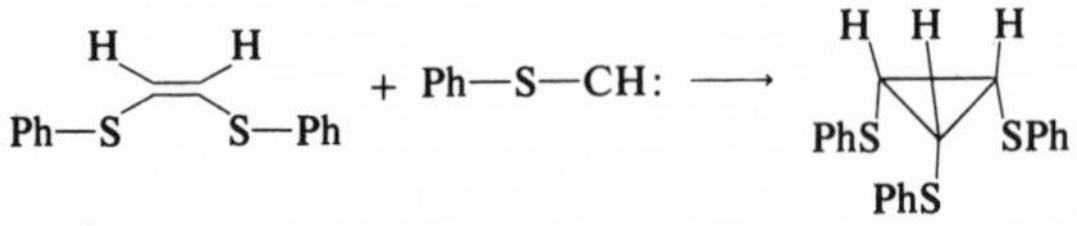

$$\text{(9a)}$$

Trialkyl orthothioformates (XVIII) are converted to tetra(alkylthio)-ethylenes (XIX) by potassium amide in liquid ammonia (*23*). A green color, attributed to the intermediate anion XX, is observed, and XX may be trapped by addition of methyl iodide. The sequence, Eq. (10), involv-ing the di(alkylthio)carbene XXI, has been proposed for the formation of XIX. Alternative paths to XIX, such as the dimerization of XXI, or a displacement reaction of XX with XVIII, were considered unlikely.

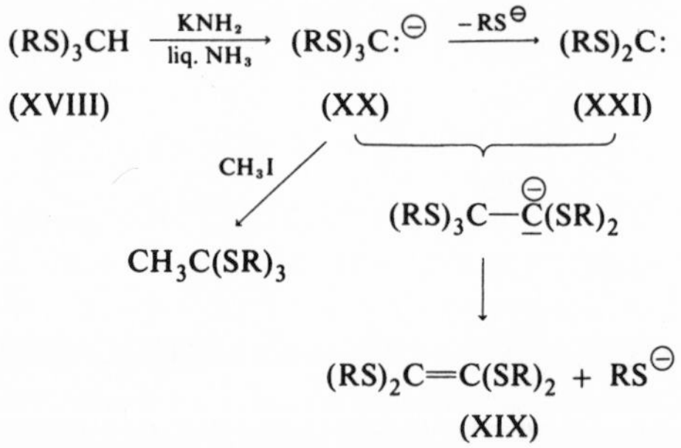

$$(RS)_3CH \xrightarrow[\text{liq. NH}_3]{\text{KNH}_2} (RS)_3C:^{\ominus} \xrightarrow{-RS^{\ominus}} (RS)_2C: \tag{10}$$

$$\text{(XVIII)} \qquad \text{(XX)} \qquad \text{(XXI)}$$

$$\text{CH}_3\text{C(SR)}_3 \qquad (RS)_3C\!-\!\overset{\ominus}{C}(SR)_2$$

$$(RS)_2C\!\!=\!\!C(SR)_2 + RS^{\ominus}$$

$$\text{(XIX)}$$

A scheme analogous to Eq. (7) represents the base-catalyzed reaction of methylmercaptide ion with chlorodifluoromethane, giving methyl di-fluoromethyl sulfide and methyl orthothioformate (*24*). The arguments in favor of a methylthiochlorocarbene intermediate are identical with those presented above.

A different approach to the chemistry of di(arylthio)carbenes utilizes the tosylhydrazones (XXII) as carbene precursors. The diazo com-pounds (XXIII) are thought to be intermediates which produce the "dimer" XXIV as the major product. The hypothetical carbenes could not be trapped by olefins such as cyclohexene, but added to enamines, ketene acetals, and triphenyl phosphine in fair yields (22b).

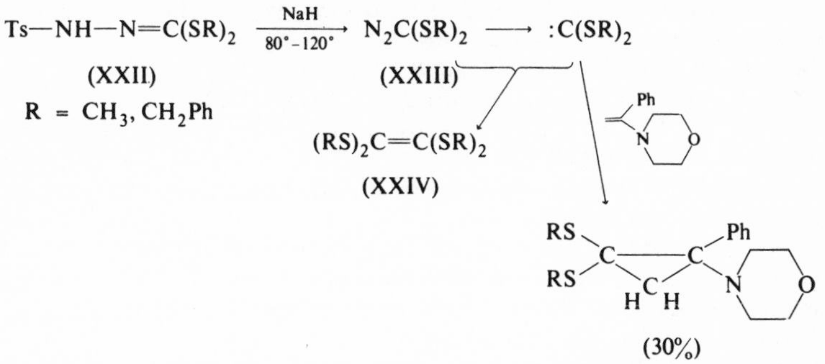

$$\text{Ts—NH—N=C(SR)}_2 \xrightarrow[80°-120°]{\text{NaH}} \text{N}_2\text{C(SR)}_2 \longrightarrow \text{:C(SR)}_2$$

(XXII)　　　　　　　　　　　(XXIII)

R = CH₃, CH₂Ph

(RS)₂C=C(SR)₂

(XXIV)　　　　　　　　　　　　　　　　　　　　　　(11)

(30%)

In contrast to the alkylthiocarbenes, bis(phenylsulfonyl)carbene, obtained from the corresponding diazo compound by photolysis, behaves as a strong electrophile (25). Its reaction with methanol afforded bis-(phenylsulfonyl)methyl methyl ether and bis(phenylsulfonyl)methane by alkylation and oxidation of the alcohol.

$$(\text{PhSO}_2)_2\text{CN}_2 \rightarrow (\text{PhSO}_2)_2\text{C:} + \text{CH}_3\text{OH} \begin{cases} (\text{PhSO}_2)_2\text{CH—OCH}_3 \\ (\text{PhSO}_2)_2\text{CH}_2 + \text{CH}_2\text{O} \end{cases}$$

## IV. PHENYLSELENOCARBENE

Many reactions in the phenylthiocarbene series may be applied to the selenium analog (24). Phenylselenocarbene has been generated according to Eq. (9) (Se instead of S). The addition to cis- and trans-2-butene was shown to be stereospecific, and the additions to cyclohexene (70% yield) and 1,3-cyclohexadiene (68% yield) afforded cis-:trans- ratios of 2:1 (configurational assignment based on the larger N.M.R. coupling constants of the major isomer).

### REFERENCES

1. L. C. Martin, *Proc. Roy. Soc.* **A89,** 127 (1913).
2. W. Jevons, *Proc. Roy. Soc.* **A117,** 351 (1928).
3. F. H. Crawford and W. A. Shurcliffe, *Phys. Rev.* **45,** 860 (1934).
4. G. Porter, *Proc. Roy. Soc.* **A200,** 284 (1950).
5. R. F. Barrow, *Discussions Faraday Soc.* **9,** 81 (1950).

6. R. G. W. Norrish, *Z. Elektrochem.* **56**, 705 (1952).

7. P. J. Dyne and D. A. Ramsay, *J. Chem. Phys.* **20**, 1055 (1952).

8. H. W. Wanzlick and E. Schikora, *Angew. Chem.* **72**, 494 (1960).

9. H. W. Wanzlick and H. J. Kleiner, *Angew. Chem.* **73**, 493 (1961).

9a. H. W. Wanzlick, F. Esser, and H. J. Kleiner, *Chem. Ber.* **96**, 1208 (1963).

10. H. W. Wanzlick and E. Schikora, *Chem. Ber.* **94**, 2389 (1961).

10a. H. W. Wanzlick and H. J. Kleiner, *Chem. Ber.* **96**, 3024 (1963).

11. D. M. Lemal and K. J. Kawano, *J. Am. Chem. Soc.* **84**, 1761 (1962).

11a. R. L. Pruett, J. T. Barr, K. E. Rapp, C. T. Bahner, J. D. Gibson, and R. H. Lafferty, *J. Am. Chem. Soc.* **72**, 3646 (1950).

11b. N. Wiberg and J. W. Buchler, *Angew. Chem.* **74**, 490 (1962); *J. Am. Chem. Soc.* **85**, 243 (1963); *Chem. Ber.* **96**, 3000 (1963).

11c. H. W. Wanzlick and H. J. Kleiner, *Angew. Chem.* **75**, 1024 (1963).

12. H. Scheibler, *Ber. deut. chem. Ges.* **59**, 1022 (1926); **60**, 554 (1927).

13. F. Adickes, *Ber. deut. chem. Ges.* **60**, 272 (1927); **63**, 3012 (1930).

14. A. E. Arbusov, *Ber. deut. chem. Ges.* **64**, 698 (1931).

15. D. Wood, Jr. and F. W. Bergstrom, *J. Am. Chem. Soc.* **55**, 3314 (1933).

16. U. Schöllkopf and A. Lerch, *Angew. Chem.* **73**, 27 (1961).

16a. R. J. Crawford and R. Raap, *Proc. Chem. Soc.* **1963**, 370.

16b. R. W. Hoffmann and H. Häuser, *Tetrahedron Letters* **1964**, 197.

16c. E. J. Corey and R. A. E. Winter, *J. Am. Chem. Soc.* **85**, 2677 (1963).

17. U. Schöllkopf, A. Lerch, and W. Pitteroff, *Tetrahedron Letters* **1962**, 241; U. Schöllkopf, A. Lerch, and J. Paust, *Chem. Ber.* **96**, 2266 (1963).

17a. U. Schöllkopf and J. Paust, *Angew. Chem.* **75**, 670 (1963).

18. G. Wittig and W. Böll, *Chem. Ber.* **95**, 2526 (1962).

19. J. Hine and K. Tanabe, *J. Am. Chem. Soc.* **79**, 2654 (1957); **80**, 3002 (1958).

20. J. Hine, R. J. Roscup, and D. C. Duffey, *J. Am. Chem. Soc.* **82**, 6120 (1960).

21. F. Ramirez, H. Yamanaka, and O. H. Basedow, *J. Am. Chem. Soc.* **83**, 173 (1961).

22. U. Schöllkopf and G. J. Lehmann, *Tetrahedron Letters* **1962**, 165.

22a. U. Schöllkopf, unpublished results (1963).

22b. U. Schöllkopf and E. Wiskott, *Angew. Chem.* **75**, 725 (1963); D. M. Lemal and E. H. Banitt, *Tetrahedron Letters* **1964**, 245.

23. J. Hine, R. P. Bayer, and G. G. Hammer, *J. Am. Chem. Soc.* **84**, 1751 (1962).

24. U. Schöllkopf and H. Küppers, *Tetrahedron Letters* **1963**, 105.

25. J. Diekmann, *J. Org. Chem.* **28**, 2933 (1963).

CHAPTER 10

# Dicarbenes

THE TASK OF PRODUCING a dicarbene involves the problem of simultaneous removal of suitable groups at different sites of a molecule. There is no difficulty in accomplishing such reactions at neighboring carbon atoms, but the immediate conversion of a 1,2-dicarbene to an acetylene may be expected. In fact, diphenylacetylene was prepared as early as 1889 (*1*) by mercuric oxide oxidation of benzil bis-hydrazone, most probably by way of formation and decomposition of a 1,2-bis-diazo compound. Occasional applications to the synthesis of other diarylacetylenes have been reported (*2, 3*). More recently, cyclic acetylenes [cyclodecyne (*4*), cyclononyne (*5*), and cyclooctyne (*6*)] have been made by the same procedure. The method has the advantage of affording acetylenes virtually free of allenes. The synthesis of an acetylenic paracyclophane has also been accomplished by hydrazone oxidation (*7*).

$$\begin{matrix} -C{=}N{-}NH_2 \\ | \\ -C{=}N{-}NH_2 \end{matrix} \xrightarrow{\text{HgO}} \begin{matrix} -C{=}N_2 \\ | \\ -C{=}N_2 \end{matrix} \rightarrow -C{\equiv}C- \qquad (1)$$

If the reaction, Eq. (1), is applied to bis-hydrazones of small-ring (< 7) 1,2-diketones, the resulting acetylenes are unstable intermediates which may be trapped by addition to dienes (*8, 9*).

The photolysis of various bis-diazoketones has been studied quantitatively (*10*). The quantum yields per diazo group compared well with those of simple diazoketones when the two reactive sites were separated by an aliphatic chain. Conjugation between the two diazocarbonyl groups *lowered* the quantum yields, as compared to the unconjugated systems. In this work there is no indication of a simultaneous ejection of *two* nitrogen molecules by *one* light quantum.

Murray and Trozzolo (*11*), however, have found some evidence for the formation of the dicarbene II from 1,4-bis(α-diazobenzyl)benzene

213

(I). When I was photolyzed in the presence of oxygen, 1,4-dibenzoyl-benzene was formed. This reaction is analogous to the oxidation of other diarylcarbenes (cf. Chapter 5, Section II,a). The formation of dibenzoylbenzene apparently does not proceed by consecutive steps, as no diazocarbonyl compound could be detected in the crude product after *partial* decomposition of I in the presence of oxygen.

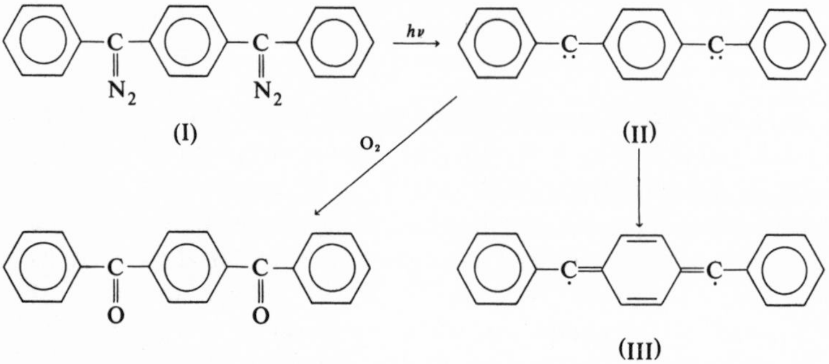

$$(2)$$

If II is assigned a triplet structure in analogy to diphenylcarbene, pairing of two of the four initially unpaired electrons would lead to the quinoid structure III. The electron spin resonance (E.S.R.) spectrum of irradiated I (solid solution in dibenzoylethane at 77°K.) indicates a low spin-spin interaction which is consistent with structure III. The E.S.R. spectrum of the photolytic products of 1,3-bis($\alpha$-diazobenzyl)benzene (*m*-isomer of I) was quite different from that of III (*11a*).

$C_3$, a major constituent of carbon vapor, was found to behave as the unique dicarbene :C=C=C: (*12*). Carbon vapor produced *in vacuo* reacted at a liquid nitrogen-cooled surface with isobutene to produce 1,1,1',1'-tetramethyl-bis-ethanoallene (IV).

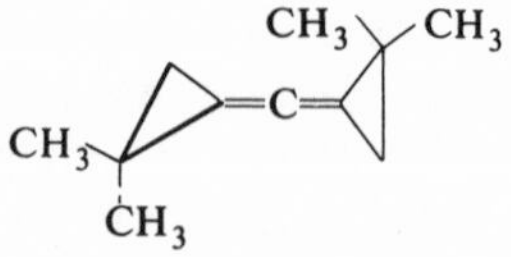

$$(3)$$

The resolution of the propene-$C_3$ adduct into three components (1:2:1) (*12*) is in accord with the geometry of the bis-ethanoallene system, the cyclopropane rings of which lie in orthogonal planes.

## References

1. Th. Curtius, *Ber. deut. chem. Ges.* **22,** 2161 (1889).
2. Th. Curtius and R. Kastner, *J. prakt, Chem.* [2] **83,** 215 (1913).
3. W. Schlenk and E. Bergmann, *Ann.* **463,** 76 (1928).
4. A. T. Blomquist, R. E. Burge, Jr., and A. C. Sucsy, *J. Am. Chem. Soc.* **74,** 3636 (1952).
5. A. T. Blomquist, L. H. Liu, and J. C. Bohrer, *J. Am. Chem. Soc.* **74,** 3643 (1952).
6. A. T. Blomquist and L. H. Liu, *J. Am. Chem. Soc.* **75,** 2153 (1953).
7. D. J. Cram and M. Cordon, *J. Am. Chem. Soc.* **77,** 4090 (1955).
8. G. Wittig, A. Krebs, and R. Pohlke, *Angew. Chem.* **72,** 324 (1960); *Chem. Ber.* **94,** 3260, 3276 (1961).
9. G. Wittig, *Angew. Chem.* **74,** 479 (1962).
10. W. Kirmse and L. Horner, *Ann.* **625,** 34 (1959).
11. R. W. Murray and A. M. Trozzolo, *J. Org. Chem.* **26,** 3109 (1961).
11a. A. M. Trozzolo, R. W. Murray, G. Smolinsky, W. A. Yager, and E. Wasserman, *J. Am. Chem. Soc.* **85,** 2526 (1963).
12. P. S. Skell and L. D. Wescott, *J. Am. Chem. Soc.* **85,** 1023 (1963).

# CHAPTER 11

# Excess Energy in Carbene Reactions
## by H. M. Frey
Chemistry Department, Southampton University, Southampton, England

CAREFUL INVESTIGATIONS of many of the simplest possible systems involving the reactions of methylene have shown them to be of considerable complexity. This complexity arises from three major causes. First, methylene is highly reactive, the energies of activation for its reactions with a large number of compounds being small. Second, methylene produced photochemically from either ketene, diazomethane, or diazirine, or thermally from diazomethane, is a "hot" radical, that is, it contains excess energy. One result of this excess energy is that in any particular system, many possible reactions of methylene occur with closely similar probabilities, the rates not being controlled by the small differences in energies of activation of the reactions. Finally, because of the highly endothermic nature of methylene ($\Delta H_f \approx 86$ kcal./mole) many of the compounds formed initially by its addition contain enough energy to undergo further reaction, and will do so unless stabilized by collision. In the gas phase this may lead to the yields of various products being pressure dependent in a manner found in very few other systems.

## I. RATES OF REACTIONS OF METHYLENE

Very few attempts have been made to obtain precise absolute values for the rates of methylene reactions. By an elegant series of experiments involving the simultaneous flash photolysis of inert gases plus ketene, and ethylene plus ketene mixtures, Kistiakowsky and Sauer (1) were able to show that methylene reacted with ketene at least as fast as once in every 200 collisions. They were not, however, able to set an upper limit to the reaction rate. A similar conclusion was reached by Kistiakowsky and Kydd (2) using a time of flight mass spectrometer. More recently, experiments on the flash photolysis of diazomethane by Herzberg and Shoosmith (3) yielded a value for the lifetime of the methylene radical which implies that methylene reacts with diazomethane *on every collision.* Much indirect evidence indicates that the reactions of methylene are extremely rapid. Thus methylene reacts at closely similar rates with a large number of saturated and unsaturated hydrocarbons, with hydrogen, carbon monoxide, ketene, diazomethane, and a number of ethers. The relative rates of these reactions have very small temperature coefficients. The simplest assumption that accounts for these findings is that the rates of these reactions are quite close to the collision frequencies. Other experimental evidence has indicated that methylene can add to ethylene before it loses excess energy carried over from the photolytic step (*4*). This again implies a very rapid reaction.

The first indication that in some systems methylene reacted as a hot radical, i.e., as one containing energy in excess of the thermal equilibrium value, came from the observation that the ratios of the products resulting from the attack of methylene on various types of carbonhydrogen bonds depended on whether the radical was generated from diazomethane or ketene (*4–6*). More detailed studies (*7, 8*) of the reactions of methylene with 2-butene and cyclobutane, which will be discussed later, suggested that methylene could have both excess translational and vibrational energy. It is probable that the indiscriminate behavior of methylene results from its being a hot radical and from the low values for the energy of activation of most of its reactions.

There is still some uncertainty about the heat of formation of methylene. Values ranging from less than 60 to nearly 100 kcal. have been suggested in the past few years. It now seems probable that $\Delta H_f$ for methylene cannot be far from 86 kcal. [For a detailed discussion of this point see reference (*9*).]

## II. UNIMOLECULAR DECOMPOSITION OF EXCITED MOLECULES FORMED BY METHYLENE REACTIONS

The initial attack of methylene on ethylene gives rise to two products: propylene by an insertion reaction in the carbon-hydrogen bonds, and cyclopropane by addition to the carbon double bond. The energetics of the reaction leading to cyclopropane are shown in Eq. (1).

$$C_2H_4 + CH_2 \rightarrow \overset{\displaystyle CH_2}{\overset{\displaystyle \diagup \diagdown}{CH_2 \!\!-\!\! CH_2}} \qquad (1)$$

$$\underset{+12.5}{\phantom{C_2H_4}} \quad \underset{+86}{\phantom{CH_2}} \qquad \underset{+12.7}{\phantom{CH_2\!-\!CH_2}} \qquad \Delta H \approx -86 \text{ kcal.}$$

The heat of the reaction $\approx -86$ kcal. must appear as vibrational excitation of the cyclopropane molecule. In fact, this is a minimum value since the cyclopropane will also contain all the excess energy carried by the (hot) methylene, and all the thermal energy originally carried by the ethylene. These additional energy contributions make it likely that the cyclopropane contains in excess of 90 kcal./mole and indeed a recent estimate (10) for the photochemical system ethylene plus methylene (from ketene) suggests a value of 103 kcal./mole. This is considerably in excess of the minimum energy required for the isomerization of cyclopropane to propylene (11) for which $E_{act} = 65$ kcal. Therefore, unless energy is rapidly removed from the excited molecule (by collision) this isomerization will occur. If the reaction were carried out in the liquid phase all the cyclopropane molecules would be stabilized, but in the gas phase the proportion of molecules stabilized will depend on the lifetime of the excited cyclopropane compared with the time taken for the molecule to undergo a collision. This latter time will clearly be dependent on the pressure of the system. We may thus write for the reactions of methylene with ethylene the following equations:

$$CH_2 + CH_2{=}CH_2 \xrightarrow{k_2} CH_3CH{=}CH_2 \qquad (2)$$

$$CH_2 + CH_2{=}CH_2 \xrightarrow{k_3} \overset{CH_2^*}{\overset{\diagup\diagdown}{CH_2{-}CH_2}} \qquad (3)$$

$$\overset{CH_2^*}{\overset{\diagup\diagdown}{CH_2{-}CH_2}} + M \xrightarrow{k_4} \overset{CH_2}{\overset{\diagup\diagdown}{CH_2{-}CH_2}} + M \qquad (4)$$

$$\overset{CH_2^*}{\overset{\diagup\diagdown}{CH_2{-}CH_2}} \xrightarrow{k_5} CH_3CH{=}CH_2 \qquad (5)$$

This system has been studied experimentally by photolyzing mixtures of ketene or diazomethane with ethylene at various pressures. In order to avoid the reactions of methylene with the propylene and cyclopropane a large ratio of ethylene to ketene (or diazomethane) was always used. This also reduced the fraction of methylene which reacted with the ketene. Under these conditions the stabilizing molecule designated by M in Eq. (4) will be ethylene. A stationary state treatment of Eqs. (2)–(5) leads to Eq. (6).

$$\frac{\text{Yield of cyclopropane}}{\text{Yields of cyclopropane + propylene}} = \frac{k_4 k_3}{k_3 + k_2} \cdot \frac{[\text{ethylene}]}{k_5 + k_4 [\text{ethylene}]} \qquad (6)$$

At low pressures when $k_5 \gg k_4$ [ethylene] the yield of cyclopropane will fall to zero, since all the excited molecules will isomerize before being collisionally deactivated. At high pressures when $k_5 \ll k_4$ [ethylene], the L. H. S. of the equation will approach the value of $k_3/(k_2 + k_3)$. The results obtained by Rabinovitch and his co-workers (12) using ketene and ethylene are shown in Fig. 1. The L. H. S. of Eq. (6) is plotted as a function of the pressure of the system. The upper curve was obtained using light of 3600 Å and the lower curve using light of 3100 Å. Both curves extrapolate to a zero value for cyclopropane at zero pressure and to ca. 0.85 at very high pressures. (The cause of the divergence of the curves at intermediate pressures will be discussed later.) The yields at high pressures give the relative values of $k_2$ to $k_3$ as 1:0.176, and since ethylene contains four equivalent carbon-hydrogen bonds the relative rate of addition to the double bond compared with insertion into a carbon-hydrogen bond is 1:0.044. (This is, of course, independent of the wavelength of the light used since both curves have the same high pressure limit.) If deactivation of the excited cyclopropane (reaction 4) occurs on every collision then the value of $k_5$ may be calculated from the equation

$$k_5 = \frac{[\text{propylene}]_p - [\text{propylene}]_\infty}{[\text{cyclopropane}]_p} \cdot \omega \tag{7}$$

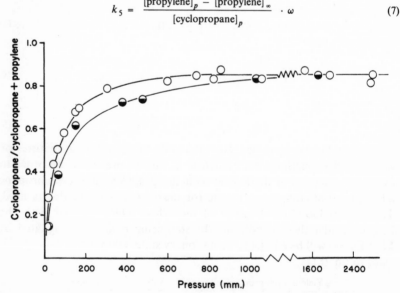

FIG. 1. Yield of cyclopropane as a function of pressure. ○ 3600 Å; ◉ 3100 Å.

where [propylene]$_p$ is the yield of propylene at pressure $p$, [propylene]$_\infty$ is the yield of propylene at high pressure, and $\omega$ is the collision frequency at pressure $p$. The mean values for $k_5$ obtained in the ketene-ethylene system were $0.65 \times 10^{10}$ and $1.11 \times 10^{10}$ sec.$^{-1}$ for light of 3600 and 3130 Å, respectively. These values, which indicate that the average lifetime of the vibrationally excited cyclopropane molecule is of the order of $10^{-10}$ sec., are to be expected for molecules of such large energy contents.

While historically the experiments just discussed were the first to be investigated in detail, a much simpler system in many respects results from the reactions of methylene with cyclobutane (8). This will be considered in some detail since it illustrates several features found in many gas phase studies of methylene reactions. Since methylene does not attack carbon-carbon single bonds, in its reactions with cyclobutane there is only one initial product, viz., methylcyclobutane:

$$CH_2 + \begin{array}{c} CH_2{-}CH_2 \\ | \qquad | \\ CH_2{-}CH_2 \end{array} \xrightarrow{k_8} \begin{array}{c} CH_3CH{-}CH_2{}^* \\ | \qquad | \\ CH_2{-}CH_2 \end{array} \qquad (8)$$

Methylcyclobutane is known to undergo a unimolecular decomposition (13) with an energy of activation of 61.2 kcal./mole. The energy content of the methylcyclobutane formed by reaction (8) is unlikely to be less than ca. 95 kcal./mole and hence this molecule will decompose unless collisionally stabilized.

$$\begin{array}{c} CH_3CH{-}CH_2{}^* \\ | \qquad | \\ CH_2{-}CH_2 \end{array} + M \xrightarrow{k_9} \begin{array}{c} CH_3CH{-}CH_2 \\ | \qquad | \\ CH_2{-}CH_2 \end{array} + M \qquad (9)$$

$$\begin{array}{c} CH_3CH{-}CH_2{}^* \\ | \qquad | \\ CH_2{-}CH_2 \end{array} \xrightarrow{k_{10}} CH_3CH{=}CH_2 + CH_2{=}CH_2 \qquad (10)$$

A stationary state treatment leads to the equation

$$[\% \text{ yield of methylcyclobutane}] = 100\, k_9 M/(k_9 M + k_{10}) \qquad (11)$$

Thus at high pressures when $k_9 M \gg k_{10}$ the yield of methylcyclobutane will approach 100%, and at low pressures when $k_9 M \ll k_{10}$ it will tend to zero. The results obtained for a series of experiments are shown in Fig. 2. Curves 1 and 2 refer to the ketene-cyclobutane system using light of 3130 and ca. 2800 Å, respectively. Curves 3 and 4 refer to the diazomethane-cyclobutane system using light of 4358 and 3660 Å, respectively. The yield of methylcyclobutane at any pressure depends on the relative

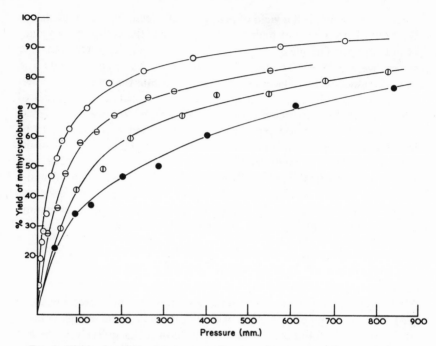

FIG. 2. Yields of methylcyclobutane as a function of pressure. ○ Curve 1 (Series 1); ⊖ Curve 2 (Series 2); ⦶ Curve 3 (Series 3); ● Curve 4 (Series 4).

magnitudes of $k_9 M$ and $k_{10}$. Since $k_9 M$ is directly proportional to the pressure, the variation of the yields of methylcyclobutane at any particular pressure with the nature of the methylene precursor, and with the wavelength of the light producing the photolysis, must be due to a corresponding variation in $k_{10}$. Since $k_{10}$ depends only on the total energy content of the methylcyclobutane, this is a clear indication that the energy content of the methylene varies with both the nature of its precursor and the wavelength of the light used.

The percentage yield of methylcyclobutane is determined from the amounts of methylcyclobutane and propylene formed. In theory the yield of ethylene could also be used, but in practice some ethylene is always formed by the reaction of methylene with either the ketene or diazomethane.

$$CH_2 + CH_2CO \rightarrow C_2H_4 + CO \qquad (12)$$

$$CH_2 + CH_2N_2 \rightarrow C_2H_4 + N_2 \qquad (13)$$

The value of the rate constant $k_{10}$ can easily be determined using the equation

$$k_{10} = \frac{[propylene]}{[methylcyclobutane]} \cdot \omega \qquad (14)$$

where $\omega$ is the collision frequency. (The usual assumption has been made that deactivation of the excited molecule occurs on every collision.) The value for $k_{10}$ varies slightly with pressure, probably because the molecules of methylcyclobutane have a small range of energies. For series 1 (curve 1) at high pressures $k_{10} = 7.81 \times 10^8$ sec.$^{-1}$, and hence the excited methylcyclobutane has an average lifetime of about $10^{-9}$ seconds. At low pressures $k_{10}$ has fallen to $4.01 \times 10^8$ sec.$^{-1}$.

The four curves shown in Fig. 2 all have the same general shape, but the fraction of excited molecules which are stabilized at any particular pressure decreases from series 1 to series 4. This is shown in Fig. 3. The curve is that obtained in series 1 and the points are those obtained in series 2, 3, and 4, the pressures in each series being divided by 2, 4, and 6, respectively. This implies that the lifetimes of the excited methylcyclobutane molecules are less by these factors in series 2, 3, and 4, respectively, than in series 1.

The dependence of the specific rate constant $k_E$ on the total energy of a reacting molecule is an essential of both the Kassel (14) and the Slater (15) theories of unimolecular reactions. If we neglect quantum or zero-point energy effects, these theories both yield an equation of the form

$$k_E = constant \left(\frac{E - E_0}{E}\right)^{n-1} \qquad (15)$$

where $E$ is the total energy of the molecule and $E_0$ is the minimum energy required for reaction, i.e., the energy of activation for the reaction. The $A$ factor in the Arrhenius equation for a unimolecular reaction may be interpreted as the limiting specific rate for molecules of very high energy (16). We may therefore replace the constant in Eq. (15) by the value of $A$ determined experimentally by the thermal decomposition of methylcyclobutane, viz., $2.4 \times 10^{15}$ sec.$^{-1}$. In the Slater theory the value of $n$ is equal to the number of vibrational modes which interact with the critical coordinate. In the Kassel theory, $n$ is equal to the number of effective oscillators in the molecule. Substitution in Eq. (15) of the value

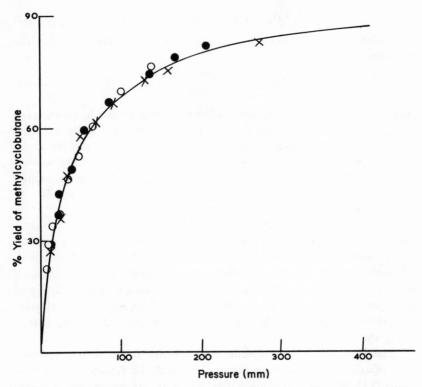

FIG. 3. Plot of yields of methylcyclobutane against "reduced" pressure. — (solid curve), series (1); × Series (2), pressure × 1/2; ● Series (3), pressure × 1/4; ○ Series (4), pressure × 1/6.

of $k_E$ for series 1 together with the value of $E_0$ and the probable value of $E$, results in the rather improbable value of $n = 15$. (The value of $n$ increases with the complexity of a molecule; for cyclopropane it is 13, for cyclobutane it is 19, so that a value of about 25 is to be expected for methylcyclobutane).

A more satisfactory relationship between $k_E$ and the energy content of the molecule takes into consideration the zero-point energy of the molecule. (For a complete discussion of this relationship, which is beyond the scope of this chapter, see reference 8.) Even this relationship is only likely to be valid for values of $E$ considerably greater than $E_0$:

$$k_E = A \left( \frac{E - E_0 + \alpha E_z}{E + \alpha E_z} \right)^{n-1} \tag{16}$$

where $E_z$ is the zero-point energy of the molecule, and $\alpha = n/(3N - 6)$, $N$ being the number of atoms in the molecule. The constant $\alpha$ is thus an approximate measure of the zero-point energy associated with the effective oscillators of the molecule. Taking $E_0 = 61.2$ kcal./mole, and $E_z = 65$ kcal./mole, and using the low pressure value of $k_{10}$, $4.01 \times 10^8$, for $k_E$, Eq. (16) yields $n = 30$ with $E = 94$ kcal./mole. This value for $E$ is about that expected from the thermochemistry of the reaction if the methylene carries very little excess energy. We may now compute the value of $E$ corresponding to $k_{10} = 7.81 \times 10^8$ sec.$^{-1}$, the value of $k_E$ obtained in series 1 at high pressures. Using $n = 30$ we obtain $E = 99$ kcal./mole. Thus in series 1 the energy spread over the majority of excited methylcyclobutane molecules is only 5 kcal./mole.

Taking the mean value of $E$ as 96.5 kcal./mole in series 1, we can now compute the corresponding values of $E$ for series 2, 3, and 4, since the values of $k_{10}$ for the various series are in the ratios 1:2:4:6. The energies obtained are 102, 107.5, and 112 kcal./mole, respectively. While Eq. (16) is certainly not an exact relationship and these values are not to be considered as precise, the differences are unlikely to be grossly in error. If we assume that the methylene in series 1 carries no excess energy, then the methylene produced from ketene using the shorter wavelength radiation contains 5.5 kcal./mole excess energy *when it reacts*. For methylene produced from diazomethane using 4358 and 3660 Å radiation, the corresponding figures are 10.5 and 15.5 kcal./mole.

As has already been mentioned, the ratios of the products resulting from the insertion reaction of methylene with a molecule containing more than one type of carbon-hydrogen bond depend on whether the methylene is produced by the photolysis of ketene or of diazomethane. In the latter case attack is virtually indiscriminate, whereas methylene from ketene inserts considerably more rapidly with tertiary carbon-hydrogen bonds than with secondary carbon-hydrogen bonds, and in both of these more rapidly than in primary carbon-hydrogen bonds. This disparity is thought to be due to the difference in kinetic energy of the methylene from the two sources (4, 6). In this context it is interesting to note that the difference in excess energy carried by the methylene in series 2 and 3 is 5.5 kcal./mole. This suggests that even if all this excess energy is kinetic the difference in the reactivity of methylene from the two precursors could only occur if the energy of activation for its reactions were less than about 5 kcal./mole, which is consistent with the extreme reactivity shown by methylene.

The reactions of methylene with isobutene (*17*) throw further light on the nature of the excess energy carried by the radical. The system is also another good example of the unimolecular decomposition of a vibrationally excited molecule. The initial attack of the methylene on isobutene gives rise to three products:

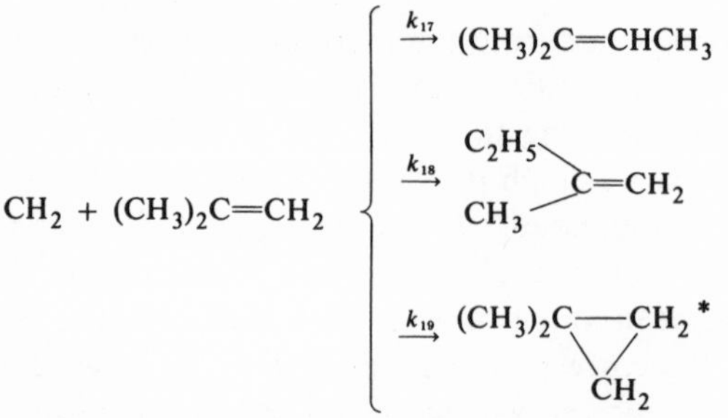

$$\xrightarrow{k_{17}} (CH_3)_2C=CHCH_3 \tag{17}$$

$$CH_2 + (CH_3)_2C=CH_2 \quad \begin{cases} & \\ & \xrightarrow{k_{18}} \begin{matrix} C_2H_5 \\ \diagdown \\ CH_3 \diagup \end{matrix} C=CH_2 \tag{18} \\ & \\ & \xrightarrow{k_{19}} (CH_3)_2C{\overset{\displaystyle{}}{\underset{\diagdown \; CH_2 \; \diagup}{\text{———}}}}CH_2{}^* \tag{19} \end{cases}$$

As in the case of cyclopropane itself, dimethylcyclopropane undergoes a unimolecular isomerization reaction (*18*) with an energy of activation considerably less than the energy content of the molecule formed by reaction 19. It will therefore decompose (to yield 2-methyl-2-butene and 3-methyl-1-butene) unless collisionally stabilized.

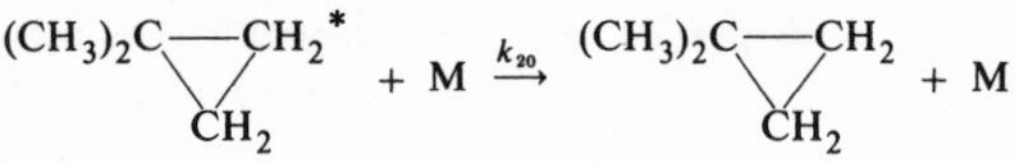

$$(CH_3)_2C{\underset{\diagdown \; CH_2 \; \diagup}{\text{———}}}CH_2{}^* + M \xrightarrow{k_{20}} (CH_3)_2C{\underset{\diagdown \; CH_2 \; \diagup}{\text{———}}}CH_2 + M \tag{20}$$

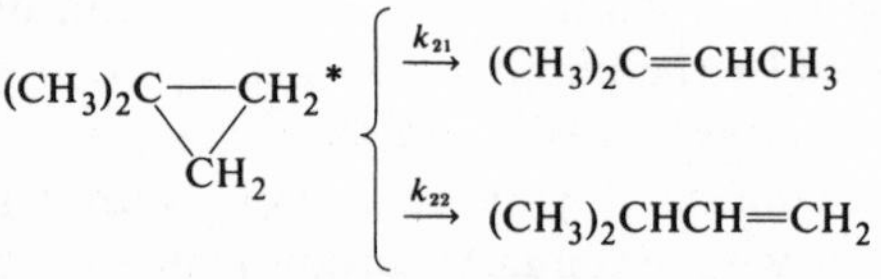

$$(CH_3)_2C{\underset{\diagdown \; CH_2 \; \diagup}{\text{———}}}CH_2{}^* \begin{cases} \xrightarrow{k_{21}} (CH_3)_2C=CHCH_3 \tag{21} \\ \\ \xrightarrow{k_{22}} (CH_3)_2CHCH=CH_2 \tag{22} \end{cases}$$

A stationary state treatment of this system gives the equation

$$\frac{[\text{yield of dimethylcyclopropane at infinite pressure}]}{[\text{yield of dimethylcyclopropane at pressure } p]} = 1 + \frac{k_{21} + k_{22}}{k_{20}p} \tag{23}$$

where it is assumed that all molecules present in the system are equally efficient at deactivating the excited dimethylcyclopropane. (In fact under the usual experimental conditions isobutene constitutes the bulk of the reaction mixture.) Thus a plot of the L. H. S. of Eq. (23) against the reciprocal of the pressure should be linear with an intercept of unity at

$p = 0$. Such a plot is shown in Fig. 4. It refers to the diazomethane-isobutene system with the unfiltered radiation of a medium pressure mercury arc and a Pyrex reaction vessel, and shows that the results are consistent with the postulated mechanism.

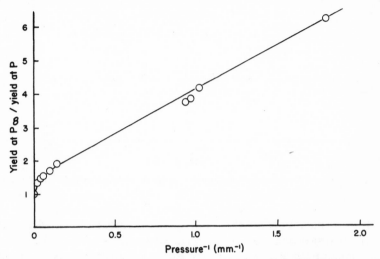

FIG. 4. Plot of the inverse of the fractional yield of 1,1-dimethylcyclopropane compared with the value at infinite pressure, against the inverse of the total pressure.

The effect on the yields of the various products, of the wavelength of the photolytic radiation, was extensively studied in the isobutene system. The yield of 2-methyl-1-butene was found to be the same using light of 4358 and 3660 Å. However, at any particular pressure the yield of the dimethylcyclopropane was greater with the longer wavelength radiation. The results obtained in this work are shown in Fig. 5.

From the dependence of the yields of dimethylcyclopropane at any particular pressure on the wavelength of the light used, it is clear that the molecules produced from diazomethane using 3660 Å radiation contain appreciably more energy than those in the 4358 Å system. However, the invariance of the yields of 2-methyl-1-butene means that the relative rates of initial attack on the isobutene, i.e., $k_{17}:k_{18}:k_{19}$, are independent of the wavelength of the photolytic radiation. This suggests that the difference in energy carried by the methylene in the two series of experiments is in the form of vibrational excitation. (An appreciable difference in kinetic energy would result in a difference in the ratios of $k_{17}:k_{18}:k_{19}$.)

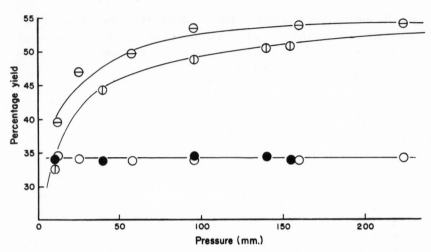

FIG. 5. Effect of wavelength of radiation on product yields. 2-methyl-1-butene: 4358 Å ○, 3660 Å ●; 1,1-dimethylcyclopropane: 4358 Å ⊖, 3660 Å ⊕.

Thus we have seen that the studies of the reactions of methylene with various hydrocarbons can be rationalized in terms of a radical which may contain both excess kinetic and excess vibrational energy. Studies of the diazomethane-isobutene system show that methylene from diazomethane contains excess vibrational energy. They also indicate that the methylene contains excess kinetic energy. It was found that the presence of a large excess of inert gas (argon, nitrogen) did lead to a change in the ratios $k_{17}:k_{18}:k_{19}$. At pressures where most of the initially formed dimethylcyclopropane was stabilized, the yield of this compound was increased from 54% to over 67% by the presence of a considerable excess of argon. It also appears that the relative values of $k_{17}:k_{18}:k_{19}$ obtained with diazomethane with a large excess of argon are within experimental error the same as those obtained with ketene and isobutene in the absence of any other added gas. A careful analysis of the results suggests that "deactivation" of the methylenes by the inert gases occurs with very high collision efficiency, which is again consistent with loss of kinetic energy. We conclude that methylene produced from diazomethane contains more kinetic energy than does methylene produced from ketene, and that this is virtually independent of the wavelength of the light-producing decomposition. Also, methylene contains excess vibrational energy and this does depend on both the precursor and the wavelength of the radiation producing decomposition.

The reactions of methylene with *trans*- and *cis*-2-butene can be explained by the same general scheme as has been given for isobutene (7). However, the system is somewhat complicated by the possibility of the 1,2-dimethylcyclopropane undergoing both a geometric and a structural isomerization. The equations below apply to the reactions of methylene with *trans*-2-butene (those with *cis*-2-butene are similar).

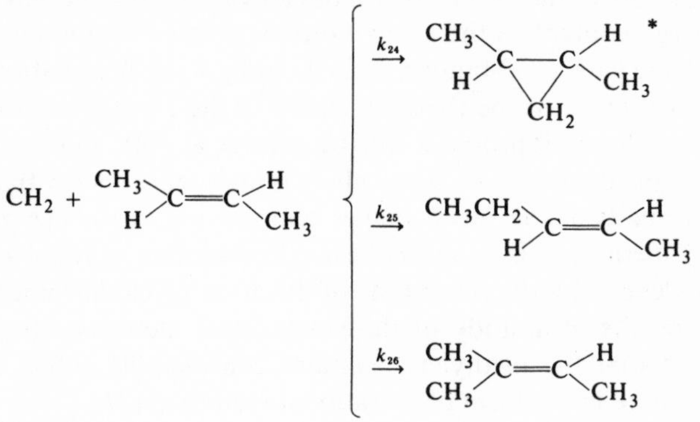

$$
CH_2 + \underset{H}{\overset{CH_3}{}}C=C\underset{CH_3}{\overset{H}{}} \quad \left\{
\begin{array}{l}
\end{array}
\right.
$$

$$\xrightarrow{k_{24}} \underset{H}{\overset{CH_3}{}}C\!\!-\!\!C\underset{CH_3}{\overset{H}{}}^{\ *} \qquad (24)$$

$$\xrightarrow{k_{25}} \underset{H}{\overset{CH_3CH_2}{}}C=C\underset{CH_3}{\overset{H}{}} \qquad (25)$$

$$\xrightarrow{k_{26}} \underset{CH_3}{\overset{CH_3}{}}C=C\underset{CH_3}{\overset{H}{}} \qquad (26)$$

$$\underset{H}{\overset{CH_3}{}}C\!\!-\!\!C\underset{CH_3}{\overset{H}{}}^{\ *} \underset{k_{-27}}{\overset{k_{27}}{\rightleftharpoons}} \underset{H}{\overset{CH_3}{}}C\!\!-\!\!C\underset{H}{\overset{CH_3}{}}^{\ *} \qquad (27)$$

$$\underset{H}{\overset{CH_3}{}}C\!\!-\!\!C\underset{CH_3}{\overset{H}{}}^{\ *} \quad \left\{
\begin{array}{l}
\xrightarrow{k_{28}} CH_3CH_2CH=CHCH_3 \qquad\qquad (28) \\
\qquad\quad cis \text{ and } trans \\
\xrightarrow{k_{29}} (CH_3)_2C=CHCH_3 \qquad\qquad (29) \\
\xrightarrow{k_{30}} CH_3CH_2(CH_3)C=CH_2 \qquad\qquad (30)
\end{array}
\right.
$$

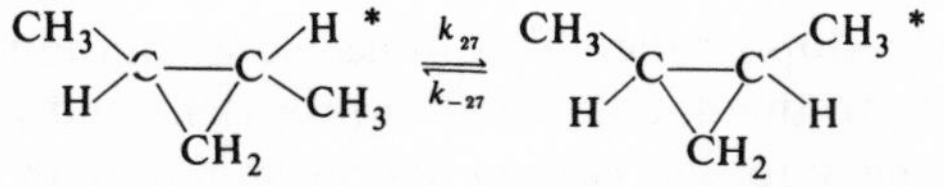

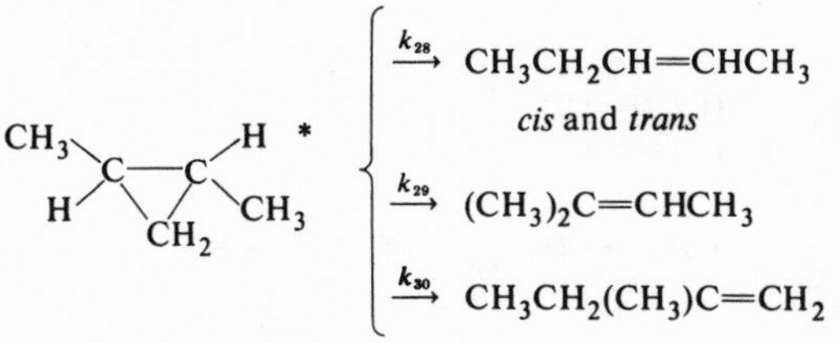

$$CH_3CH\!\!-\!\!CHCH_3^{\ *} + M \xrightarrow{k_{31}} CH_3CH\!\!-\!\!CHCH_3 + M \qquad (31)$$

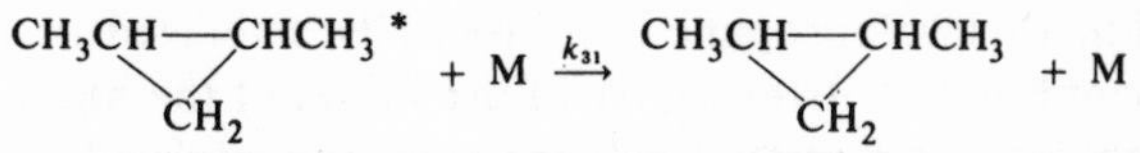

The results obtained fully support the mechanism suggested by Eqs. (24)–(31), and the effects of wavelength of light and addition of inert gas are fully consistent with the explanations given to account for the results given for isobutene. By working at high pressures the formation of *trans*-2-pentene [Eq. (25)] was shown to be stereospecific since no *cis*-

compound was detected. At low pressures, however, there is some evidence that this molecule does contain sufficient energy to undergo a reversible geometrical isomerization to the *cis*-compound.

Methylene can be produced by the *thermal* decomposition of diazomethane (*19*) at temperatures above about 200°C. Studies of the reactions of methylene produced in this way with *cis*-2-butene indicate that at about 350°C the resulting 1,2-dimethylcyclopropane has about the same energy content as the same molecule formed by the *photolysis* of diazomethane with *cis*-2-butene at 25°C using 4358 Å radiation (*20*). Since the contribution of the thermal energy of the 2-butene toward the total energy of the cyclopropane will be greater at 350° than at 25°C, the methylene produced photochemically has even more energy than that produced thermally at the much higher temperature, a further demonstration that methylene is a hot radical. Yet another method of producing methylene is by the photolysis of diazirine (cyclodiazomethane). Preliminary results of a study of the reactions of methylene from this source suggest that the methylene contains considerable excess energy which is almost all in the form of vibrational excitation (*21*).

The production of the same excited molecule by two distinct paths has been used by Butler and Kistiakowsky (*22*) in their studies of the decomposition of methylcyclopropane. This molecule was produced by the addition of methylene to the double bond in propylene and also by the insertion of methylene into the carbon-hydrogen bonds in cyclopropane:

$$CH_2 + CH_3CH{=}CH_2 \xrightarrow{k_{32}} \underset{CH_2}{CH_3CH{-}CH_2{}^*} \tag{32}$$

$$CH_2 + \underset{CH_2}{CH_2{-}CH_2} \xrightarrow{k_{33}} \underset{CH_2}{CH_3CH{-}CH_2{}^*} \tag{33}$$

The excited methylcyclopropane is collisionally stabilized or isomerizes to a mixture of butenes. Irrespective of the values of the heats of formation of methylene and methylcyclopropane, the molecule formed by reaction 33 will have about 7.9 kcal./mole more energy than that formed by reaction 32 ($\Delta H_f$ cyclopropane–$\Delta H_f$ propylene). The lifetime of the molecule derived from cyclopropane was found to be less than one third of that from propylene. This is a striking demonstration that the lifetime of these excited molecules is highly dependent on their energy contents.

The reactions of methylene with butadiene and the subsequent decomposition of some of the excited initial products, are a good example of the complications (and consequent analytical difficulties) of even the simplest systems involving this reactive radical. This system also illustrates in yet another way the high energy content of the molecules formed by methylene reactions. The initial attack of methylene produces *cis*- and *trans*-penta-1,3-diene, isoprene, and vinylcyclopropane:

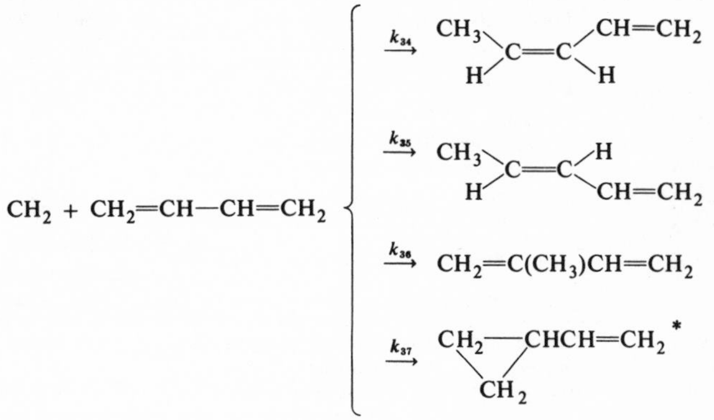

$$\mathrm{CH_2 + CH_2{=}CH{-}CH{=}CH_2}$$

$$\xrightarrow{k_{34}} \quad \begin{matrix} \mathrm{CH_3} \\ \phantom{x} \\ \mathrm{H} \end{matrix}{>}\mathrm{C}{=}\mathrm{C}{<}\begin{matrix} \mathrm{CH{=}CH_2} \\ \phantom{x} \\ \mathrm{H} \end{matrix} \quad (34)$$

$$\xrightarrow{k_{35}} \quad \begin{matrix} \mathrm{CH_3} \\ \phantom{x} \\ \mathrm{H} \end{matrix}{>}\mathrm{C}{=}\mathrm{C}{<}\begin{matrix} \mathrm{H} \\ \phantom{x} \\ \mathrm{CH{=}CH_2} \end{matrix} \quad (35)$$

$$\xrightarrow{k_{36}} \quad \mathrm{CH_2{=}C(CH_3)CH{=}CH_2} \quad (36)$$

$$\xrightarrow{k_{37}} \quad \overset{*}{\underset{\mathrm{CH_2}}{\mathrm{CH_2{-}CHCH{=}CH_2}}} \quad (37)$$

The hot vinylcyclopropane is stabilized by collision or isomerizes:

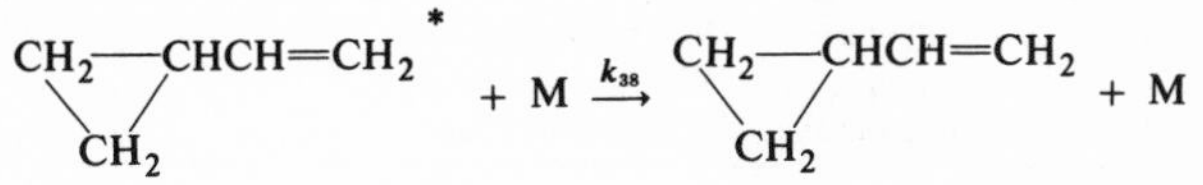

$$\overset{*}{\underset{\mathrm{CH_2}}{\mathrm{CH_2{-}CHCH{=}CH_2}}} + \mathrm{M} \xrightarrow{k_{38}} \underset{\mathrm{CH_2}}{\mathrm{CH_2{-}CHCH{=}CH_2}} + \mathrm{M} \quad (38)$$

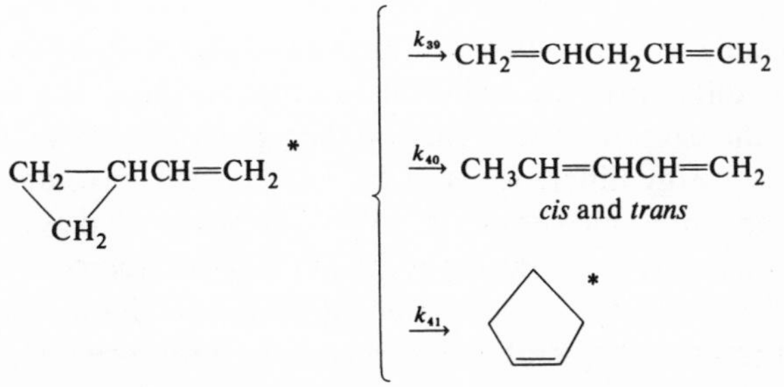

$$\overset{*}{\underset{\mathrm{CH_2}}{\mathrm{CH_2{-}CHCH{=}CH_2}}}$$

$$\xrightarrow{k_{39}} \mathrm{CH_2{=}CHCH_2CH{=}CH_2} \quad (39)$$

$$\xrightarrow{k_{40}} \mathrm{CH_3CH{=}CHCH{=}CH_2} \quad (40)$$
$$\text{\textit{cis} and \textit{trans}}$$

$$\xrightarrow{k_{41}} \quad \overset{*}{\bigcirc\!\!=} \quad (41)$$

All the products shown in Eqs. (39)–(41) were found to be formed by the isomerization of the hot vinylcyclopropane. In the thermal isomerization of vinylcyclopropane (at about 370°C.), cyclopentene is the major product with only trace amounts of the other dienes. This is because the

TABLE I

RATE CONSTANTS FOR DECOMPOSITION OF MOLECULES PRODUCED
BY METHYLENE REACTIONS

| $CH_2$ source | Other source | Activated molecule | Rate constant $\times 10^8 sec^{-1}$ | Ref. |
|---|---|---|---|---|
| $CH_2N_2$, 4358 Å | Ethylene | Cyclopropane | 450 | 20 |
| $CH_2N_2$ thermal, 325°C | Ethylene | Cyclopropane | 380 | 20 |
| $CH_2CO$, 3200 Å | Ethylene | Cyclopropane | 180 | 20 |
| $CH_2CO$, 3200 Å | Ethylene-$d_2$ | 1,2-Cyclopropane-$d_2$ | 1580 cis-trans | 20 |
| $CH_2CO$, 3320 Å | Ethylene-$d_2$ | 1,2-Cyclopropane-$d_2$ | 1180 cis-trans | 20 |
| $CH_2N_2$ (unfiltered light) | Propylene | Methylcyclopropane | 12.0 | 22 |
| $CH_2CO$, 3100 Å | Propylene | Methylcyclopropane | 5.9 | 22 |
| $CH_2N_2$ (unfiltered light) | Cyclopropane | Methylcyclopropane | 43.5 | 22 |
| $CH_2CO$, 3100 Å | Cyclopropane | Methylcyclopropane | 27.8 | 22 |
| $CH_2N_2$ (unfiltered light) | Isobutene | 1,1-Dimethylcyclopropane | 1.6 | 17 |
| $CH_2N_2$, 4358 Å | Isobutene | 1,1-Dimethylcyclopropane | 0.6 | 17 |
| $CH_2N_2$, 4358 Å | trans-2-Butene | trans-1,2-Dimethylcyclopropane | 9.0 (cis-trans) | 7 |
|  |  |  | 1.4 (structural) | 7 |
| $CH_2N_2$, 3660 Å | trans-2-Butene | trans-1,2-Dimethylcyclopropane | 18 (cis-trans) | 7 |
| $CH_2N_2$, 4358 Å | Allene | Methylenecyclopropane | 24.7 | 24 |
| $CH_2N_2$, 3660 Å | Allene | Methylenecyclopropane | 38.1 | 24 |
| $CH_2CO$, 3130 Å | Allene | Methylenecyclopropane | 12.8 | 24 |
| $CH_2N_2$, 4358 Å | Cyclobutane | Methylcyclobutane | 20 | 8 |
| $CH_2N_2$, 3660 Å | Cyclobutane | Methylcyclobutane | 34 | 8 |
| $CH_2CO$, 3130 Å | Cyclobutane | Methylcyclobutane | 7.8 | 8 |
| $CH_2N_2$, 4358 Å | Butadiene | Vinylcyclopropane | 8.7 | 25 |
| $CH_2N_2$, 3660 Å | Butadiene | Vinylcyclopropane | 12.4 | 25 |
| $CH_2CO$, 3130 Å | Butadiene | Vinylcyclopropane | 5.3 | 25 |

reactions leading to these other products have higher energies of activation, and the differences are sufficient to suppress them almost entirely. However in the case of excited vinylcyclopropane formed by methylene addition, this energy difference is of far less consequence, and approximately as many molecules isomerize to give dienes as yield cyclopentene.

Cyclopentene itself can decompose (23) to give cyclopentadiene and hydrogen with an energy of activation of 58.8 kcal./mole. Thus while the result of reaction 41 yields a relatively more stable product, the cyclopentene still has sufficient energy to decompose into cyclopentadiene and hydrogen unless it is itself collisionally stabilized:

$$\text{cyclopentene}^* + M \xrightarrow{k_{42}} \text{cyclopentadiene} + M \qquad (42)$$

$$\text{(structure)} \xrightarrow[\phantom{xx}]{\overset{*}{k_{43}}} \text{(structure)} + H_2 \qquad (43)$$

A stationary state treatment of Eqs. (34)–(43) shows that the yield of cyclopentene should go through a maximum, and this is in fact found experimentally (*25*).

Table I shows the rate constants for the decomposition of excited molecules produced by methylene reactions. It can be seen that there is a marked correlation between the magnitude of the rate constants and the complexity of the decomposing molecule. This is in complete accordance with the present theories of unimolecular reactions.

### REFERENCES

1. G. B. Kistiakowsky and K. Sauer, *J. Am. Chem. Soc.* **80**, 1066 (1958), **78**, 5699 (1956).
2. G. B. Kistiakowsky and P. H. Kydd, *J. Am. Chem. Soc.* **79**, 4825 (1957).
3. G. Herzberg and J. Shoosmith, *Nature* **183**, 1801 (1959).
4. H. M. Frey and G. B. Kistiakowsky, *J. Am. Chem. Soc.* **79**, 6373 (1957).
5. W. v. E. Doering, R. G. Buttery, R. G. Laughlin and N. Chaudhuri, *J. Am. Chem. Soc.* **78**, 3224 (1956).
6. H. M. Frey, *J. Am. Chem. Soc.* **80**, 5005 (1958).
7. H. M. Frey, *Proc. Roy. Soc.* **A251**, 575 (1959).
8. H. M. Frey, *Trans. Faraday Soc.* **56**, 1201 (1960).
9. H. M. Frey, *Prog. in Reaction Kinetics* **2**, 131–164.
10. B. S. Rabinovitch, private communication.
11. T. S. Chambers and G. B. Kistiakowsky, *J. Am. Chem. Soc.* **56**, 399 (1934); W. E. Falconer, T. E. Hunter, and A. F. Trotman-Dickenson, *J. Chem. Soc.* **1961**, 609.
12. B. S. Rabinovitch, E. Tschuikow-Roux, and E. W. Schlag, *J. Am. Chem. Soc.* **81**, 1083 (1959).
13. M. N. Das and W. D. Walters, *Z. physik. Chem.* **15**, 22 (1958).
14. L. S. Kassel, "Kinetics of Homogeneous Gas Reactions." Chemical Catalogue Co., New York, 1932.
15. N. B. Slater, *Proc. Roy. Soc.* **A194**, 112 (1948); *Phil. Trans.* **A246**, 57 (1953).
16. N. B. Slater, *Trans. Faraday Soc.* **55**, 5 (1959).
17. H. M. Frey, *Proc. Roy. Soc.* **A250**, 409 (1959).
18. M. C. Flowers and H. M. Frey, *J. Chem. Soc.* **1959**, 3953.
19. B. S. Rabinovitch and D. W. Setser, *J. Am. Chem. Soc.* **83**, 750 (1961).
20. D. W. Setser and B. S. Rabinovitch, *Can. J. Chem.* **40**, 1425 (1962).
21. H. M. Frey and I. D. R. Stevens, *Proc. Chem. Soc.* **1962**, 79.
22. J. N. Butler and G. B. Kistiakowsky, *J. Am. Chem. Soc.* **82**, 759 (1960); **83**, 1324 (1961).
23. D. W. Vanus and W. D. Walters, *J. Am. Chem. Soc.* **70**, 4035 (1948).
24. H. M. Frey, *Trans. Faraday Soc.* **57**, 951 (1961).
25. H. M. Frey, *Trans. Faraday Soc.* **58**, 516 (1962).

# CHAPTER 12

# The Spin States of Carbenes

by Peter P. Gaspar[1] and George S. Hammond

California Institute of Technology, Pasadena, California[1a]

## I. INTRODUCTION

DERIVATIVES OF DIVALENT CARBON, known variously as carbenes or methylenes, have in recent years fascinated both organic chemists and theoreticians. Such species are important transients in many organic reactions and as the simpler members of the series seem to provide especially attractive cases for development of methods of *ab initio* treatment of structural problems by quantum mechanics. Among the most intriguing structural problems are those arising from the fact that there should be two relatively low-lying electronic states of carbenes. The possibilities are illustrated by methylene, the simplest member of the series. Since carbon atoms have four low-energy bonding orbitals, $H_2C$: is obviously an electron-deficient species. Two orbitals are used by the four C—H bonding electrons leaving two more for occupation by the two nonbonding electrons. If the two orbitals are equivalent, the electrons should, according to Hund's rules, be assigned to different orbitals with parallel spins. On the other hand, if the two available orbitals are not degenerate, the two electrons would probably occupy the lower of the available orbitals with consequent spin-pairing. The species with unpaired spins would have a net electronic angular momentum ($S = 1$) and would therefore be a triplet state. The spin-paired species would be a singlet. The relationships are shown in Scheme 1.

---

[1]*Present address*: Department of Chemistry, Washington University, St. Louis 5, Missouri.

[1a]Contribution No. 3036 from the Gates and Crellin Laboratories of Chemistry.

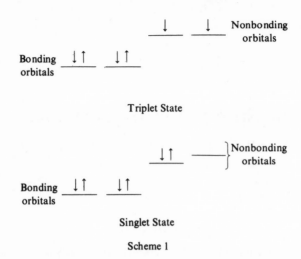

Scheme 1

Skell (*1*) has suggested that triplet states of divalent carbon compounds be named methylenes and that the singlets should be called carbenes. Although this system of nomenclature has some merit, there is real doubt that it will become standard. Theoretical chemists have for many years referred to "singlet-" and "triplet-methylene" and organic chemists have referred to "carbenes" without much regard for ambiguities arising from spin multiplicity. Interchangeable use of the terms carbene and methylene to designate compounds containing divalent carbon, and addition of the terms "singlet" and "triplet" to specify spin states, is likely to continue to be accepted practice. There seems to be little reason for existence of abominable names such as "methylene biradical."

Both experimental evidence and theory concerning methylene and its relatives have tarnished but interesting histories. The following discussion will deal first with structural theories and then with experimental evidence. Since nearly all theoretical work and much of the pertinent experimental study have centered on methylene itself, that species will receive predominant attention.

## II. STRUCTURAL THEORY

Despite the relative simplicity of $H_2C$:, the molecule is far too complex for treatment by nonapproximate quantum mechanics. All treatments, both simple and sophisticated, have ignored higher $3s$, $p$, and $d$ orbitals of carbon, $2s$ and $2p$ orbitals of hydrogen and have attempted to construct descriptions of the molecule by using hydrogen $1s$ and carbon $2s$ and $2p$ orbitals as basic functions. Carbon $1s$ electrons are often included in detailed calculations but have little influence on results. All but the most superficial descriptions have invoked group theory to simplify the problem and present the results. Methylene could conceivably belong to only one of two symmetry classes. If the molecule is linear it would fall in class $D_{\infty h}$. All bent forms having equivalent C—H bonds would belong to class $C_{2v}$. The higher symmetry of the linear form, if it exists, would impose rigid restrictions on the electronic formulation. Two low-lying orbitals must be respectively $\sigma_g$ and $\sigma_u$, i.e. symmetric and antisymmetric with respect to reflection through the center of the molecule and symmetric with respect to rotation about the molecular axis as is indicated by the cross-sectional drawings in Scheme 2.

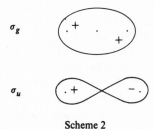

$$\sigma_g$$

$$\sigma_u$$

Scheme 2

Chemical intuition dictates choice of the $\sigma_g$ and $\sigma_u$ orbitals for description of the C—H bonding electrons. The next lowest orbitals would be a degenerate pair of $\pi_u$ orbitals which are antisymmetric with respect to planes containing the molecular axis and not transformed into each other by any of the covering operations (rotations, reflections, etc.) of the $D_{\infty h}$ group. These orbitals should, according to Hund's rule, each hold an electron and the two electrons should have paired spins, i.e., the linear molecule must be a triplet. The $\pi_u$ orbitals have just the properties of two $p$ orbitals with axes perpendicular to the molecular axis (Scheme 3).

$\pi_u$ orbitals

Scheme 3

As has been concisely pointed out by Walsh (2), bending of the molecule would remove the degeneracy of the $\pi_u$ orbitals and convert them to $A_1$ and $B_1$ orbitals of the $C_{2v}$ group. Therefore, bent molecules *could* be singlet states; however, it is not at all obvious that the energy minimum of the triplet state would inevitably have the linear configuration although such has sometimes been assumed to be the case. Because bending would be accompanied by rehybridization, the relative amounts of $s$ and $p$ character in both the bonding and the nonbonding orbitals would change with consequent changes of the binding energies of both the bonding and the nonbonding electrons. If the levels of the $A_1$ and $B_1$ orbitals are close together, relief of electron-electron repulsion might very easily be enough to compensate for the promotion energy required to put one unshared electron in the higher orbital, allowing the bent molecule to be a triplet.

The perpendicular molecule is the most extreme bent configuration that has been given serious consideration. Although the symmetry class would be the same as for any other bent configuration, formulation of the 90° molecule seems straightforward on the basis of simple valence theory. The bonding orbitals would be formulated as involving two of the carbon $2p$ orbitals and the unshared pair of electrons would be assigned to the carbon $2s$ orbital leaving a $p$ orbital vacant. The energy required to promote an electron from the $s$ orbital to the vacant $p$ orbital *in atomic carbon* was estimated by Slater (3) to be 199 kcal./mole. Granting that the method of calculation may admit some error and that introduction of two hydrogen atoms may modify electron-electron repulsion, one is still forced to conclude that perpendicular $CH_2$ would be a singlet and that excitation to a perpendicular triplet would require a large amount of energy. The view that promotion energy should be a dominant effect and that the perpendicular singlet should be the stable state was prominent in early discussion of the problem (4, 5). However, Voge (6) pointed out that a very strong compensating influence would be formation of stronger bonds if $sp$ hybrid orbitals were used for bonding.

Early theoretical work was fairly strongly influenced by the erroneous suggestion (7) that the group of lines around 4050 Å in the spectra of comets was due to $CH_2$. The problem was not helped by over-reliance on early estimates (4, 5, 8) of the heat of formation of methylene from methane (9, 10) and diazomethane (5). Since the early thermochemical estimates indicated a very small endothermicity ($\Delta H \cong + 25$ kcal. per mole) for the reaction, $\cdot CH_3 \rightarrow CH_2 + H\cdot$, Norrish (5) reasoned that bond breaking must be largely compensated by reorganization energy. Granted the premise, the conclusion that methylene contained carbon in close to its atomic configuration is eminently reasonable. Consequently the first structural assignments indicated that the ground state should be a singlet. The assignment also seemed reasonable in view of the belief that methylene had absorption in the visible. The triplet should have no allowed, low-energy transitions since transitions between the partially vacant, low-energy orbitals would require spin inversion.

Mulliken (11) gave the first purely theoretical treatment of methylene. He used $2s$, $2p_x$, $2p_y$, and $2p_z$ orbitals of carbon and $1s$ orbitals of hydrogen to formulate sets of molecular orbitals belonging to the same irreducible representations of the $C_{2v}$ point group. The molecular orbitals were labeled $s$, $x$, $y$, and $z$, and in the formulation of the molecule the $x$ orbital was left vacant giving the configuration $1s^2(s)^2(y)^2(z)^2$ for the ground singlet ($^1A_1$). The lowest excited state would then be $1s^2$ $(s)^2$ $(y)^2$ $(z)$ $(x)$ and should be the triplet, $^3B_1$, and the other low lying excited state would have the corresponding singlet configuration, $^1B_1$. The result seems to be an almost necessary consequence of choosing a bent configuration and ignoring electron-electron repulsion since the $z$ and $x$ orbitals (Walsh's $A_1$ and $B_1$ orbitals) must be nondegenerate. Lennard-Jones (12) considered the problem by a united-atom treatment. The procedure consisted of removing protons from the nucleus of atomic oxygen to make first NH and then $CH_2$. Application of the non-crossing rule, consideration of the maximum overlap criterion for bonding and use of group theory led to a correlation diagram which ordered the valence orbitals in the same way as had been done by Mulliken, and the prediction that the ground state should be $^1A_1$ was reinforced.

As was mentioned earlier, Voge (6) commented on the methylene problem as an aftermath of his detailed treatment of methane by the valence bond method. Using the solutions of the energy matrix for methane, and guidance from the expected symmetries of $CH_3$ and $CH_2$, Voge calculated that the stepwise removal of hydrogen atoms from methane should involve nearly evenly spaced energy changes. While Voge did not comment explicitly on the problem of spin assignment, his thesis attacked the principal grounds for preference for the ground singlet assignment.

Walsh's first discussion (13) of methylene included reanalysis of thermochemistry of the successive stages in the dissociation of methane.

The heat of atomization of methane is well known (if the value of the heat of sublimation of carbon is accepted) as is the bond dissociation energy of methane. The energy of the sole remaining bond in CH is also reliably estimated from spectroscopic data. The energies involved in the steps $\cdot CH_3 \rightarrow CH_2 + H\cdot$ and $CH_2 \rightarrow CH + H\cdot$ had no firm experimental basis in 1947. All arguments concerning the stepwise dissociation involve the notion that somewhere in the course of atomization there should be a gain in reorganization energy of about 70 kcal. (14) due to the change of carbon from its valence state to the $^3P$ state of the atom. One or more steps in the dissociation process should be characterized by a low energy requirement. The relatively low value for D(C—H) of $\approx$ 80 kcal. [present best value is 81.7 kcal. at 298° (15)] indicates that, although some reorganization may accompany the last dissociative step, some must also precede it. By assigning a large amount of reorganization to the step, $\cdot CH_3 \rightarrow CH_2 + H\cdot$, Norrish (5) had arrived at the conclusion that methylene must be a ground-state singlet. Walsh reserved reorganization for the last two steps and thereby reached the conclusion that methylene might very possibly have a ground triplet state although he also predicted that the lowest singlet and triplet would be very close in energy. The only experimental evidence introduced into the argument was the 145° bond angle that Herzberg had attributed to methylene on the basis of the (incorrect) assignment of the 4050 Å absorption in the spectra of comets (7). From empirical relationships between bond angle and bond length and between bond length and bond energy, Walsh derived a value for the bond energies in $CH_2$ which indicated that the species had not been rehybridized. The result was justified by qualitative analysis of anticipated effects of rehybridization on the character of the C—H bonds. In brief, it was argued that H—H repulsions in perpendicular methylene should be large, partly because a carbon-hydrogen bond involving a carbon $p$ orbital should be polar in the sense $C^{\delta+}-H^{\delta-}$. Introduction of $s$ character into the bonding orbital could reasonably be expected to decrease the polarity as well as accommodating movement of the hydrogen atoms away from each other.

Walsh's discussion initiated a lively controversy. Laidler and Casey (16) strongly maintained that a bond angle of 140° was entirely compatible with a singlet spin state but that a triplet could have only the linear configuration. Rationalization of the wide-angle singlet was based upon qualitative examination of the possibilities for modification of the limiting, perpendicular geometry by configuration interaction involving "ionized" states for which larger angles might be expected. Consideration of analogous interactions in the triplet gave them no grounds for expecting the triplet to bend. The importance of $sp$ hybridization was considered but dismissed in a rather summary fashion. However, Duffey (17) raised objection to the apparent reluctance of Laidler and Casey to assign unshared electrons in the triplet to any except unhybridized $p$ orbitals. In essence he pointed out that if the methane structure were maintained in methylene, the unshared electrons of the triplet could be assigned to two different, nonbonding tetrahedral orbitals. While the remarks were pertinent, no explicit mention was made of the fact that the two orbitals would have to be combined, with formation of symmetric and antisymmetric combinations, to give proper symmetry orbitals. This operation would inevitably remove the degeneracy. However, a near degeneracy might very likely occur and would be expected by anyone who accepts the description of methane in terms of four localized bond eigenfunctions. A later attempt by Laidler and Casey (16) to repeat the analysis of thermochemistry of the dehydrogenation of methane confirmed their opinion that methylene must be a singlet containing bent atomic carbon. The principal new data used were derived from a study of the kinetics of the reaction of sodium with methylene chloride (18). Although the reaction was at the time presumed to produce methylene, there was no strong evidence to that effect, and, in retrospect, it now appears that methylene was probably not formed.

During the past 15 years a number of serious attempts to carry out "exact" calculations of the energy and configuration of methylene have yielded variable but interesting results. Niira and Oohata (19) used the valence bond approach to a calculation by the variation method. The treatment was the first serious attempt to deal quantitatively with non-limiting configurations. Six wave functions based on ground state carbon ($s^2p^2$ configuration) and seven based on valence state carbon ($sp^3$ configuration) were used. Both singlet and triplet linear combinations of the thirteen wave functions were classified by the irreducible representations of the $C_{2v}$ point group giving secular equations of various orders. The secular determinants were solved and the roots evaluated. The procedure must have involved an enormous amount of labor because a Hamiltonian including interactions between all pairs of particles was used[2]; there is no indication of the use of machine calculations. The

---

[2]Reduction of the number of terms (9!) expected in each integral was accomplished by assuming that all atomic orbitals were orthogonal to each other.

integrals were evaluated using Zener functions and an attempt was made to include interactions between $1s$ electrons of carbon and hydrogen $1s$ electrons by use of a constant interaction term.[3] The important value of the promotional energy required to excite carbon from the ground state to the valence state was taken as 7.90 e.v. (182 kcal.), the separation between the $^3P$ and $^3D$ states of atomic carbon. The C—H distance was taken as 1.12 atomic units, the observed value in CH. The calculation was made for a series of bond angles. The results indicated that the ground state should be $^3B_1$ with a bond angle close to 140°. The result, which appears to be in stunning agreement with present experimental evidence, loses some of its glamour when other results are considered. The next lowest state, $^1B_1$, is predicted to lie 35 kcal. above the ground state and the $^1A_1$ state, which is ordinarily expected to be the lowest singlet, is predicted to lie 12 kcal. above $^1B_1$. Furthermore, Niira and Oohata seem to accept without qualms the conclusion that the triplet should be the lowest lying state for all bond angles from 90°–180°!

Gallup (20) initiated quantitative LCAO-MO treatment of methylene. Linear combinations of carbon $2s$, $2p_x$, and $2p_y$ and two hydrogen $1s$ orbitals[4] were grouped to form symmetry orbitals and the reduced determinants were solved and the roots evaluated with inclusion of overlap integrals. Coulomb integrals were given empirical values for AO energies of carbon and hydrogen and resonance integrals were given the values $\frac{1}{2}$ $(H_{ii} + H_{jj} = 10.0)$ $S_{ij}$ as an admitted crude approximation. Calculations were carried out for various values of the bond angle. The energies of three of the MO's were calculated to lie below that of the noninteracting $p_z$ orbital for all bent configurations. This is, of course, a necessary consequence of the fact that basis functions having energies equal to or lower than the $2p_z$ orbital were fed into the MO treatment. Filling the three lowest orbitals without regard for electron-electron repulsion would give a singlet ground state. However, Gallup preferred to boost the level of the singlet above that of the triplet by adding 1.5 e.v. (the separation between the $^1D$ and $^3P$ states of carbon) as the energy required to pair electrons in a nonbonding carbon orbital. Both singlet

[3]This interaction term was gotten in some way as an adjustable parameter in a calculation of the (known) energy levels and dissociation energy of CH. Since the reported results of the latter calculation *only* give good agreement with observed value for the highest excited state, a reader develops scepticism of the results of the calculation for methylene.

[4]The carbon $2p_z$ orbital is considered orthogonal to all the other orbitals and therefore does not contribute to delocalized MO's.

and triplet curves had energy minima at $\approx 160°$ bond angles. Although Gallup's treatment was presented unobtrusively, it evoked an attack by Gray (21) who rediscovered the arguments set forth by Norrish (5) at a much earlier date, i.e., that the triplet must contain valence state carbon whereas the singlet can be based on the ground state of the atom. Exchange of comments did not advance the state of science materially since Gallup defended his stand on the basis of the experimental value of the bond angle, despite the fact that the original basis for assignment had been shown to be erroneous in 1950 (22).

The advent of high-speed digital computers has triggered an avalanche of refined calculations. Reports of three extended calculations have appeared (23–25). It is interesting that the three groups either predict (23, 24) or accept as theoretically demonstrated (25) that the lowest state of methylene is $^3B_1$ and that there is a very shallow minimum in an energy versus angle curve for that state. Using a semi-empirical method, Jordan and Longuet-Higgins (26) have also concluded that the triplet is the lowest state. Confidence of the recent authors in the significance of their results was fortified by the reports by Herzberg (27, 28) that methylene has finally been cornered and the absorption spectra of its two lowest states have been observed. Evidence that the lowest state is a triplet with a large bond angle and that the lowest singlet has a bond angle of $\approx 103°$ will probably guide future theoretical work and may already have provided some guidance.

Foster and Boys (23) used the MO method, with configuration interaction, to calculate the energies of the $^3B_1$, $^1A_1$, and $^1B_1$ states for 12 different bond angles. Atomic orbitals of the Slater type were used and a method for varying investigation of the consequences of modest variation in the functions was included. The influence of carbon $1s$ electrons was also included. Two and three center integrals were computed and automatically assembled into orthonormal functions. Table I shows the properties calculated for the equilibrium configurations of the three lowest states.

Padgett and Krauss (24) used a self-consistent field molecular orbital method. The basis functions were again Slater orbitals for carbon and hydrogen including the carbin $1s$ functions; the usual nodeless $2s$ orbital of carbon was modified to make it orthogonal to the $1s$ function. The method of Roothaan (29) was used to determine the best combination of orbitals for the $^1A_1$ state. The results were then used to calculate energies of other states. The results were then further improved by introduction of some configurational interaction using a second-order per-turbation calculation. The computations were carried out for a series of angles; the C—H distance in the CH radical (1.12 Å) was used so that values of two center integrals already at hand could be employed. Perti-nent results are shown in Table 1. The authors pointed out that their results must surely be somewhat inaccurate since the calculated value of the energy of atomization was much lower than would be compatible with the generally accepted range of experimental values.

King and Malli (25) extended the range of calculations with con-figuration interaction to include a larger number of excited states. How-ever, their attentions were limited to the linear configuration and for some reason they seem to ignore the indications of both the other groups that the linear triplet should be unstable with respect to suitably bent configurations by 2–3 e.v. Since experimental evidence concerning the configuration of the triplet ground state is still inconclusive (28),

TABLE I

CALCULATED PROPERTIES OF LOWEST STATES OF $CH_2$

| State | Excitation energy (kcal) | | Bond angle | | C—H bond length |
|-------|------|------|------|------|------|
| | FB[a] | PK[b] | FB[a] | PK[b] | FB[a] |
| $^1A_1$ | 0 | 0 | 90° | 90° | 1.17 |
| $^1B_1$ | 60 | 64 | 132° | $\approx 120°$ | 1.11 |
| $^3B_1$ | 24 | $\approx 0$ | 129° | $\approx 120°$ | 1.11 |

[a]Foster and Boys (23).
[b]Padgett and Krauss (24).

there is no very obvious way of deciding whether or not King and Mali have significantly improved the estimates of the energies required for vertical transitions in the linear molecule. If suitable comparisons with experiment can be made, they would be of considerable value in apprais-ing the validity of the omission of a number of "higher" states in the calculation and the exclusion of higher atomic orbitals of carbon and hydrogen from the set of basis functions.

The most recent theoretical discussion is an interesting semi-empiri-cal treatment by Jordan and Longuet-Higgins who preface their paper by saying, "It may be that future theoretical progress will require elaborate variational calculations such as those of Foster and Boys on $CH_2$; but until the results of such machine experiments can be interpreted phy-sically, there would seem to be a place for more empirical theories such as that which we now describe." Irrespective of their reaction to the particular treatment, many chemists who have shuddered at the prospect of having all wisdom generated within the bowels of computers will endorse the general proposition. The authors presented an analysis of AH, $AH_2$, and $AH_3$ molecules in which they attempted to render in quantitative terms the qualitative concepts concerning hybridization, promotional energy, and bond strength that have long been discussed in connection with methylene and other molecules. The total energy of the molecule is expressed in Eq. (1).

$$E_{total} = E_A(\lambda) + nE_{AH}(\lambda) + nE_H \tag{1}$$

where $\quad E_A(\lambda)$ = the energy required to promote A atoms to their effective valance state in $AH_n$

$E_{AH}(\lambda)$ = A—H bond energy

$E_H$ = the ground state energy of the hydrogen atom

$\lambda$ = the $2s$ character in the bonding orbitals of A

The value of $E_{total}$ is minimized with respect to $\lambda$, a measure of the state of hybridization, and the calculations are repeated for various values of the bond angles (in $AH_2$ or $AH_3$). Of course, $E_A(\lambda)$ and $E_{AH}(\lambda)$ must be expressed as explicit functions of $\lambda$. Antisymmetrized wave functions are formulated for the molecules assuming perfect pairing and writing the bond eigenfunctions as antisymmetric combinations of atomic orbitals of A and hydrogen $1s$ orbitals. The bonding A orbitals are, in turn, formulated as hybrids of the form, $\sqrt{\lambda}s + \sqrt{1 - \lambda} \, p_A$. The promotional energy of A is then estimated by extracting the terms from the wave function in which the $A_{orbitals}$ occur, giving the terms statistical weights proportional to their coefficients, and then identifying those terms as components of excited states of the A atom. The effective valence state energy is then calculated as the appropriate statistical mixture of ground and excited states. Values of the strengths of perfectly oriented[5] hybrid A—H bonds are obtained from suitable thermochemical and spectroscopic data. These members are then decomposed into "contributions" from $s$ and $p$ character in the bonding orbitals by the presumption that $E_{AH}$ will depend upon $\lambda$ in the same way as a two-electron exchange integral between the centers A and H. Finally, the effect of distortion of the molecular geometry (variation of the angle in $AH_2$) is investigated by writing an expression for $E_{AH}$ in a general form

---

[5]Bonds in which the internuclear direction is the axis of the hybrid orbital.

for hybrid orbitals that do not point directly at hydrogen atoms. The energy of the system is then minimized with the angle between the bonds and the molecular symmetry axis.

Application of the method to methylene gave very interesting results. The lowest state is found to be the linear triplet; the next state is $^1A_1$ with an equilibrium bond angle of 106° and an excitation energy of 3440 cm.$^{-1}$ (9.8 kcal.). The results are strikingly similar to those obtained by more sophisticated machine calculations. The estimated excitation energy of the $^1A_1$ state is intermediate between the estimates by Foster and Boys and by Padgett and Krauss. Conclusions concerning geometry of the lowest states are also similar since the more elaborate calculations predict that the minimum for the triplet will be very shallow. Perhaps the most outstanding difference lies in the prediction by both MO calculations that a rather sharp rise in the energy would occur as the triplet approached the linear configuration.

Pedley (30) and Ellison (31) have both carried out semi-empirical calculations conceptually very similar to those of Jordan and Longuet-Higgins. The interplay between excitation energy of the carbon valence state and hybridization-controlled bond energy were pitted against each other and compromised to obtain the most stable configuration. The ultimate conclusions were strikingly similar to those of the treatments discussed above.

While theoretical work has not yielded any really definitive answers concerning the structure of methylene, the results have been instructive, both as to methodology and as to the limitations of even the best currently available theoretical tools. A thought-provoking lesson is told by the tendency of theoretical conclusions to become more guarded as the work becomes more quantitative and sophisticated.

## III. SPECTROSCOPIC EVIDENCE

Observation and analysis of the spectra of a species as simple as methylene should give very detailed information concerning both ground and excited states of the molecule. Furthermore, if the energy separation between the lowest levels of the singlet and triplet manifolds is as low as has been estimated, both singlet-singlet and triplet-triplet transitions should be observable. This potentially profitable work has usually been thwarted by the great chemical reactivity of methylene.

Assignment of a group of lines at 4050 Å in the spectra of comets to methylene (7) gave a great deal of useful guidance in early discussions of methylene even though it later turned out that the lines were due to $C_3$ rather than $CH_2$ (22). In 1959 Herzberg (27, 28) finished a 17-year hunt for the elusive methylene and obtained spectra of both the lowest singlet and triplet states. Straightforward observations show that, since the singlet state decays to the triplet, the latter must have the lower energy content. There is as yet no experimental measure of the energy separating the two.

Before the successful experiments by Herzberg and Shoosmith (27) there were a number of other attempts to observe the spectrum of methylene in the vapor phase and by matrix isolation techniques. The first real success involved $CF_2$ rather than $CH_2$. The emission spectrum of an excited state of difluoromethylene was reported by Venkateswarlu (32, 33) and by Andrews and Barrow (34), and absorption by the ground state of the species was observed by Laird, Andrews and Barrow (35). Venkateswarlu passed an electric discharge through a stream of $CF_4$ and observed an extensive system of emission bands between 2400 and 3250 A. The band structure showed strong resemblance to that of the absorption spectrum of $NO_2$. Analysis of the vibronic structure of the spectrum resulted in assignment of stretching and deformation frequencies in both the upper and the lower states. Occurrence of the two strong vibrational bands indicated that the molecule is nonlinear; the same conclusion was reached by analysis of the rotational fine structure. Duchesne and Burnelle (36) used all available spectral data to carry out an anlysis of both ground and excited states. They concluded that the upper limits of the FCF angle in the lower and upper states were 110° and 120° respectively. They also concurred with Venkateswarlu that the ground state must be a singlet. It is worth noting that the data gave no information concerning the triplet states of $CF_2$ except that Laird, Andrews and Barrow showed that the lower state of the species under observation is rather long-lived. If there were a lower-lying triplet state, the singlet-triplet decay rate would be enormously slower than is the case with $CH_2$. However, it is entirely possible that a triplet state lies between the two singlets which have been characterized spectroscopically.

Attempts to preserve $CH_2$ for spectroscopic observation by matrix isolation (37–40) have led to ambiguous results. Pimentel and his co-workers (37, 38) irradiated diazomethane in argon and nitrogen matrices at 20°K. under various conditions. They observed many new infrared absorption bands, some of which disappeared when the matrix was warmed to 40°K. to permit diffusion. During the warming period a red glow, attributed to chemiluminescence, was observed. The systems were then cooled again to 20°K. and spectral measurements were repeated. Spectra of stable species such as ethylene, polyethylene, methane, propylene, and cyclopropane appeared during the warming period. The results were taken to indicate that an ethylene precursor, probably methylene, was present in the matrices after irradiation. Certain infrared bands were tentatively assigned to methylene. Irradiation with a filter which excluded light below 3400 Å gave significantly different results than were obtained with unfiltered light. Since little or no ethylene was formed on warming solutions irradiated with the filter, the authors presumed that such systems did not contain methylene. Absorption maxima at 4182, 3968, and 3050–3300 Å were then assigned as *possible* methylene absorption bands. Robinson and McCarty (*40*) studied the absorption of matrices formed by deposition of $CH_2N_2$, $CHDN_2$, and $CD_2N_2$ in krypton at 4.2°K. Irradiation was carried out *during deposition*. The spectra of the matrices were extraordinarily different from those reported by the Berkeley group (*37, 38*). When irradiation was carried out with a 3340 Å filter the spectra of products were rich in ultraviolet absorption bands including an interesting group of sharp lines close to 3000 Å. Unfiltered light gave none of these bands, and the spectra were bleached by postirradiation with unfiltered light. These lines all showed isotope effects and, therefore, arise from species containing hydrogen (or deuterium). The well-known spectrum of CH (or CD) was also observed. If the Robinson and McCarty results were viewed alone, one would almost surely conclude that methylene was formed and was responsible for sharp absorption lines near 3000 Å and, furthermore, that irradiation with high energy light destroys the species. However, the results are in direct contrast to those of Pimentel using the same filter. As Robinson has pointed out, there are sufficient differences in the irradiation procedures, in the nature of the matrices, and in the temperatures to account for the results, but none of the rationalizations are much help in assigning particular bands to methylene. To a casual observer it appears that Robinson's experiments should have produced some methylene, if it is ever to be obtained in a matrix, since the technique of photodeposition should lead to photolysis in the vapor, on the crystal surface, and in the interior. If some other ethylene precursor could be devised to account for Pimentel's experiments with ethylene production on warming, the results could be accounted for easily. We see no likely candidates for the role and conclude that the moderate tone of all authors in interpreting their results is warranted.

De More, Pritchard, and Davidson irradiated diazomethane, diazo-cyclopentadiene, and diphenyldiazomethane in nitrogen or perfluoro-ether matrices at 20°K. Some interesting spectra were obtained but none that could be assigned to the desired carbenes with any conviction.

Flash photolysis of gaseous diazomethane in the presence of nitrogen finally led to observation of the spectra of two species of methylene (27). Experiments were done using $CH_2N_2$, $CDHN_2$, and $CD_2N_2$. The species first observed absorbed close to 1415 Å. The positions of the bands for $CH_2$, CHD, and $CD_2$ were, respectively, 1414.5, 1415.5, and 1415.8 Å, showing unequivocally that the species involved contained two and only two hydrogen atoms. The rotational fine structure of $CD_2$ showed Panel Q branches with alternating ($J_{odd}$ lines strong) intensities, whereas there was no alternation of the rotational lines in the spectrum of CHD. These features are accommodated by a linear structure but the fact that the rotational lines of odd $J$ are strong would require that the molecule be in a nontotally symmetric electronic state. Accordingly the state is believed to be $^3\Sigma_g^-$ and the transition is believed to be $^3\Sigma_u^- \leftarrow {}^3\Sigma_g^-$ even though triplet splitting of the lines has not been resolved. An alternate analysis of the spectrum was made on the assumption that the molecule is bent and the rotational structure arises from coupling with the rotation about the $C_2$ axis. Using moments of inertia obtained from the isotopic species this analysis led to a bond angle of 140° and a C—H distance of 1.071 Å. However, side bands due to transitions from higher rotational levels of the ground state were not observed, providing grounds for preference for a linear or nearly linear state.

A new band system spread from 5500–9500 Å was observed when higher ratios of $CH_2N_2/N_2$ were used. Apparently the first product of photolysis has long wavelength absorption but decays rapidly to the triplet absorbing at 1415 Å. The rotational fine structure of the three bands indicated the absorbing species is bent with a bond angle of about 103° (C—H distance = 1.12 Å) and a linear upper state. No triplet splitting of spectral lines could be found despite the fact that the doublet splitting in the analogous spectrum of $NH_2$ is very clear. Assignment of the absorbing state as $^1A_1$ seems straightforward.

It is interesting that Herzberg also saw faint bands in the 3000–3500 Å region. Appearance of the lines was not favored by conditions which maximize the triplet absorption at 1415 Å. Consequently Herzberg feels that, if the lines are due to methylene, the absorbing species must be $^1A_1$. If the absorption is to be associated with the sharp lines found by Robinson and McCarty, and attributed to $CH_2$, a problem arises since the species seen at 4.2°K. was obviously long-lived.

Recently electron spin resonance has been used to characterize triplet states of substituted (*41–43*) carbenes. Such measurements indicate that diphenylcarbene, phenylcarbene, and fluorenylidene have triplet ground states. The magnitude of the triplet splitting at zero field and the hyperfine interactions with protons indicate that in diphenylcarbene the two phenyl groups lie close to, but not exactly, perpendicular planes. Surprisingly, the extent to which the unpaired electrons are constrained to stay at the central carbon atom is about the same in diphenylcarbene and in fluorenylidene despite their different geometries (Scheme 4).

Diphenylmethylene          Fluorenylidene
                        (with *sp*$^3$ hybridization)

Scheme 4

## IV. CHEMICAL EVIDENCE

Attempts to draw inference concerning the spin state of methylene from chemical reactivity, and vice versa, have a long and sometimes undistinguished history. Early attempts to characterize methylene in gas streams involved removal of tellurium, selenium, arsenic, and antimony mirrors, and the tellurium method (*44*) was a favorite for "detection" of methylene until it was shown (*45*) that mirror removal was due largely to reaction with other species, at least when methylene was produced by photolysis of ketene. Methylene also reacts with iodine to give $CH_2I_2$ (*46, 47*) and with carbon monoxide to form ketene (*48, 49*). Diphenylcarbene reacts with oxygen to give benzophenone (*43*). Methylene and its derivatives would probably react with many other materials if given the chance since, in either the singlet or triplet state it is a highly reactive species. It is doubtful that any but the most detailed study of randomly chosen reactions would yield much information concerning the characteristic chemical properties of singlets and triplets.

In retrospect, assumptions such as low reactivity of singlet methylene (50) or clearly "radical-like reactivity" of the triplet seem either wrong or harmfully oversimplified.

Reactions which have been most studied are insertion reactions (2):

$$:CH_2 + H_2 \rightarrow CH_4$$
$$:CH_2 + RH \rightarrow RCH_3 \tag{2}$$

and addition to carbon-carbon double bonds (3).

$$:CH_2 + \underset{/}{\overset{\backslash}{C}}=\underset{\backslash}{\overset{/}{C}} \rightarrow \underset{\underset{CH_2}{/ \backslash}}{\overset{\backslash}{C} - \overset{/}{C}} \tag{3}$$

These reactions have been studied in great detail and much of the related discussion relates to chemistry of singlets and triplets. A major complication in interpretation of the data arises from the fact that the reactions are highly exothermic so products are formed with very large excitation energies. Consequently, drastic chemical changes may occur before the product has cooled to its equilibrium energy state. Although no completely rigorous argument can be generated using currently available data, we believe that the net evidence is strongly in favor of the view that singlet and triplet methylene show significantly different behavior and that study of insertion and addition reactions can distinguish between the species. An opposite point of view has been eloquently and thoughtfully propounded by DeMore and Benson (51)[6].

## A. The Insertion Reaction

The insertion of $:CH_2$ into C—H bonds was first reported by Meerwein, Rathjen, and Werner (52) in 1942. Photolysis of $CH_2N_2$ in diethyl ether, isopropyl alcohol, and tetrahydrofuran gave all the products expected from C—H insertion by methylene. This remarkable result, which suggests strongly the unique reactivity of $:CH_2$, was unappreciated. In 1956 Doering, Buttery, Laughlin, and Chaudhuri (53) showed that methylene reacts almost indiscriminately with the C—H bonds of n-pentane and 2,3-dimethylbutane, and the direct insertion reaction then became widely recognized. These reactions in the liquid phase gave a not quite statistical distribution of products. The relative

---

[6]We are much indebted to Dr. DeMore and Dr. Benson for prepublication copies of their manuscript and for extensive discussions. Although we arrive at fairly definite conclusions, the route is much less sure than we had originally conceived to be the case.

rates of insertion into the various bonds were: $2°C—H:1°C—H = 1.04$ and $3°C—H:1°C—H = 1.23$.

The liquid phase photolysis of $CH_2N_2$ in $C_7$, $C_8$, and $C_9$ alkanes was carefully investigated by Richardson, Simmons, and Dvoretzky (54) who found, within the error of their analytical method, *totally random insertion*. Dvoretzky concluded that the insertion in the liquid phase is a reaction of $:CH_2$ in an excited singlet state, the insertion taking place more rapidly than transition from a singlet to a triplet electronic state. The explanation is reasonable since methylene is presumed to be *formed* as a singlet by the photolytic dissociation $CH_2N_2 \rightarrow :CH_2 + N_2$ (27) and collision frequencies in the liquid phase are very high, on the order of $10^{12}$ per second. A serious and persistent objection must be raised at this point. Dvoretzky's argument depends on the reaction of methylene before it intersystem crosses to a triplet, i.e., it must react in the first few collisions. This means that $:CH_2$ must also react before it has been able to dissipate its excess energy, which it must also do by collision. Does the relative inability of methylene to discriminate between various carbon-hydrogen bonds in the liquid phase simply reflect the fact that it reacts as an energy-rich species independent of its spin state? This question in one form or another will arise throughout this discussion.

Whereas $:CH_2$ from the photolysis of $CH_2N_2$ indiscriminately attacks C—H bonds in the liquid phase, this is not the case in the gas phase. The photolysis of mixtures of diazomethane and large excesses of alkanes in the gas phase at total pressures in the range 200–1200 mm. gave the following product ratios independent of pressure (55):

| | |
|---|---|
| $:CH_2$ + *n*-propane $\rightarrow$ *n*-butane + isobutane | ratio 2.62:1 |
| $:CH_2$ + *n*-butane $\rightarrow$ *n*-pentane + isopentane | ratio 1.25:1 |
| $:CH_2$ + isobutane $\rightarrow$ isopentane + neopentane | ratio 6.06:1 |

After statistical correction, the rates of insertion into secondary and tertiary C—H bonds are, respectively, about 20 and 50% higher than the rates of insertion into primary bonds. Frey and Kistiakowsky (56) had earlier studied ketene and found that the reactivity of secondary C—H bonds relative to primary hydrogen atoms was 1.7, independent of total pressure (90–1560 mm.) with constant ketene: propane ratio. However, discrimination was increased by addition of inert gases; the order of decreasing efficiency of added gases in increasing selectivity was: $CO_2 > A > He$. Although the results with ketene are a little difficult to interpret since methylene reacts with carbon monoxide and ketene as well as with propane, there does seem to be some factor that increases selectivity as a consequence of repeated collisions with inert gases. Two possibilities were considered: (1) a deactivation process involving methylene and (2) deactivation of an energy-rich reaction product. The second possibility was ruled out because, in the absence of inert gases, the selectivity ratio was independent of total pressure; propane should be relatively effective in dissipation of excess vibrational and rotational energy. Consequently it appeared that methylene was believed to be the species that underwent vibrational and rotational relaxation on collision with inert molecules. The possibility that the change also involved singlet-triplet transition of $CH_2$, or that the excited state of ketene might undergo intersystem crossing before decomposition, was not considered.

Inspired by the observations of Herzberg (27, 28), Richardson, Simmons, and Dvoretzky (54) explained the relatively high selectivity of gaseous methylene by the hypothesis that some decay to the triplet occurs in all of the vapor phase experiments. They presumed that insertion by the triplet is a selective process and, furthermore, that it involves free radicals as intermediates [Eq. (4)].

$$\downarrow \downarrow CH_2 + RH \rightarrow \cdot CH_3 + R \cdot \rightarrow CH_3R \tag{4}$$

That some radicals are formed in the reactions had already been indicated by the work in which Frey (57) found ethane, n-hexane, 2-methylpentane, and 2,3-dimethylbutane, along with the butanes as products of reaction of methylene with propane. Methylene was generated by photolysis of both diazomethane and ketene. Addition of oxygen removed the products of radical coupling. From the change in product distribution in the presence of oxygen, Frey calculated that 22% of the reaction in the absence of oxygen involved hydrogen abstraction as a first step. Although one cannot infer from the results whether or not all of the scavenging involves capture of some species of methylene, the result is certainly compatible with Dvoretzky's explanation of the contrast between vapor phase and liquid phase experiments, except for the fact that even in the presence of oxygen the vapor phase results do not indicate entirely random attack on propane.

Doering and Prinzbach (58) reported some elegant experiments with 2-methyl-(1-C$^{14}$-)prop-1-ene. In the vapor phase, methylene generated from diazomethane reacted with the labeled hydrocarbon to give 8% 2-methyl(3-C$^{14}$-)but-1-ene indicating that 16% of the reaction might have taken the radical path in reaction (5).

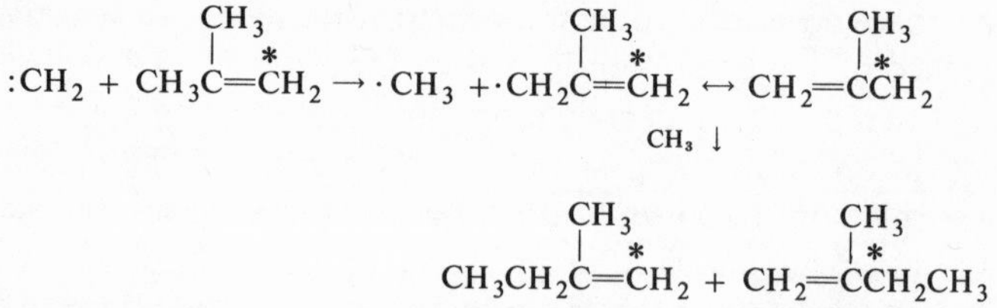

$$:CH_2 + CH_3\overset{\underset{\displaystyle |}{CH_3}}{C}{=}\overset{*}{CH_2} \rightarrow \cdot CH_3 + \cdot CH_2\overset{\underset{\displaystyle |}{CH_3}}{C}{=}\overset{*}{CH_2} \leftrightarrow CH_2{=}\overset{\underset{\displaystyle |}{CH_3}}{\overset{*}{C}}CH_2$$

$$CH_3 \downarrow$$

$$CH_3CH_2\overset{\underset{\displaystyle |}{CH_3}}{C}{=}\overset{*}{CH_2} + CH_2{=}\overset{\underset{\displaystyle |}{CH_3}}{\overset{*}{C}}CH_2CH_3 \tag{5}$$

In the liquid phase only 2% rearrangement occurred. However, Doering also pointed out the rearrangement could be due, not to radical reactions, but to rearrangement of "hot" methylcyclopropane formed by an addition reaction (6).

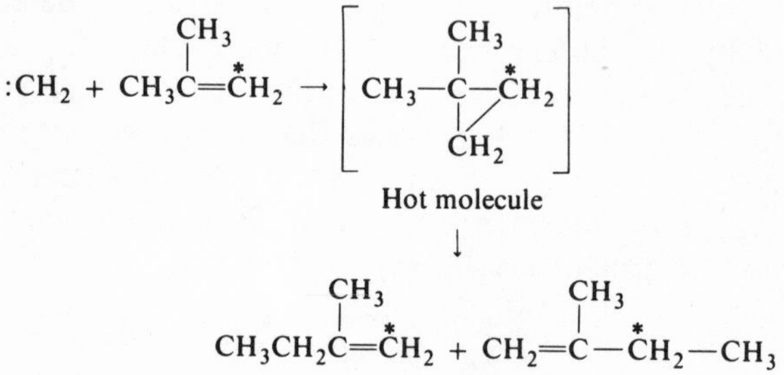

$$:CH_2 + CH_3\overset{\underset{\displaystyle |}{CH_3}}{C}{=}\overset{*}{CH_2} \rightarrow \left[ CH_3-\overset{\underset{\displaystyle |}{\underset{\displaystyle CH_2}{C}}}{\overset{\displaystyle |}{C}}-\overset{*}{CH_2} \right]$$

Hot molecule

$$\downarrow$$

$$CH_3CH_2\overset{\underset{\displaystyle |}{CH_3}}{C}{=}\overset{*}{CH_2} + CH_2{=}\overset{\underset{\displaystyle |}{CH_3}}{C}-\overset{*}{CH_2}-CH_3 \tag{6}$$

A similar, hot molecule hypothesis could also account for the production of radicals in the gas phase experiments with methylene and propane. The possibility has been investigated more thoroughly by Frey (59) using cyclobutane as the substrate. Appearance of ethylene and propylene is attributed to decomposition of excited methylcyclobutane [reaction (7)].

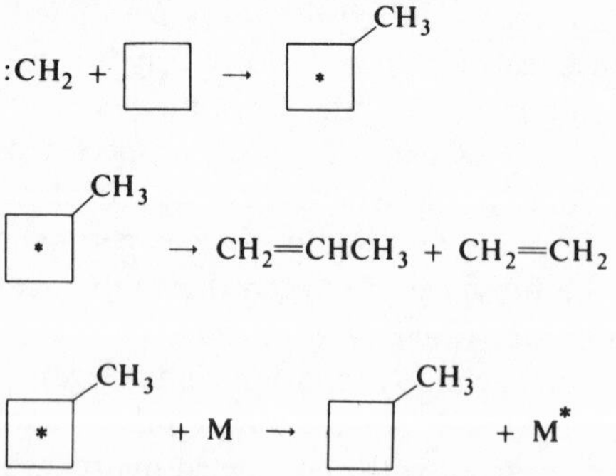

$$:CH_2 + \square \rightarrow \square^{\cdot}\text{-}CH_3$$

$$\square^{\cdot}\text{-}CH_3 \rightarrow CH_2{=}CHCH_3 + CH_2{=}CH_2$$

$$\square^{\cdot}\text{-}CH_3 + M \rightarrow \square\text{-}CH_3 + M^* \tag{7}$$

Both wavelength and pressure were varied and the results, which are discussed in more detail in Chapter 11 are compatible with the view that methylene does not return to thermal levels before it reacts with cyclo-butane if it is produced from diazomethane or by irradiation of ketene with light of short wavelength. The results were fitted to the Rice-Rampsberger-Kassel theory (*60*, *61*) of unimolecular reaction rates in a consistent, but not compelling manner.[7]

None of the results make the variation in selectivity in insertion between liquid and vapor phase really easy to explain. It is tempting to speculate that in solution vibrational relaxation should always be essentially complete before chemical reaction occurs since methylene is probably coupled to solvent phonon bands as soon as it is born. However, such a hypothesis would contradict the intuitive expectation that the "hottest" attacking species should be least selective since selectivity is at a minimum in solution. As an alternative we suggest the view that the reactions in solution resemble those obtained *at the low pressure extreme* in the gas phase. Such a seemingly ridiculous circumstance could obtain if, in solution, reaction is assisted in some way by coupling to the environment whereas in the vapor phase a number of unfruitful collisions with substrates usually precede reaction.

The effect of oxygen on the product distribution almost surely points to at least a duality of chemical processes in the vapor phase. However, it is not *necessary* to invoke two spin states of $CH_2$ to accommodate the results. There is no evidence that singlet methylene cannot effect hydro-gen abstraction. Since the hot-molecule hypothesis in some form is demanded, the principle of Occam's razor would suggest the view that radicals arise from hot molecules. Conversely, there is no reason to eliminate the notion that high selectivity is characteristic of the reactions of triplets with alkanes—should involvement of triplet methylene be demanded by other experiments. In short, "cooling" of methylene before reaction is demanded, whether or not intersystem crossing is also involved remains a moot question.

Insertion reactions of other carbenes have also been studied. Doering and Knox (*62*) photolyzed ethyl diazoacetate and ethyl diazomalonate in saturated hydrocarbons and obtained the following results.

[7]In the experiments in which the wavelength of the exciting light was varied, the cal-culated spread in the energies of the methylene species was less than the spread in the energy of the primary excitation. This may simply mean that deactivation of more ener-getic species occurs more rapidly, i.e., Frey's rate constant for deactivation is not really a constant. No explicit account is taken of the possibility of partial or total vibrational deactivation of excited ketene molecules before they decompose.

| Hydrocarbon | Ratio | $:CH_2$ | $:CHCO_2Et$ | $:C(CO_2Et)_2$ |
|---|---|---|---|---|
| 2,3-Dimethylbutane | 3°/1° | 1.2 | 2.9 | 12.5 |
| Isobutane | 3°/1° | — | 3.1 | 21.0 |
| n-Butane | 2°/1° | — | 2.3 | 8.4 |

The effect of carbethoxy groups has apparently been to produce transition states for reaction with various C—H bonds which reflect the strengths of the bonds being broken. This is to be expected since elementary arguments about delocalization indicate that the carbethoxy group should stabilize a carbene. Since they are more stable the exothermicity of their reactions with C—H bonds must be considerably less than for methylene. Therefore it is reasonable to assume greater C—H bond stretching in the transition states since the reduced exothermicity of the reaction should result in a decreased resemblance of the transition state to the reactants (63). This argument is consistent, but not synonymous, with the introduction of polar character in transition states as suggested by Doering. Such polarity would obviously favor reaction at tertiary centers [reaction (8)].

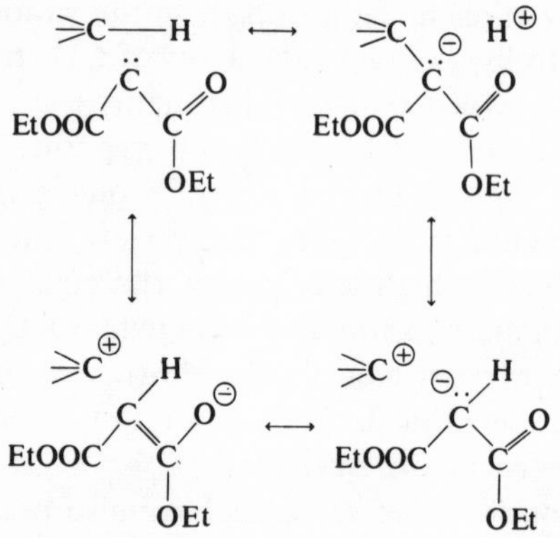

$$\tag{8}$$

Several other carbenes have been shown to give C—H insertion products. Cyclopentadienylidene reacts with the $\alpha$-C—H bonds of diethyl ether 23 times as fast as with the $\beta$-C—H bonds (64). With the same substrate carbethoxycarbene shows a 7.7-fold preference (64) and methylene a 1.23-fold preference (65). It is noteworthy that for cyclopentadienylidene both sp-hybridized linear and unhybridized 90° bond angles are highly unlikely for the divalent carbon atom on steric grounds.

The most likely ground states are $sp^2$-hybridized singlet and $sp^3$-hybridized triplet (*64*).

Phenylcarbene, shown by electron spin resonance (ESR) spectroscopy to possess a triplet ground state (*41, 42*), attacks the secondary C—H bonds of *n*-pentane $6.0 \pm 0.3$ times as fast as the primary (*66*). Chloromethylene, from the photolysis of chlorodiazomethane, is *reported* to insert into the primary C—H bonds of *n*-pentane at 0.05 the rate of insertion into secondary C—H bond (*67*) (this is likely to be a typographical error). Diphenylmethylene, for which ESR studies (*41, 42*) as well as symmetry considerations (*67*) indicate a triplet ground state, only gives C—H insertion products with hydrocarbons such as fluorene and diphenylmethane which contain readily abstractable hydrogen atoms (*68*). Cyclohexane is not attacked by $(C_6H_5)_2C:$. The reactivity of diphenylcarbene seems to present real evidence for an abstraction reaction by triplet methylenes. Propargylene, $H\dot{C}=C=\dot{C}H$, also assigned a triplet ground state on grounds of symmetry, does not seem to insert into the C—H bonds of 2-butene (*69*). Fluorenylidene, also shown by ESR to have a triplet ground state, inserts into the C—H bonds of cyclohexane on photolysis (*68, 71*) and pyrolysis (*70, 71*) and reacts with isobutane to give exclusively 9-*tert*-butylfluorene with no isobutyl derivative being formed. Dichloro- and dibromocarbene do not insert into C—H bonds (*71*).

The greater ability to discriminate among C—H bonds, and the total lack of ability to insert, exhibited by some substituted methylenes, can once again be rationalized on the basis of greater stability and lower energy content. The ability of fluorenylidene to insert into the C—H bonds of cyclohexane and also to discriminate between the tertiary and primary bonds of isobutane, speaks for hydrogen abstraction and radical recombination as the mode of reaction, rather than direct insertion. The temptation is strong to associate the abstraction process with the triplet electronic state, even though energetic arguments alone are sufficient to account for the results.

De More and Benson propose a mechanism for the insertion reaction (*51*) in which attack by methylene on a hydrogen atom leads to an intermediate which is equivalent to a recombination complex for the radicals $CH_3\cdot$ and $\cdot C\!\!<$ [reaction (9)].

$$\begin{matrix}H\\ \phantom{}\\ H\end{matrix}\!\!>\!\!C: \;+\; H\!-\!C\!\!<\; \rightarrow \left[ \begin{matrix}H\\ \phantom{}\\ H\end{matrix}\!\!>\!\!C \cdot\cdot H\!-\!C\!\!< \;\leftrightarrow\; \begin{matrix}H\\ \phantom{}\\ H\end{matrix}\!\!>\!\!C\!-\!H\cdot\cdot C\!\!< \right] \quad (9)$$

The high efficiency of alkyl radical recombination (ca. one in six collisions) is cited as lending support to this mechanism, and the attractive potential between the loosely associated radicals is partially ascribed to contribution by ionic states (Scheme 5).

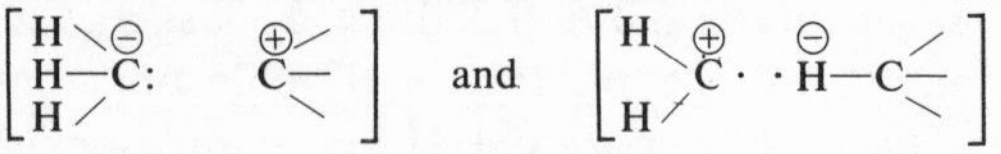

$$
\left[\begin{array}{c} H \searrow \ominus \\ H-C: \quad \overset{\oplus}{C}- \\ H \diagup \end{array}\right] \quad \text{and} \quad \left[\begin{array}{c} H \searrow \oplus \\ \phantom{H}\overset{\ominus}{C}\cdot\ \cdot H-C \diagdown \\ H \diagup \end{array}\right]
$$

Scheme 5

Although the geometry that De More and Benson have in mind is different, the suggestion of ionic character is reminiscent of that of Doering (62) who invoked ionic character in triangular transition states.

Using parameters derived from the pyrolytic dissociation of ethane into methyl radicals, the rate of dissociation of excited ethane produced by the reaction of :$CH_2$ with $CH_4$ was shown to be ten times as great as the rate of collisional deactivation (assuming unit efficiency) if the complex were formed from methylene containing 10 kcal./mole excess energy. If the complex were formed from unexcited methylene, the rate of dissociation should be more than an order of magnitude smaller than the rate of collisional deactivation. This calculation rationalizes the detection of methyl radicals in the reaction of methylene with methane under conditions such that the reacting methylene contains excess energy.

Production of methyl radicals by dissociation of excited ethane does not substantiate DeMore and Benson's mechanism for the insertion since hot ethane might also be formed by a one-step direct insertion describable by a triangular transition state such as that proposed by Knox and Trotman-Dickenson (72) and Doering (62). The discussion by De More and Benson does support the point of view that energy-rich methylene inserting into a C—H bond by a highly exothermic reaction can lead to the formation of radicals *without* involving a direct abstraction mechanism. However, the presumption that the insertion reaction has a high cross-section has not been experimentally investigated in the vapor phase.

## B. Addition Reactions

The most incisive information concerning the chemical characteristics of singlet and triplet methylene comes from study of addition reactions involving carbon-carbon double bonds. Two kinds of data have been used to adduce information concerning the spin states of the attacking species; both approaches seem to have been first suggested by Skell (73, 74). The first involves study of relative reactivities of various olefinic substrates toward carbenes using the competitive method. It was Skell's original notion (73) that triplet carbenes should show selectivity reminiscent of that of typical free radicals. Competitive experiments in the liquid phase showed that dibromomethylene does not select among olefinic substrates in the same way as the tribromomethyl radical. What little selectivity was observed paralleled the relative reactivities of olefins toward electrophilic reagents such as peracids and bromine. Doering and Henderson reported similar results with both dichloro- and dibromocarbene (75). Application of the Skell criterion would indicate that the dihalocarbenes react as electron-deficient singlet states. There seems to be no good grounds for questioning the conclusion since spectroscopic data indicate that the lowest state of difluoromethylene is a singlet and the methods of generation of dihalocarbenes would not be expected to produce triplets selectively. Without independent evidence, we would be inclined to question the *a priori* basis of the Skell theory since free radicals do show significant sensitivity to polar effects (76); conceivably a highly reactive radical having a high electron affinity and a substantial dipole moment might show selectivity such as is demonstrated by dihalomethylenes.

Skell's second criterion involved the stereospecificity of addition (74). He reasoned that a singlet carbene might add to a double bond in a single concerted step since such a step *could* occur with spin conservation [reaction (10)].

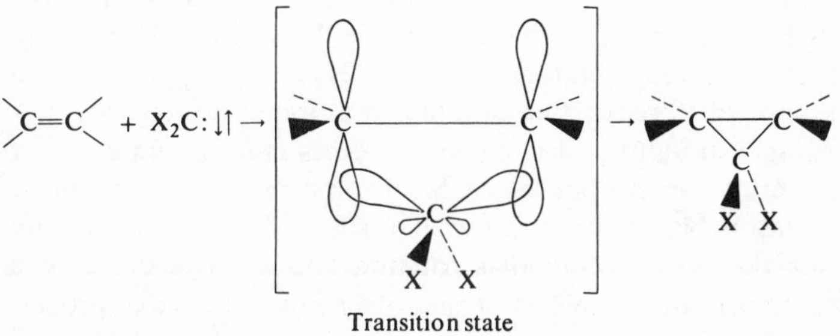

$$\text{C=C} + X_2C: \uparrow\downarrow \rightarrow \quad \text{[Transition state]} \quad \rightarrow \qquad \tag{10}$$

Transition state

Conversely it was reasoned that addition of a triplet might be expected to involve two adiabatic bond-making processes, with spin inversion being a discrete, intermediate step. Since spin inversion was expected to be "slow" (77), it was presumed that "fast" rotations of the intermediate would destroy the steric relationships originally present in the olefin [reaction (11)].

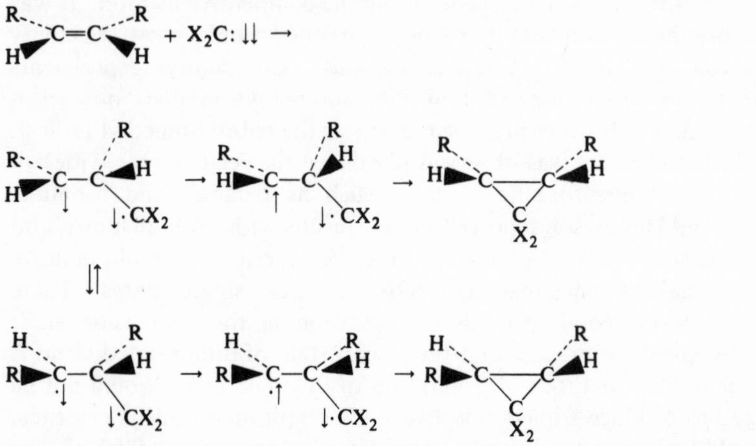

(11)

Since dihalomethylenes, and methylene generated by direct photolysis of diazomethane, add stereospecifically to alkenes in solution (74, 78), it has been inferred that singlet reagents are involved. Methylene produced by irradiation of diazomethane in the vapor phase in the presence of a high pressure of inert gases (79–81) gives nonstereospecific addition to the 2-butenes, as does the species produced by photolysis sensitized in solution by benzophenone (82) and in the vapor phase by mercury (83). An obvious interpretation seems to lend weight to the Skell hypothesis. The sensitized reactions should produce triplet methylene and direct irradiation is known to produce the singlet. In the presence of a high pressure of inert gas, singlet :CH$_2$ has an opportunity to decay to the triplet before reacting with the unsaturated substrates.

The seemingly straightforward picture becomes much cloudier under thoughtful scrutiny. In the first place, Skell's first suggestion should be regarded as reasonable intuition rather than sound theory. There is no firm basis for the presumption that rotation about single bonds will necessarily be much more rapid than spin inversion. The latter process is slow in comparison with radiative transition times but is not well placed on the time scale of most physical events. This is especially true of events in solution in which spin-lattice relaxation can become very important (84). Conversely, it is not at all certain that addition of singlet methylene to a double bond *must* be a one-step process just because it *might be* without violating spin conservation. Consequently one could readily conceive of both stereospecific triplet addition and nonstereospecific singlet addition. Finally, as has been clearly pointed out by Frey (*80*), the cyclopropane formed by addition of singlet methylene to an alkene with conservation of energy would be "hot" enough to undergo a variety of isomerization reactions if it were not deactivated rapidly and efficiently. By a wide margin the most popular point of view is that Skell's second hypothesis, like the first, has turned out to be correct. However, DeMore and Benson (*51*) have taken the view that all of the chemistry of methylene addition *may* be explained in terms of a singlet spin state if proper account is taken of energy transfer from excited methylene and reaction intermediates to other molecules in the environment. Although the argument seems, to us, to be untenable, we will examine it with care.

Data pertinent to the problem are abundant. The first significant studies were reported by Butler and Kistiakowsky (*85*) who studied the reactions of methylene with cyclopropane. If all species involved were cooled instantaneously to their equilibrium states, one product, methylcyclopropane, would be expected. However, under normal gas-phase conditions mixtures of all the butenes are also formed. Methylene was produced by irradiation of both diazomethane and ketene at various total pressures, both with and without added inert gases. The ratio of butenes to methylcyclopropane decreased as the pressure was increased, and with either source of methylene, the results could be fitted to a rate law involving competition between isomerization of hot methylcyclopropane and cooling by collision with other species. Since methylene from diazomethane gave more butenes than was found in comparable experiments with ketene, Kistiakowsky drew the inference that methylene was produced from diazomethane in a relatively high state of excitation. The excess energy was believed to be largely translational since the results could only be accommodated by the assumption that cooling by and reaction with cyclopropane have similar specific rate constants. Clearly, cyclopropanes produced by addition of methylene to double bonds should also be excited, both because of the exothermicity of the addition reaction and because of the excitation of $:CH_2$ at the time of reaction.

Frey studied the effect of inert gas on the reaction of $:CH_2$ with isobutene (*80*). In the absence of inert gas the yield of dimethylcyclo-

propane increased with increase of total pressure (initial ratio diazo-
methane/isobutene, 1:10) approaching asymptotically a limiting yield
of greater than 50% of the total yield of $C_5$ hydrocarbons at 300 mm.;
at 1200 mm. the yield is 57%. The yield of 2-methyl-1-butene was independent of pressure over the 0–300 mm. range studied (ca. 34%). The
yields of 2-methyl-2-butene and 3-methyl-1-butene decreased asymptotically to limits of ca. 8 and 0%, respectively, and the variation in yields
with pressure clearly indicated that hot dimethylcyclopropane isomerized
to 3-methyl-1-butene and 2-methyl-2-butene at relative rates of 1:2.2.

When irradiations of diazomethane-isobutene mixtures were carried
out with monochromatic light of 3660 and 4358 A the *lifetime* of excited
cyclopropane was shorter, at any given pressure, with light of shorter
wavelength, but the yield of 2-methyl-1-butene was independent of wavelength. The limiting yield of dimethylcyclopropane at high pressure
was also independent of wavelength. Therefore the ratios of *primary*
rate constants (for attack at the double bond and the two C—H bonds)
are independent of wavelength, even though the variation of the extent
of isomerization of hot cyclopropane indicate that :$CH_2$ *when it reacted*
with isobutylene contained varying amounts of energy, depending on
wavelength of the exciting light.

Inert gas experiments were performed using 1:10 diazomethane-
isobutene mixtures and adding enough inert gas so that the total pressure
was 600–700 mm. The butene pressure was lowered as the inert gas
pressure was increased. At this total pressure it was assumed that
primary products would be wholly collisionally deactivated before
isomerization and that variation of the composition of the product mixture would reflect variation in the translational energy of methylene at
the time of reaction.

The yield of dimethylcyclopropane did increase (from 54 to 67%) as
the percentage of inert gas was increased and the yield of 2-methyl-1-
butene decreased, indicating that inert gas influences competition
between addition and insertion. Frey estimated the number of collisions
necessary to "deactivate" methylene by plotting the yield of dimethylcyclopropane against the fraction of methylene molecules which had
undergone one, two, and three collisions with inert gas molecules before
encountering an isobutylene molecule. For both argon and nitrogen,
the plot of cyclopropane yield against fraction of methylenes which had
suffered two collisions is linear, but is markedly curved for one and three
collisions. Thus *two* collisions are required to deactivate methylene

assuming that one set of primary rate constants is operative above a critical translational energy content and another below. Collision diameters of relative magnitudes 1, 0.6, and 0.65 were assumed for isobutylene, argon, and nitrogen, respectively. Although Frey maintained that unit collisional reaction efficiency was implied by these plots, it seems to us that the results merely imply that the efficiency of reaction with butene is twice as high as the efficiency of deactivation by inert gases. Both processes *could* be significantly less efficient than was estimated.

The low number of collisions required to deactivate methylene is taken as indicating that translational energy being removed, since quanta of vibrational energy are thought to be removed only after many collisions. Since the ratios of primary rate constants did not change when the wavelength of the exciting light was changed from 4358 to 3660 Å, the amount of kinetic energy imparted to methylene in the photolysis of $CH_2N_2$ is apparently independent of wavelength. Discrimination between allyl and vinyl C—H bonds (insertion reactions) did not change on addition of inert gas although discrimination between addition and insertion increases. Frey postulated that the energy of activation for attack at C—H is greater than for attack on double bonds.

A plot of the ratio of dimethylcyclopropane yield at $p_{infinity}$ to that at $p$ against $1/p$ is linear, as would be expected either if the rate of rearrangement of activated molecules is *independent* of energy or if the activated molecules are mono-energetic. Frey considers the latter explanation more likely and that most of the excess energy of hot dimethylcyclopropane comes from the heat of reaction; slight curvature in the plots is attributed to small dispersion in the energy of methylene at the time of reaction.

Just as attack of methylene on isobutylene initially forms three products [reaction (12)].

$$:CH_2 + \quad \xrightarrow{k_1} \quad \xrightarrow{k_2} \quad \xrightarrow{k_3} \qquad (12)$$

so Frey considered that attack by methylene on *trans*-2-butene should give three primary products (*80*) [reaction (13)].

$$:CH_2 + \quad \xrightarrow{k_1} \quad \ast$$

$$\xrightarrow{k_2} \quad \ast \tag{13}$$

$$\xrightarrow{k_3} \quad \ast$$

In the gas phase the hot *trans*-dimethylcyclopropane can isomerize [reaction (14)]

$$\ast \quad \underset{k_{-4}}{\overset{k_4}{\rightleftarrows}} \quad \ast$$

$$\xrightarrow{k_5} \quad CH_3CH_2CH{=}CHCH_3 \text{ cis and trans} \tag{14}$$

$$\xrightarrow{k_6}$$

$$\xrightarrow{k_7}$$

or be deactivated ($k_8$) to *trans*-dimethylcyclopropane. Hot *cis*-dimethylcyclopropane can also be deactivated ($k_9$) or isomerize. Hot *trans*-2-pentene can isomerize to hot *cis*-, both of which can be collisionally deactivated. Hot 2-methyl-2-butene will not undergo isomerization under these conditions.

The yield of *trans*-dimethylcyclopropane increased asymptotically to a limit at high total pressure (ca. 49%) and fell off rapidly below 150 mm. Analysis of the data indicated that at 8 mm. half of the initially formed *trans*-dimethylcyclopropane isomerized before deactivation. The *cis*-dimethylcyclopropane yield went through a maximum (ca. 7% at 10 mm.) (yields expressed as % of C$_5$ product) and approached zero asymptotically. *trans*-2-Pentene yield remained constant, after an initial slight rise, at about 43%, and *cis*-2-pentene and 2-methyl-1-butene declined asymptotically to zero as the pressure was increased. That the yield of *cis*-dimethylcyclopropane goes through a maximum was accounted for by the assumption that the geometrical isomerization is much faster than structural isomerization. At very low pressure, increase in pressure produces more cold *cis*-dimethylcyclopropane by increased stabilization of hot *cis-* formed from hot *trans-*, while a further increase in pressure deactivates hot *trans-* at a rate comparable and finally more rapid than geometrical isomerization.

Irradiation with monochromatic light of 4358 and 3660 Å apparently produced *trans*-dimethylcyclopropane of differing energy content. The primary rate constants, $k_1$, $k_2$, and $k_3$ remained in constant ratio, but at any given pressure the yield of *cis*-dimethylcyclopropane was lower at 4358 than at 3660 Å. Thus, at any given total pressure, the *apparent* stereospecificity was a function of the energy content of the methylene when it reacted.

Use of high pressures of inert gases gave nearly the same product distribution as was obtained with high pressures of reactants. Small deviations were attributed to lower efficiency of nitrogen and argon, as compared to *trans*-2-butene, in deactivation of hot *trans*-dimethylcyclopropane. The presence of inert gas altered the yields of *both trans*-dimethylcyclopropane *and trans*-2-pentene indicating that the primary rate constants were affected. This was attributed to removal of the excess translational energy of methylene before reaction. No figures on relative yields of *trans-* and *cis*-dimethylcyclopropane were included, so a reanalysis of Frey's argument in this paper in terms of methylene spin state is profitless until further work has been examined.

It was determined that methylene reacts with diazomethane 2.4 times as rapidly as with butene. If this is correct then most methylene molecules *must* be partially deactivated by collision with butene even in the absence of inert gas. Therefore Frey's determination of the number of collisions required for translational deactivation must be *relative*, i.e. two *times* the number of collisions with inert gas as with butene lead to deactivation as collisions with butene lead to reaction.

The data on isomerization of initially formed hot *trans*-dimethylcyclopropane according to the reaction (15)

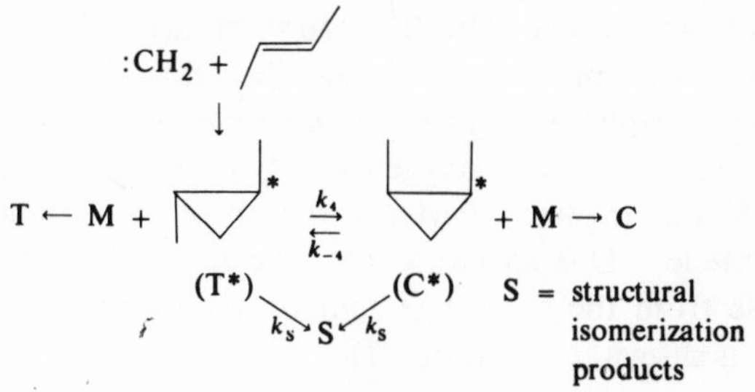

were fitted to the following kinetic expressions assuming only one collision necessary to deactivate any of the excited species. The fact that the pressure, $p$, has been used in such a way as to attach the units of $t^{-1}$ to it, does not invalidate the use made of the equations in (16).

$$k_s = \frac{pS}{T + C}$$

$$\frac{C}{T} = \frac{k_4}{k_{-4}} - \frac{pC(S + C + T)}{T(C + T)} \frac{1}{k_{-4}} \tag{16}$$

A plot of $C/T$ against $pC(S + C + T)/T(C + T)$ gave an average intercept, for 4358 Å, (unfiltered) and 3660 Å radiation, of $0.33 = k_4/k_{-4}$ which represents an equilibrium constant between excited *cis*- and *trans*-dimethylcyclopropanes while the slopes gave geometrical isomerization constants in the ratio 1:1.36:1.6, respectively. Thus excess vibrational energy increases the rate of geometrical isomerization of hot cyclopropanes. Rate constants for geometrical isomerization are greater than for structural isomerization ($k_{-4}/k_s$, 6–18:1) and the ratio increases with decreasing pressure. The rate constants for geometrical isomerization are independent of pressure in the range studied.

The limiting yield for *cis*-dimethylcyclopropane from *trans*-2-butene at low pressure is 25% (of total cyclopropane) since $k_4/k_{-4}$ is 0.33. Experimental values approached this figure.

In a second paper on the reaction of methylene with *cis*-2-butene, Frey (*81*) claims to have obtained an important further effect of inert gas, namely *the conversion of singlet methylene to triplet methylene*. Mixtures of diazomethane and *cis*-2-butene were irradiated at high pressure (2100–3200 mm.). In all experiments part of the pressure was supplied by nitrogen or argon. Despite the fact that total pressures were above the high pressure limits established in the earlier work, large variations in the relative amounts of products were observed as the ratio of inert gas to reactants was varied. The data are summarized in Table II.

The striking effect of inert gas was attributed to conversion of singlet methylene to the triplet *prior to reaction with butene*. The dramatic influence of a small amount of oxygen was believed to be due to specific scavenging of the triplet. Perhaps the most important product is 3-methyl-1-butene. This species cannot be formed by direct insertion but must arise from the rearrangement of some primary product. An obvious path is shown in reaction (17).

$$H_2C: \downarrow \downarrow + \quad \diagup\!\!=\!\!\diagdown \quad \rightarrow \quad \underset{H}{\overset{H_3C}{\diagdown}}C\!\!-\!\!C\underset{\underset{\downarrow}{H}}{\overset{CH_3}{\diagup}}\!\!\overset{CH_2}{\underset{\downarrow}{}} \quad \rightarrow CH_2\!\!=\!\!CH\!\!-\!\!CH(CH_3)_2 \qquad (17)$$

Since the yields of the terminal alkene, *trans*-dimethylcyclopropane and *trans*-2-pentene increase monotonously as the argon pressure is increased, it seems inevitable that these products must be formed from some low-energy intermediate. DeMore and Benson disagree with Frey as to the formulation of this intermediate. The former maintain that all the data may be explained by a single mechanism involving only one spin state of methylene. All variation in products is attributed to varying initial energy content and relative rates of deactivation of an intermediate biradical of unspecified spin state. Extensive use is made of data obtained in the isomerization of *cis*- and *trans*-cyclopropane-$d_2$ (*86*) and by study of the addition of methylene, generated by photolysis of ketene, to *trans*-1, 2-ethylene-$d_2$ (*87*).

Rabinovitch (*87*) measured the relative amounts of *cis*- and *trans*-cyclopropane-$d_2$ and propylene formed at various total pressures with both 3100 and 3600 Å irradiation. The ratio of ketene to ethylene was maintained essentially constant so the average degree of "thermalization" of methylene before reaction with ethylene should be constant. At high total pressure the yield of propylene became constant at ~ 15%

TABLE II

EFFECT OF ARGON PRESSURE ON PRODUCTS
OF REACTION OF METHYLENE WITH *cis*-2-BUTENE

| Ratio argon to *cis*-2-butene | % Yields of $C_5$ products | | | | | |
|---|---|---|---|---|---|---|
| | △⌐ | △⌐ | ∧∧∨ | ⌐═∨ | ⌇∨ | ⌐═⌇ |
| 1600 | 27.1 | 28.1 | 16.5 | 17.0 | 10.5 | 4.0 |
| 850 | 24.0 | 28.4 | 12.7 | 19.1 | 9.2 | 6.6 |
| 356 [a] | 3.6 | 50.9 | 0.9 | 27.7 | 1.8 | 15.0 [a] |
| 314 | 22.1 | 30.7 | 10.7 | 21.8 | 8.2 | 6.3 |
| 300 | 20.8 | 31.1 | 11.1 | 22.4 | 7.5 | 6.9 |
| 134 | 18.0 | 33.3 | 8.8 | 24.9 | 6.6 | 8.4 |
| 69 | 16.3 | 35.4 | 7.8 | 26.4 | 5.8 | 8.4 |
| 15 3 | 10.6 | 41.4 | 3.6 | 29.9 | 2.9 | 11.4 |
| 7.6 | 9.5 | 44.3 | 2.4 | 30.4 | 1.9 | 12.9 |

[a] Four mm. $O_2$ present.

with both 3100 and 3600 Å irradiation. The yield of *trans*-cyclopropane-$d_2$ approached zero at high pressures but was still changing significantly in a pressure range ($\sim$ 2000 mm.) where the propylene yield was reduced to its limiting value. At intermediate pressures 3100 Å light produced more propylene and *trans*-cyclopropane-$d_2$ than did 3600 Å light. The relative amounts of the stereoisomeric cyclopropanes were not measured at high pressure in the experiments with 3100 Å excitation.

not measured at high pressure in the experiments with 3100 Å excitation.

Benson has attempted to fit the data by the mechanism in (18).

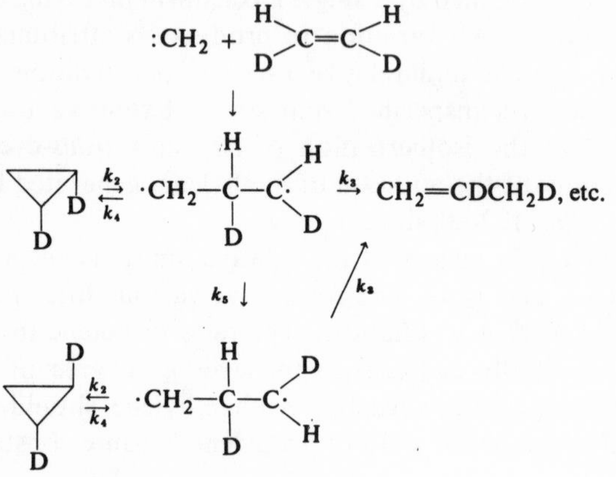

$$(18)$$

The kinetic parameters shown in Table III were extracted from the data for thermal isomerization of cyclopropane.

TABLE III

KINETIC PARAMETERS INVOLVED IN
ISOMERIZATION OF CYCLOPROPANE

| Reaction | Log A | $E_{act}$ (kcal./mole) |
|---|---|---|
| 2 | 13.0 | 8.2 |
| 3 | 12.2 | 9.5 |
| 4 | 16.0 | 64.2 |

The relative rates of ring closure, rotation, and rearrangement to propylene can be estimated for any presumed energy content of the trimethylene biradical using Rice-Rampsberger-Kassel theory (*60, 61*) [Eq. (19)].

$$k = A \left( \frac{E - E_{\text{act}}}{E} \right)^{n-1} \tag{19}$$

where $n$ = number of internal degrees of freedom = 12

$E$ = exothermicity of addition + $nRT$

$\cong 25.5 + 7.2 = 32.7$ (at 300°)

The value of 25.5 is inferred by use of the values of 80 and 67 kcal. per mole for $\Delta H_f(CH_2)$ and $\Delta H_f(\cdot CH_2CH_2CH_2\cdot)$. The rates of cyclization and propylene formation then become those in Eq. (20).

$$\frac{k_2}{k_3} = \frac{10^{13.0}}{10^{12.2}} \left( \frac{\delta E + 32.7 - 8.2}{\delta E + 32.7 - 9.5} \right)^{11} \tag{20}$$

where $\delta E$ = variation in energy content of the biradical, positive at the outset if $CH_2$ is excited and negative at later times if some deactivation precedes reaction.

If $\delta E$ is zero, the rate of cyclization is calculated to be ten times the rate of propylene formation. If the biradicals were to undergo complete relaxation ($\delta E = -32.7$ kcal.), the relative rates of the two activated processes would be given by Eq. (21).

$$\frac{k_2}{k_3} = \frac{10^{13}}{10^{12.2}} e^{(-8.2 + 9.5)/RT} \cong 10^2 \text{(at 300° K)} \tag{21}$$

At high pressure, where no reopening of the cyclopropane will occur, the yield of propylene might well be expected to be 10% or less. This conclusion is certainly compatible with the data of Rabinovitch and suggests the possibility that some propylene formed at high pressure might come from a biradical as well as by direct attack on C—H bonds. At low pressure much propylene would be produced both by rearrangement of the initially formed biradical and by reentry of the cyclopropane into the reaction scheme via reaction (4). However, we cannot see that any resolution of the problem is achieved. Since about 50% of the propylene must come from cyclopropane at the low pressure limit, one is left with a problem similar to that of deciding whether or not the first fowl preceded the first egg!

DeMore and Benson maintain that *if the rate of rotation of the biradical is low enough* stereospecific ring closure could occur. We do not see how kinetic parameters for the rotation process can be chosen so as to make this a real possibility. The barrier to rotation is unlikely to exceed 3 kcal. and there is no reason to expect the frequency factor to be less than $10^{13}$. Therefore, in a highly excited biradical, ($\delta E$ very large), the rate of rotation should at least equal the rate of cyclization. For finite $\delta E$ the rate of rotation should exceed the rate of cyclization, and the factor would become larger as relaxation of the radical occurred ($10^{1.4}$ for $\delta E = 0$). Consequently, we conclude that, if the interpretation of the data for thermal isomerization is correct, *any* biradical must be considered to be a free rotator during the time required to close the ring. This conclusion is independent of assumptions concerning spin states; if the biradical were a triplet, ring closure might be even slower, but the difference in over-all stereochemical result might be undetectably different from that observed with a singlet. We believe that stereospecific addition in the vapor phase[8] *demands* that addition involves simultaneous formation of two bonds. Such reaction could only be an adiabatic process if the attacking species is a singlet.

The converse proposition is not necessarily true. Nonstereospecific addition cannot be taken as a proof that an attacking species is a triplet unless it has also been shown that under some other conditions a species of the same composition can give stereospecific addition. For example, Skell's observation (1) that diphenylmethylene, produced by photolysis of diphenyldiazomethane, adds nonstereospecifically to the 2-butenes could not be regarded as unequivocal evidence that the carbene was a triplet. The presence of the two phenyl groups might well have been sufficient to allow the singlet to react by a biradical mechanism which would almost certainly be somewhat nonstereospecific. Closs and Closs (88) have found that a species, generated from dibromodiphenylmethane by a halogen-metal interconversion with methyllithium, reacts stereospecifically with olefins. The reagent in the latter case may be an organometallic compound; if it is not, the comparison of the two experiments would show that Closs generated a singlet species and that photolysis produces at least some triplet. The fact that diphenylcarbene is now known to have a triplet ground state (41, 42) is not a great deal of assistance since an arbitrarily chosen preparative method might produce the singlet which could react before decaying to the triplet.

Both fluorenylidene (89) and propargylene ,(69) add nonstereospecifically. Since the former is known to have a triplet ground state

---

[8] In a liquid phase, intermolecular interactions might well contrive to slow the rate of rotation.

(43), the evidence suggests, but does not demand, that addition in both cases involves triplets.

The most extensive systematic study of various methods for production of carbenes has involved methylene itself. Duncan and Cvetanovic (83) found that decomposition of ketene, photosensitized by the excited triplet state of mercury atoms, produced a species showing little tendency to undergo random insertion reactions. The species did, however, add nonstereospecifically to the 2-butenes and also gave the substitution products expected from rearrangement of a biradical by 1,3-hydrogen migration. As is shown in Table IV, the product distribution was very similar to that found in the presence of a high pressure of inert gas by Frey.

TABLE IV

PRODUCTS OF REACTION OF METHYLENE FORMED BY
MERCURY SENSITIZED DECOMPOSITION OF KETENE

| Olefin |  | 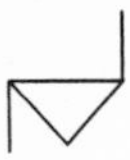 |  |  | 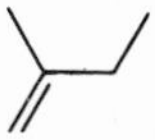 | 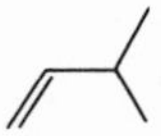 | 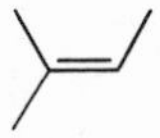 |
|---|---|---|---|---|---|---|---|
| trans-2-Butene | 13.5 | 51.9 | 5.6 | 18.7 | 0.7 | 6.8 | 2.8 |
| cis-2-Butene | 24.6 | 31.3 | 19.3 | 12.3 | 0.7 | 8.1 | 3.7 |

The results are clearly consistent with a mechanism in which triplet ketene, formed by transfer of excitation from mercury triplets, decomposes with direct formation of triplet methylene [reaction (22)].

$$Hg^{*(3)} + CH_2CO \rightarrow Hg + CH_2CO^{*(3)}$$
$$CH_2CO^{*(3)} \rightarrow CO + H_2C: \downarrow \downarrow$$
(22)

A very similar result was obtained in solution using benzophenone as the photosensitizer for decomposition of diazomethane (82). Other studies (90) offer persuasive evidence that excitation of benzophenone is followed rapidly by intersystem crossing to the triplet [reaction (23)].

$$(C_6H_5)_2CO \xrightarrow{h\nu} (C_6H_5)_2CO^{*(1)}$$
$$(C_6H_5)_2CO^{*(1)} \xrightarrow[\text{crossing}]{\text{Intersystem}} (C_6H_5)_2CO^{*(3)}$$
(23)

Transfer of energy from the triplet state of the ketone to diazomethane should effect the same over-all results as are obtained using mercury sensitization with ketene in the vapor phase. The species produced added nonstereospecifically to the 2-butenes. No substitution products were formed in significant amounts, perhaps indicating that the latter arise from radical chain reactions in the vapor phase. The reaction was not entirely stereo random, much more cis-dimethylcyclopropane was produced from cis-2-butene than from the trans isomer. The result may have been due to failure to remove all traces of light absorbed by diazomethane or it may indicate that in solution spin inversion in the biradical and cyclization are rapid enough to compete with rotation.

Despite the recent extensive interest in methylene chemistry, much additional study is required before comprehensive generalizations concerning the characteristic reactivity of singlets and triplets will be warranted. Among experiments which have not, to our knowledge, been carried out as yet is one of a most intriguing nature suggested in the literature no less than 19 years ago (91).

### REFERENCES

1. R. M. Etter, H. S. Skovronek, and P. S. Skell, *J. Am. Chem. Soc.* **81**, 1008 (1959).
2. A. D. Walsh, *J. Chem. Soc.* p. 2260 (1953).
3. J. C. Slater, *Phys. Rev.* **98**, 1093 (1955).
4. R. Mecke, *Z. Elektrochem.* **36**, 589 (1930).
5. R. G. W. Norrish, *Trans. Faraday Soc.* **30**, 103 (1934).
6. H. Voge, *J. Chem. Phys.* **4**, 581 (1936).
7. G. Herzberg, *Rev. Mod. Phys.* **15**, 195 (1942).
8. R. Mecke, *Z. physik. Chem.* **7B**, 108 (1930).
9. L. S. Kassel, *J. Am. Chem. Soc.* **54**, 3949 (1932).
10. L. Belchetz, *Trans. Faraday Soc.* **30**, 170 (1934).
11. R. S. Mulliken, *Phys. Rev.* **41**, 751 (1932); **43**, 279 (1932).
12. J. E. Lennard-Jones, *Trans. Faraday Soc.* **30**, 70 (1934).
13. A. D. Walsh, *Discussions Faraday Soc.* **2**, 18 (1947).
14. L. H. Long and R. G. W. Norrish, *Proc. Roy. Soc. (London),* **A187**, 337 (1946).
15. T. L. Cottrell, "The Strength of Chemical Bonds," 2nd ed. Academic Press, New York, 1958.
16. K. J. Laidler and E. J. Casey, *J. Chem. Phys.* **17**, 213 (1949).
17. G. H. Duffey, *J. Chem. Phys.* **17**, 840 (1949).
18. K. J. Laidler and E. J. Casey, *J. Chem. Phys.* **17**, 1087 (1949).
19. K. Niira and K. Oohata, *J. Phys. Soc. Japan* **7**, 61 (1952).
20. G. A. Gallup, *J. Chem. Phys.* **28**, 716 (1957).
21. B. F. Gray, *J. Chem. Phys.* **28**, 1252 (1957).
22. A. Monfils and B. Rosen, *Nature* **164**, 713 (1949).
23. J. M. Foster and S. F. Boys, *Revs. Mod. Phys.* **32**, 305 (1960).
24. A. Padgett and M. Krauss, *J. Chem. Phys.* **32**, 189 (1960).
25. G. W. King and G. L. Malli, *Can. J. Chem.* **39**, 1652 (1961).

26. P. C. H. Jordan and H. C. Longuet-Higgins, *Mol. Phys.* **5**, 121 (1962).
27. G. Herzberg and J. Shoosmith, *Nature* **183**, 1801 (1959).
28. G. Herzberg, *Proc. Roy. Soc. (London),* **A262**, 291 (1961).
29. C. C. J. Roothaan, *Revs. Mod. Phys.* **23**, 69 (1951).
30. J. B. Pedley, *Trans. Faraday Soc.* **58**, 23 (1962).
31. F. O. Ellison, *J. Chem. Phys.* **36**, 3107 (1962).
32. P. Venkateswarlu, *Phys. Rev.* **77**, 79 (1950).
33. P. Venkateswarlu, *Phys. Rev.* **77**, 676 (1950).
34. E. B. Andrews and R. F. Barrow, *Nature* **165**, 890 (1950).
35. R. K. Laird, E. B. Andrews, and R. F. Barrow, *Trans. Faraday Soc.* **46**, 803 (1950).
36. J. Duchesne and L. Burnelle, *J. Chem. Phys.* **21**, 2005 (1953); **19**, 1191 (1951).
37. D. E. Milligan and G. C. Pimentel, *J. Chem. Phys.* **29**, 1405 (1958).
38. T. D. Goldfarb and G. C. Pimentel, *J. Am. Chem. Soc.* **82**, 1865 (1960).
39. W. B. DeMore, H. O. Pritchard, and N. Davidson, *J. Am. Chem. Soc.* **81**, 5874 (1959).
40. G. W. Robinson and M. McCarty, Jr., *J. Am. Chem. Soc.* **82**, 1859 (1960).
41. R. W. Brandon, G. L. Closs, and C. A. Hutchison, *J. Chem. Phys.* **37**, 1878 (1962).
42. R. W. Murray, A. M. Trozzolo, E. Wasserman, and W. A. Yager, *J. Am. Chem. Soc.* **84**, 3213 (1962).
43. A. M. Trozzolo, R. W. Murray, and E. Wasserman, *J. Am. Chem. Soc.* **84**, 4990 (1962).
44. F. O. Rice and A. Glasebrook, *J. Am. Chem. Soc.* **56**, 2381 (1934).
45. G. B. Kistiakowsky and K. Sauer, *J. Am. Chem. Soc.* **78**, 5699 (1956).
46. L. Belchetz, *Trans. Faraday Soc.* **30**, 170 (1934).
47. L. H. Gevantman and R. R. Williams, Jr., *J. Phys. Chem.* **56**, 569 (1952).
48. G. B. Kistiakowsky and W. L. Marshall, *J. Am. Chem. Soc.* **74**, 88 (1952).
49. T. Bremer-Wilson and G. B. Kistiakowsky, *J. Am. Chem. Soc.* **80**, 2934 (1958).
50. R. G. W. Norrish and G. Porter, *Discussions Faraday Soc.* **2**, 97 (1947).
51. W. B. DeMore and S. W. Benson, "Advances in Photochemistry," Vol. II. Wiley, New York, in press.
52. H. Meerwein, H. Rathjen, and H. Werner, *Ber.* **75**, 1610 (1942).
53. W. von E. Doering, R. G. Buttery, R. G. Laughlin, and N. Chaudhuri, *J. Am. Chem. Soc.* **78**, 3224 (1956).
54. D. B. Richardson, M. C. Simmons, and I. Dvoretzky, *J. Am. Chem. Soc.* **82**, 5001 (1960); **83**, 1934 (1961).
55. H. M. Frey, *J. Am. Chem. Soc.* **80**, 5005 (1958).
56. H. M. Frey and G. B. Kistiakowsky, *J. Am. Chem. Soc.* **79**, 6373 (1957).
57. H. M. Frey, *Proc. Chem. Soc.* p. 318 (1959).
58. W. von E. Doering and H. Prinzbach, *Tetrahedron* **6**, 24 (1959).
59. H. M. Frey, *Trans. Faraday Soc.* **56**, 1201 (1960).
60. O. K. Rice and H. C. Rampsberger, *J. Am. Chem. Soc.* **49**, 1617 (1927); **50**, 617 (1928).
61. L. S. Kassel, *J. Phys. Chem.* **32**, 225 (1928).
62. W. von E. Doering and L. H. Knox, *J. Am. Chem. Soc.* **78**, 4947 (1956); **83**, 1989 (1961).
63. G. S. Hammond, *J. Am. Chem. Soc.* **77**, 334 (1955).
64. J. E. Basinski, Doctoral Dissertation, Yale University, New Haven, Connecticut, (1961).

65. W. von E. Doering, L. H. Knox, and M. Jones, Jr., *J. Org. Chem.* **24**, 136 (1959).
66. C. D. Gutsche, G. Bachman, and R. S. Coffey, *Tetrahedron* **18**, 617 (1962).
67. G. L. Closs and J. J. Coyle, *J. Am. Chem. Soc.* **84**, 4350 (1962).
68. W. Kirmse, L. Horner, and H. Hoffmann, *Ann.* **614**, 20 (1958).
69. P. S. Skell and J. Klebe, *J. Am. Chem. Soc.* **82**, 247 (1960).
70. A. A. Lamola, Bachelors Thesis, Massachusetts Institute of Technology (1961).
71. M. Jones, Jr., Doctoral Dissertation, Yale University, New Haven, Connecticut (1963).
72. J. H. Knox and A. F. Trotman-Dickenson, *Chem. Ind. (London)* 268 (1957).
73. P. S. Skell and A. Y. Garner, *J. Am. Chem. Soc.* **78**, 5430 (1956).
74. P. S. Skell and R. C. Woodworth, *J. Am. Chem. Soc.* **78**, 4496 (1956).
75. W. von E. Doering and W. A. Henderson, Jr., *J. Am. Chem. Soc.* **80**, 5274 (1958).
76. G. A. Russell, *Tetrahedron* **8**, 101 (1960).
77. K. J. Laidler, "Chemical Kinetics," p. 386, McGraw-Hill, New York 1950.
78. W. von E. Doering and P. LaFlamme, *J. Am. Chem. Soc.* **78**, 5447 (1956).
79. F. A. L. Anet, R. F. W. Bader, and A. -M. Van der Auwera, *J. Am. Chem. Soc.* **82**, 3217 (1960).
80. H. M. Frey, *Proc. Roy. Soc. (London)* **A250**, 409 (1959); **A251**, 575 (1959).
81. H. M. Frey, *J. Am. Chem. Soc.* **82**, 5947 (1960).
82. K. R. Kopecky, G. S. Hammond, and P. A. Leermakers, *J. Am. Chem. Soc.* **83**, 2397 (1961); **84**, 1015 (1962).
83. F. J. Duncan and R. J. Cvetanovic, *J. Am. Chem. Soc.* **84**, 3593 (1962).
84. N. E. Bloembergen, E. M. Purcell, and R. V. Pound, *Phys. Rev.* **73**, 679 (1948).
85. J. N. Butler and G. B. Kistiakowsky, *J. Am. Chem. Soc.* **82**, 759 (1960); **83**, 1324 (1961).
86. B. S. Rabinovitch, E. W. Schlag, and K. B. Wiberg, *J. Chem. Phys.* **28**, 504 (1958).
87. B. S. Rabinovitch, E. Tschuikow-Roux, and E. W. Schlag, *J. Am. Chem. Soc.* **81**, 1081 (1959).
88. G. L. Closs and L. E. Closs, *Angew. Chem.* **74**, 431 (1962).
89. W. von E. Doering and M. Jones, Jr., *Tetrahedron Letters* p. 791 (1963).
90. W. M. Moore, G. S. Hammond, and R. P. Foss, *J. Am. Chem. Soc.* **83**, 2789 (1961).
91. *Walt Disney's Comics and Stories,* **4**, No. 8, 2 (1944).

# AUTHOR INDEX

Numbers in parentheses are reference numbers and are included to assist the reader in locating the references where the authors' names are not mentioned in the text. Numbers in italics indicate the pages on which the complete references are listed.

## A

Abend, P. G., 12(61), 28(61), *43*, 88(59), *94*, 99(22), *112*, 170(115), *198*
Adams, Ch. E., 119(19), *141*
Adickes, F., 206(13), *212*
Aeberli, M., 120(39), *141*
Agre, C. L., 103(54), *113*
Akiyoshi, S., 99(16), *112*
Alder, K., 36(161), *46*, 102(50), *113*
Alder, R. W., 56(54b), *66*
Alexander, E. R., 16(86), *44*, 181(154), *200*
Alink, R. J. H., 123(61), *142*
Allen, T. L., 152(44), *196*
Alleston, D. L., 173(119d), *199*
Allinger, N. L., 122(52a), *142*
Aman, H., 130(96a), *143*
Amende, J., 119(20), *141*
Anantakrishnan, S. V., 164(91), *198*
Anderson, J. C., 161(82a), *197*
Andreades, S., 159(76), 162(76), *197*
Andrews, E. B., 159(70), *197*, 247(35), *273*
Anet, F. A. L., 27(128), *45*, 260(79), *274*
Anthes, E., 5(21), *6*, 83(51), 84(51), *94*
Applequist, D. E., 47(9), 59(9), 61(60), *64*, *66*
Arbusov, A. E., 206(14), *212*
Arkell, A., 128(92), *142*
Armanious, E. R., 72(20a), *76*
Arndt, F., 119(20, 22), 120(22), 141
Arnold, R. T., 126(80), *142*
Ashcraft, A. C., 31(139f), *45*
Aston, J. G., 152(43), *196*
Atkinson, E., 159(75), *197*
Augestad-Jensen, H., 105(72), *113*
Ayrey, G., 37(168), *46*
Ayscough, P. B., 158(68), *197*

## B

Babad, H., 61(60), *66*
Bachman, G. L., 85(56), 87(56), 88(56), *94*, 257(66), *274*
Bachmann, W. E., 118(10), *140*
Badea, F., 154(52, 53), 166(52, 53), *197*
Baddeley, G., 128(90), *142*
Bader, R. F. W., 27(128), *45*, 260(79), *274*
Badger, G. M., 104(65), 105(71, 73), *113*
Bahner, C. T., 205(11a), *212*
Balenović, K., 122(49), *141*
Ball, W. J., 176(128), *199*
Baltazzi, E., 103(58), *113*
Bamberger, E., 124(69), *142*
Bamford, W. R., 48(13), *64*, 85(57), 86(57), 90(57), *94*
Banitt, E. H., 211(22b), *212*
Bank, J., 181(149), *200*
Barr, J. T., 205(11a), *212*
Barrow, R. F., 159(70), *197*, 203(5), *211*, 247(35), *273*
Bartels-Keith, J. R., 103(55, 56), 107(55, 56), 108(55, 56), *113*
Bartlett, P. D., 84(53), *94*
Basedow, O. H., 209(21), *212*
Basinski, J. E., 256(64), 257(64), *273*
Bassett, H., 185(161), *200*
Battiste, M., 100(33, 34), *112*
Baum, M., 124(69), *142*
Baum, S. J., 54(52a), *65*
Bawn, C. E. H., 5(24, 25, 26), *6*, 12(53, 60), 13(60), 16, 18(81, 82, 83), *43*
Bayer, R. P., 210(23), *212*
Bayes, K., 50(32), *65*
Beal, Ph. F., 120(37), *141*
Belchetz, L., 238(10), 250(46), *272, 273*

275

# SUBJECT INDEX